Department of Psychiatry
Cornell University
Medical College

Psychiatry

W9-CZX-888

The FOUNDERS *of* NEUROLOGY

Discipulus est prioris posterior dies.

P. Publilius Syrus

The FOUNDERS *of* NEUROLOGY

One Hundred and Thirty-Three Biographical Sketches

**Prepared for the
Fourth International Neurological Congress in Paris**

By

Eighty-Four Authors

Edited by

WEBB HAYMAKER, M.D.

*Chief, Neuropathology Section
Armed Forces Institute of Pathology
Washington, D.C.*

With the bibliographical and editorial assistance of

KARL A. BAER

*Bibliographer
Army Medical Library, Washington, D.C.*

CHARLES C THOMAS · PUBLISHER

Springfield · Illinois · U.S.A.

CHARLES C THOMAS • PUBLISHER

BANNERSTONE HOUSE

301–327 East Lawrence Avenue, Springfield, Illinois

Published simultaneously in the British Commonwealth of Nations by

BLACKWELL SCIENTIFIC PUBLICATIONS, LTD., OXFORD, ENGLAND

Published simultaneously in Canada by

THE RYERSON PRESS, TORONTO

This monograph is protected by copyright. No part of it may be reproduced in any manner without written permission from the publisher.

Copyright 1953, by CHARLES C THOMAS • PUBLISHER

Printed in the United States of America

FOREWORD

*I*t is with great pleasure that I write this foreword to *The Founders of Neurology* prepared by the Armed Forces Institute of Pathology and the Army Medical Library, U.S.A., for presentation to the Fourth International Neurological Congress. This biographical work, prepared under the direction of Webb Haymaker, M.D., of the Armed Forces Institute of Pathology, provides concrete recognition of those scientists whose labors have resulted in the present status of Neurology throughout the world.

It is doubtful whether any other organizations in the world are today in a better position to prepare and publish a volume for the purpose of surveying the contributions of the founders and proponents of our discipline than the United States Armed Forces Institute of Pathology and the Army Medical Library. As editor of the present volume, Dr. Haymaker has had at his disposal not only the extensive historical and scientific treasures of the Army Medical Library and the Armed Forces Institute of Pathology but also the personal individual resources of the neurologists of the United States. Drawing upon this wealth of information, the present volume has memorialized those whose patient investigative efforts and brilliant incisive reasoning have penetrated the darknesses of the neural jungle, and often brilliantly and always honestly, pieced together the hypotheses, the suspicions, the intuitive inspirations and the solid hard work at the bedside, the deadhouse and the laboratory which represent our knowledge of the branch of medicine we profess.

Bernard Sachs, the President of the First International Neurological Congress, which met in Bern in 1931, was, more than any other individual, responsible for this series of Congresses, and the preparation of *The Founders of Neurology* does honor to him and to those from our sister countries who have made these Congresses famous in the memories of all of us.

It may be hoped that we shall continue to be inspired by the labors of those who have preceded us, and that it shall be our endeavor to pass on the lamp which they have lighted to those who so urgently press forward upon our retreating footsteps.

As the Vice-President for the United States, it gives me the greatest pleasure to express my thanks and appreciation to Major General Raymond W. Bliss, The Surgeon General, United States Army; Brigadier General Raymond O. Dart, Director of the Armed Forces Institute of Pathology; Colonel Joseph H. McNinch, Director of the Army Medical Library; and Dr. Webb Haymaker, for the preparation of *The Founders of Neurology*.

HENRY ALSOP RILEY, M.D.
Vice-President for the United States
The Fourth International Neurologi-
cal Congress
Paris, France 1949.

FOREWORD

*I*t has been both a privilege and a pleasure for the staff of the Army Medical Library to collaborate with Dr. Webb Haymaker in the preparation of this volume. In this, we of the staff are proud to carry out the bibliographic tradition of the Army Medical Library.

This Library had its beginning in 1836 as a small collection of books in the office of Surgeon General Joseph Lovell. Following the Civil War and the administration of Surgeon General William A. Hammond, a pioneer in neurology, the growing collection was received and catalogued in cramped quarters across the street from the White House and then sent to Library Hall in Ford's Theater, that melancholy scene of President Lincoln's assassination. But the Library owes its real growth and development to Dr. John Shaw Billings, under whose direction for 30 years it became one of the world's greatest repositories of medical information.

Today the Army Medical Library has the responsibility, in-so-far as possible, of collecting all the medical literature of the world, and of making known its vast resources through its published bibliographies, catalogs and indexes. These resources are at the service of physicians and scientists, not only in the United States but also throughout the world, by personal visit, inter-library loan, microfilm or photoprint.

To you of the Fourth International Neurological Congress we send our greetings. We extend to you a cordial invitation to use the resources and services of the Army Medical Library.

J. H. McNINCH
Colonel, Medical Corps
Director, Army Medical Library

FOREWORD

The Medical Department of the United States Army, under the direction of Major General Raymond W. Bliss, The Surgeon General, takes great pleasure in presenting to the Fourth International Neurological Congress this tribute to the departed world-famous neurologists of the past century.

This volume contains biographical sketches of 133 outstanding investigators, authors, and teachers in the field of neurology. Together with an exhibit prepared especially for this memorable event, it represents the collaborative effort of a large number of civilian neurologists in America, who contributed the biographies and many of the portraits, and of two well-known national institutions—the Armed Forces Institute of Pathology and the Army Medical Library. This presentation is made by The Surgeon General, Department of the Army, with a view to stimulating greater collaboration between military and civilian scientists in educational and research programs through the use of the vast facilities of these two institutions: one a comprehensive collection of well-documented pathologic material and the other a great storehouse of medical literature, which constitute a combination unique in the history of medicine.

The Director and the Staff of the Armed Forces Institute of Pathology extend cordial greetings to the participants of the Fourth International Neurological Congress, and anticipate the announcement of scientific discoveries of great consequence to the advancement of neurology in the world.

RAYMOND O. DART
Brigadier General
Director, Armed Forces Institute
of Pathology

PREFACE

During the meeting of the American Neurological Association in Atlantic City in June, 1948, a small group of members foregathered on the boardwalk late one evening and, while chatting, conceived the idea of preparing an historical account of the achievements in neurology for presentation to the Fourth International Neurological Congress to be held in Paris the succeeding year. The idea quickly took form, and a committee of 20 was appointed to select the 100 most outstanding neurologists of the past century, exclusive of those still living, on whom to concentrate our efforts. The choices of the committee members far exceeded the number to be selected (who would expect any two persons to see exactly eye-to-eye in judging greatness?); and as a consequence it was decided not to restrict ourselves to so arbitrary a number as 100, which might, by the roundness of its digits, suggest finality.

The request for biographical sketches met with an enthusiastic response from all parts of the United States. Many chose to write of their teachers or associates, while others selected those in whose works they had a special interest. When 133 sketches had been completed a halt had to be called, even though some important personages had not yet been included. Portraits came down from the walls or out of the portfolios of the authors of the sketches, and many are published here for the first time. Each of the contributors, including several from abroad, has helped, in one way or another, to preserve the precious past from oblivion.

This volume was intended to serve as a *vade mecum* to an exhibit sent to the Congress by the Armed Forces Institute of Pathology—an exhibit which included the portraits and chief works of well over 100 neurologists—but untoward circumstances prevented its being printed by the appointed time. These portraits and volumes were put on display in the great Salle des Pas-Perdus of the École de Médecine where they provided evidence of the rich heritage left by such immortals as Claude Bernard, Cajal, Charcot, Gowers, Helmholtz, Hughlings Jackson, and Pavlov, to remind us—as we congregated there to exchange ideas—that the history of neurology cannot be divorced from its pursuit and that scientific achievement knows no national boundary. This volume makes that exhibit more tangible.

WEBB HAYMAKER, M.D.

ACKNOWLEDGMENTS

*T*hose to whom I am most indebted for suggestions on the biographical sketches—for this was a joint effort in which the sketches were freely circulated among the authors—are Dr. Gerhardt von Bonin, Dr. Stanley Cobb, Dr. D. Denny-Brown, Dr. Walter Freeman, the late Dr. George B. Hassin, Dr. J. R. M. Innes, Dr. Hartwig Kuhlenbeck, the late Dr. F. H. Lewey, Dr. Henry R. Viets, Dr. Paul I. Yakovlev, and, above all, Dr. Robert Wartenberg, who took on the task of correcting the assembled galley proof. Those in other countries who assisted by checking biographical details and contributing valuable data were Dr. Ilse Foerster of Baden-Baden; Mme. le Docteur Sorrel-Dejerine of Paris; Lady Elliot Smith and Prof. LeGros Clark of Oxford (on Elliot Smith); Dr. Rudolf Altschul of Saskatoon, Canada (on Mingazzini); Dr. Pierre Astruc of Paris (on Lasègue); Signe Henschen and Prof. Folke Henschen of Stockholm (on Henschen, Retzius and Wickman); Prof. Hans Hoff of Vienna (on Viennese neurologists); Dr. Maurice-Levy of Paris (on Foix); Dr. Moises Polak of Buenos Aires (on Hortega); Prof. Willibald Scholz of Munich (on Spielmeyer); Prof. Hugo Spatz of Giessen (on Nissl); and Prof. Oskar Vogt and Cécile Vogt of Neustadt/Schwarzwald (on Henschen, Bárány, Hitzig, Liepmann, Nissl and others). Among those in the United States who lent their assistance were Dr. Lauretta Bender (on Schilder); Dr. Tilly Edinger and her sister, Mrs. Dora L. Lindley (on their father); Mrs. Dora Pick Fuchs (on Pick); Dr. Jan Cammermeyer (on Gerlach and Nansen); Dr. Hugo V. Raubitschek (on Weigert); Dr. Charles Rupp (on Spiller); Dr. Hans Smetana (on Redlich and Schilder); Dr. Alphonse R. Vonderahe (on Coghill); Dr. Theodor Wagner-Jauregg (on his father); and Dr. Harry M. Zimmerman (on Spielmeyer).

To those who so freely loaned the portraits for reproduction goes much credit for the final product; their names appear beneath each photograph. The greatest number of photographs were received through the courtesy of the Army Medical Library, the portrait files of which have been enriched during the past century by innumerable donors. Several fine portraits came through the courtesy of Dr. Maurice Genty, Director of the Library of the Académie de Médecine, Paris. Others who were especially generous

were Mrs. Malvine Marburg, New York City; Prof. Ludo van Bo-
gaert, Antwerp; Prof. Dott. Paolo Colombo, Verona; Dr. Macdonald
Critchley, London; Dr. John F. Fulton, New Haven, Connecticut;
Prof. Folke Henschen, Stockholm; Dr. J. R. M. Innes, Washington,
D. C.; Dr. Foster Kennedy, New York City; Dr. W. Krücke, Frank-
furt-am-Main; Dr. Leon Roizin, New York City; Prof. Hugo Spatz,
Giessen; and Dr. Robert Wartenberg, San Francisco.

Members of the Staff of the Armed Forces Institute of Pathology
who collaborated in this undertaking were Mr. Herman Van Cott,
who drew the vignettes of Campbell, Dawson, Liepmann and Nageotte, and Dr. Edward Gunn, who was in charge of the arrangements for the exhibit in Paris. To Mrs. Helen Knight Steward and
Miss Jessie Clare Tomlinson go my special thanks for their invaluable
assistance in editing. Brigadier General Raymond O. Dart, former
Director of the Armed Forces Institute of Pathology, and Colonel
J. H. McNinch, former Director of the Army Medical Library, were
the two who, by their active support, made this venture possible.

The authors of these sketches join in expressing their appreciation
to Mr. Charles C Thomas not only for this display of his professional
skill but also for his wholehearted cooperation in making available
another chapter on the history of medicine.

WEBB HAYMAKER, M.D.

THE MEANING OF SOME OF THE ACADEMIC TERMS
USED IN THESE BIOGRAPHIES

*S*ince the reader may not be entirely familiar with such terms as *agrégé, habilitation, venia legendi, Professor Extraordinarius* and *Bachelor of Medicine,* frequently used in this volume to denote an individual's position in the academic hierarchy, a few words of explanation seem in order.

France. The word *faculty* (from *facultas*—meaning facility) carries with it a different connotation in France than in some other countries. Thus, in English universities the word faculty refers to the teaching personnel of a university, whereas in countries of the European continent the word signifies a division or a department of the university. Thus, *Faculté de Médecine* means the School of Medicine of a French university. In medieval times, universities were municipal civic organs and, so, preeminently democratic institutions of learning. With the end of the feudal period and with the increasing assertion of centralized monarchical statism of the XVIth and XVIIth centuries, they became "royal" universities, and since then have remained state-governed agencies of higher education, usually under the budgetary and political dominion of the state ministry of public education. In France, as in most other countries of continental Europe, there are no private or corporate universities or schools of medicine as they are known in the countries of Anglo-Saxon lineage.

The degree of Bachelor of Arts from a *lyceé* (college) has for centuries been a prerequisite of matriculation at the Faculty of Medicine of a French university. In the early 1900's another requirement was introduced, namely, a certificate of premedical study in physics, chemistry, and natural history. Once matriculated, the student embarks on five years (until recently, at any rate) of formal instruction.

A distinctive feature of the French system is that clinical training begins in the first year of medicine. On completing this year the student is eligible for a competitive examination in anatomy, medicine and surgery for an appointment as *externe des hôpitaux*—a part-time, non-resident hospital position. The successful candidates are placed in any one of the municipal hospitals in the Public Welfare Administration of the City of Paris. Those who do not seek or do not receive the appointment of externe (about one-half of the

applicants fail to pass the examination for this appointment) are
required, nevertheless, to complete the "stages" of clinical training
in medicine, surgery, obstetrics, and certain major specialties in
various municipal hospitals affiliated with the university. Completion of these "stages" during the third to fifth year is necessary before
a student is eligible for graduation.

The externeship marks the beginning of the formal medical *training* of the student at the hospital services and is quite distinct from
his medical *education* at the Faculty of Medicine. The maximum
duration of the externeship is six years. A minimum of two years
is required before the medical student is eligible for competitive
examination for an appointment as interne at one of the municipal
hospitals (*interne des hôpitaux*).

The examination for interneship is highly competitive in Paris,
for usually there are more externes seeking interneship appointments than there are vacancies available. The functions and status
of the *interne des hôpitaux* are equivalent to those of the full-time
resident house officer in an American hospital, except for one difference: the *interne des hôpitaux*, even though he has completed the
five-year curriculum of the medical school and two years of externat,
does not yet have the degree of Doctor of Medicine. He is a physician "de facto" but not yet "de jure," so to speak. The duration of
interneship is from one to four years. Many of the distinguished
physicians of France made their first important contributions while
they were still internes, i.e., mere apprentices of clinical medicine
and surgery.

All students who have completed the curriculum of five years at
the Faculty of Medicine and have fulfilled the required two-year
minimum of the "stage" clinical experience (and regardless of
whether or not they have been externes or internes) are eligible
for the *examens d'état* (final examinations) in which a final sifting
of the students takes place. Those who pass are permitted to present a doctoral thesis before a commission of professors appointed
by the Dean. After the thesis is successfully "defended"—seldom
is the defense unsuccessful—and after it is published at the candidate's expense, a diploma of Doctor of the University of Paris (or
elsewhere) is granted.

Such is the traditional pattern of what may be called the professional education and training of the French physician.

The system of higher competitive examination for hospital training and appointments has been much criticized of late, and for valid reasons. It tended to stifle the youthful energies by the cut and dried formalities of dogmatic medicine. But it has had, at least in the past, its incontestable merit. The French system of hospital interneship has provided an incomparable clinical experience. It is this system, later adopted in other countries, which has reared the outstanding clinicians for which France is so legitimately renowned. Someone has rightly stated: "There is nothing in clinical medicine that some French clinician hasn't already seen and described."

The professional and academic medical career in France is rooted in the clinical experience of interneship. An interne who shows the inclination and has the ability to advance in the academic field of medicine has the opportunity of becoming *chef de clinique* of the hospital service of a faculty professor in charge of the service. This, as far as we know, is not a competitive appointment, but is made on the basis of personal qualities and scientific work done during interneship. Only former internes who have received their doctorate are eligible for the appointment. A *chef de clinique* has the privilege of seeing private patients outside the University. His official duties are thus part-time, and consist of supervision of the service and teaching of internes, externes and medical students of the service. The status of a *chef de clinique* is very similar to that of an assistant professor in an American university hospital. The title indicates, therefore, not only a university rank but also a municipal hospital position. The duration of the appointment is unlimited.

The position of chef de clinique usually affords the opportunity of following an academic career at the University. Competitive examination and presentation of a *thèse d'agrégation* lead to the next university rank—that of *professeur agrégé* (associate professor). Only a few ever become full professors.

Different titles are employed in the non-clinical fields. Thus, the equivalent of instructor in such academic pursuits as histology, anatomy, physiology, pathology, etc., is called a *préparateur*; the equivalent to the rank of assistant professor in these fields in the School of Medicine of a University is referred to as *chef des travaux à la Faculté*; and the equivalent to an assistant professor in charge of clinical and/or pathological laboratories of a hospital service, under a *médecin des hôpitaux* who was university status of either *professeur* or *professeur agrégé*, is called a *chef de laboratoire à la faculté*. All three of these positions are non-competitive ones filled by appointment.

The crowning achievement in the professional career of the French physician is that of being appointed *médecin* (or *chirurgien*) *des hôpitaux*. Only chefs de clinique are eligible for this appointment, for which there is the keenest competition. Not only must written and oral examinations in clinical and academic fields be passed, but the candidate, to be successful, must have achieved a high measure of personal and academic distinction.

A *médecin* (or chirurgien) des hôpitaux is a physician-in-chief (a reputed practitioner by definition) of a service in a municipal hospital. The appointment carries no university rank or status. Many a renowned *médecin* (or chirurgien) des Hôpitaux de Paris had no university status beyond that of former chef de clinique, although his prestige was equal to or even greater than that of a professor. Babinski, for instance, was *chef de clinique* of Charcot at the Salpêtrière but never received the rank even of *professeur agrégé*.

A most distinguished few among the médecins (or chirurgiens) des hôpitaux are elected to the Academy of Medicine and, indeed, very few, and usually when they have reached a venerable age, receive the highest academic honor by election to the Institut de France (Academy of Sciences).

It should be pointed out that while the pattern of the professional and academic career in neurology was the same as that in other fields of medicine, the educational system in psychiatry took a different turn rather early in the XIXth century. The mental hospitals, or *asiles d'aliénés,* as the French with the straightforward honesty of their Gallic logic still call them, are under the Ministry of the Interior and are administered by the governments of the regional "departments" into which France is divided. Thus, the asylums in metropolitan Paris are under the administration of the Department of Seine. In these asylums competitive examinations are held for the position of *interne des asiles d'aliénés de la Seine* (a training appointment in psychiatry), *assistant des asiles d'aliénés* (equivalent to senior physician in most American state hospitals), and *médecin des asiles* (equivalent to psychiatrist-in-chief).

At the hospice de Ste.-Anne in Paris, which is a psychiatric clinic and teaching hospital for the Faculty of Medicine of the University of Paris, the head of the psychiatric services is usually a professor at the Faculty of Medicine.

Paul I. Yakovlev

Germany. After obtaining his M.D. and his medical license—when he is granted *Ärztliche Approbation*—the young physician who aspired to university life usually began as *Assistent* in a university clinic or institute. After several years of scientific work documented by a number of original publications, his professor then sponsored him for nomination as *Privatdozent.* After he had been elected he obtained *venia legendi* (*venia,* permission; *legendi,* of lecturing) that is he became entitled to give courses of lectures in his particular field. This made him officially a junior member of the faculty. The complex procedure through which the candidate had to make his way in order to earn his venia legendi was known as *Habilitation.* A prerequisite was the submission of an original major research work known as the *Habilitationsschrift.* The candidate was also required to give a lecture before the faculty, after which each faculty member could engage him in discussion. If he passed this test he was then entitled to give an official public lecture known as the *Antrittsvor-lesung,* to which the faculty members, the student body, and the public were invited. After the completion of this requirement the venia legendi was granted. This did not carry any official salary but entitled the Privatdozent to collect lecture fees from his students. In order to make a living, he usually continued in his position as Assistent. Some, however, went into private practice and relinquished their assistantship.

After several years of successful activity, the *Privatdozent,* upon recommendation of the faculty, received the title of (*nichtbeamteter, ausserplanmässiger*) *ausserordentlicher Professor,* or *Extraordinarius.* This means that he was given the title of professor without salary. There were, however, a few positions such as (*beamteter, planmässiger*) *ausserordentlicher Professor,* or *planmässiger Extraordinarius,* which carried a salary.

The climax of the academic career was the appointment as *ordentlicher öffentlicher Professor,* or *Ordinarius,* in charge of an established chair, usually combined with the directorship of a clinic or institute. The appointment was made by the government upon recommendation by the faculty.

If a chair was vacant, not only could an Extraordinarius of that university qualify as a candidate for the position, but also an Ordinarius, Extraordinarius or even Privatdozent of any other university.

After a number of years of successful work, the government usually conferred on the Professor the honorary title of *Geheimrat* (privy councillor) or *Hofrat* (court councillor). A still higher title was *Wirklicher Geheimer Rat* or *Wirklicher Geheimer Hofrat* (actual privy councillor, etc.) which often carried also the title *Exzellenz* (or *Prädikat*) (your excellency).

A full professor was never retired but was merely relieved of his official duties (*von den amtlichen Pflichten entbunden*) and of his directorship; he continued to receive his full salary. This, however, was only part of the earnings of a professor, who derived most of his income from lecture fees and, in the case of clinicians, from private practice. Much the same applied in Austria except that the professor was retired on reaching a certain age.

Hartwig Kuhlenbeck
E. A. Spiegel

Great Britain. In Great Britain neurological medicine was first fostered and established as a special interest of general physicians whose practice covered the whole range of internal medicine. About 25 years ago appointments as neurologist, or physician-in-charge of the department for nervous diseases, began to be made at Guy's and some other London hospitals. The Universities still do not recognize any status in neurology. The highest status of a practising neurologist was therefore that of *honorary physician* to one of the great hospitals where he had charge of a full service in internal medicine. In London the neurologist was, in addition, usually a physician to a special neurological hospital (the National Hospital for the Paralyzed and Epileptic [now the National Hospital for Nervous Diseases], the Maida Vale Hospital for Nervous Diseases, or the West End Hospital). The first staff appointment to any of these hospitals was as assistant physician, then by a laborious promotion by seniority to *physician-to-outpatients,* and finally *full visiting physician.* All these appointments were purely honorary. The first full time appointment in neurology in Britain was that of director of the research unit at the National Hospital in 1932. Gowers was physician to University College Hospital and to the National Hospital, and Jackson to the London Hospital and to the National Hospital. Head was physician to the London Hospital alone. Ferrier was physician to King's College Hospital and physician to the National Hospital, with an honorary title of Professor of Neuropathology in King's College of the University of London.

The most valued civil distinction given to neurologists is the royal bestowal of one of the classes of the various orders of knighthood. These could be respectively member, officer, commander, or knight. Conferral of the last of these honours entitled the recipient to the prefix "Sir" before his first name. He is then no longer addressed as "Dr." It is customary to place initials of these decorations after the name: O.B.E. for example, indicates an officer of the Order of the British Empire, C.B. a Commander of the Order of the Bath. Gowers became Sir William Gowers in 1897. Ferrier was knighted in 1911. The Order of Merit, instituted in 1902, is given for outstanding achievement. Sherrington and Adrian have been the only neurological recipients. No neurologist has been raised to the peerage, nor have any with hereditary titles chosen a neurological career. The most coveted scientific honour is election to Fellowship of the Royal Society (F.R.S.).

In Britain, licence to practice medicine is granted to those who graduate from a university as *Bachelor of Medicine* and *Bachelor of Surgery*, and also to licentiates of the Royal Colleges of Physicians. The Royal Colleges are professional corporations entirely separate from the Universities. The consultant physician is expected to have obtained the M.D. by further examination and thesis, and also to have passed the membership examination of one of the Royal Colleges of Physicians (which entitles him to the qualification M.R.C.P.). Elevation to Fellowship of a Royal College of Physicians (F.R.C.P.) is by election, after an interval of at least five years from obtaining the membership.

The first neurosurgeons in Britain also practised general surgery, and held appointments as honorary surgeon to general hospitals, as well as honorary visiting surgeon to special hospitals. Fellowship of the College of Surgeons of London, Edinburgh or Ireland is gained by special examination, and is essential for a surgical consultant. By tradition all surgeons are called "Mr." instead of "Dr." The universities confer the degree of Bachelor of Surgery, together with the M.B., on graduation. Some aspiring to consultant practice in surgery now take the advanced degree of Master of Surgery by special examination. The same civil and scientific awards may be made to surgeons as to physicians.

D. DENNY-BROWN

CONTENTS

xxiii

Section II

NEUROPHYSIOLOGISTS

Section III

NEUROPATHOLOGISTS

Section IV

CLINICAL NEUROLOGISTS

SECTION V

NEUROSURGEONS

The FOUNDERS *of*
NEUROLOGY

I

NEUROANATOMISTS

NICOLÁS ACHÚCARRO (1880–1918)

Achúcarro occupies a unique position in the Spanish school of histology as favorite pupil of Cajal and inspired teacher of del Río Hortega. His brilliant career was cut short by Hodgkin's disease when he was only 37.

He was born in Bilbao. After preliminary medical studies in Madrid at the turn of the century, he set out on a pilgrimage to several scientific world capitals. In Paris he came under the guiding genius of Pierre Marie; in Munich he worked with Kraepelin and Alzheimer; and in Florence he profited by his association with Lugaro. Returning to Madrid, he obtained the M.D. in 1906. Two years later he accepted the invitation of I. W. Blackburn to work in the laboratory of the Government Hospital for the Insane in Washington, D. C. (now St. Elizabeth's Hospital). His studies there led to the publication in 1909[1] and 1910[2] of five articles on neurohistology and neuropathology, all of which were illustrated with unmatchable grace by his own hand.

Possessed of learning uncommon for his years, a thorough knowledge of the classical techniques of Cajal, and an incisive clinical sense, Achúcarro, on his return to Madrid, proceeded with extraordinary energy to tackle one basic problem after another in neurohistology and neuropathology, and to carry his deductions into the clinical and physiological fields. The delineation of the nature of the various cell types in the human cerebral cortex in 1910[3] and the development of the silver tannate method in 1911[4] were among his earlier accomplishments. The investigations of Cajal on neuroglia awakened in Achúcarro an interest in this subject, with the result that important studies, some in collaboration with Cajal, were published in 1908[5] and 1913.[6] Of equal distinction were his works, alone and in association with Sacristan, on the pineal body.[7] From Achúcarro, Hortega learned the art and magic of silver impregnation which were to lead him to the discovery of the microglia.

Achúcarro's contributions to neuropathology were no less outstanding. When only 30, he was invited by Nissl to collaborate in the preparation of a series of articles on the cerebral cortex for the *Nissl-Alzheimer Arbeiten;* he responded by providing a masterful study of rabies.[8] Other authoritative studies were those on general

5

Nicolás Achúcarro

paresis (1911),[9] brain tumors, including ganglioneuroma of the central nervous system (1913),[10] and Alzheimer's disease (1914).

Achúcarro was known not only for his happy disposition, intellectual vigor, and broad culture, but also for the cutting sarcasm with which he castigated the careless and the mediocre. No one was better able than Hortega to assess the nature of the man. In his as yet unpublished autobiography, Hortega wrote as follows: "The sad event of the death of Achúcarro has left a deep impression on us. There was tragedy not only in the physical suffering which he endured without palliatives, but also in the moral suffering of this man of action, who although intensely desirous of life, lay conquered by the inability to act, knowing he was to die. How much more fruitful work might have been accomplished through the vigor of his mind! His dominant traits were lucid intelligence, fine sensibility, and sharp criticism. As an investigator he possessed

Portrait, courtesy of Prof. J. F. Tello, Madrid, Spain. (Photograph was obtained from Achúcarro's mother in 1949.)

ingenuity in the construction of hypotheses, a rare passion for analysis, and an equanimity of judgment. His scientific productions demonstrate his clear perception of the meaning of his observations, even though some of the structures he sought to stain were poorly defined because of the primitiveness of the equipment at his command; like the brilliant Cuvier, he was able on the basis of only slender clues to reconstruct the whole. Death, however, has folded his wings. Only his spirit accompanies us. He was a benevolent master. Through the ardor of my gratitude for his guidance and through the faith kindled by his inspiring example, I was able in some small measure to utilize at least some of the stimulus to work which he provided."

BUENOS AIRES, ARGENTINA   M. POLAK

References

[1]Govt. Hosp. for Insane, Bull. No. 1. Washington, D. C., Govt. Printing Office, 1909; p. 43–54.   [2]*Ibid.*, Bull. No. 2, 1910; p. 81–90, 91–103, 104–114, 115–117.   [3]Tr. Lab. invest. biol. Univ. Madrid, 1910, 8: 169–176.   [4]*Ibid.*, 1911, 9: 269–288.   [5]*Ibid.*, 1908, 6: 95–122.   [6]*Ibid.*, 1913, 11: 187–217.   [7]Rev. clín. Madrid, 1912, 8: 336–340.   [8]*Histologische und histopathologische Arbeiten* (Nissl-Alzheimer). Jena, 1909, 3: 143–199.   [9]*Zschr. ges. Neur. Psychiat.*, 1911, 7: 375–383.   [10]Fol. neurobiol., Lpz., 1913, 7: 524–538.

References to Biography: 1) Tr. Soc. biol., Barcel., 1918, 6: 13–14 (not signed).   2) Presse méd., 1918, 26: 418 (Azoulay).

CORNELIUS UBBO ARIËNS KAPPERS (1877–1946)

*A*riëns Kappers was born in Groningen, The Netherlands. After attending schools at Leeuwarden he went to the University of Amsterdam, where Winkler and van Rees were among his teachers. Here he soon found his life work and followed it consistently.

His doctoral thesis, based on his research at the Marine Biological Station at Naples, on the structure of the brain of teleosts and selachians, won honors in 1904. He then received an appointment in neuropathology at the University Hospitals in Amsterdam, but in 1906 joined Edinger's Senckenbergisches Pathologisches Institut at Frankfurt-am-Main, and shortly was made chief of the laboratory. Here a great part of his future thinking was determined, and in many

ways he followed and expanded Edinger's methods and concepts, particularly in regard to the neo-, archi-, and paleo-subdivisions of the various parts of the brain.

In 1907 he published his first paper on neurobiotaxis,[1] and as years went by he continued to develop this theory of nuclear position which so greatly intrigued him. Although the early postulates as to the mechanisms involved have not been verified, and a number of exceptions to the rule are now apparent, the theory, as restated

Portrait, courtesy of A. Ariëns Kappers, Jr., Amsterdam. (Photograph taken in 1928 on receiving Honorary Doctorate of Science at Yale University.)

in 1927,[2] has been of great use in stimulating research and in drawing attention to certain general principles in comparative neuroanatomy.

In 1908 Kappers was unanimously elected director of the Central Institute for Brain Research in Amsterdam, which was founded, in part for him, by the Royal Dutch Academy of Science; the Institute was patterned after the Edinger Institute in Frankfurt. He remained loyal to the Institute in spite of invitations to professorships of much greater personal advantage from the Universities of Leiden and Yale. A just reward came in 1929 when he was elected to the chair of comparative neuroanatomy at the University of Amsterdam. He held these two positions for the rest of his life. Many honors were accorded him; among them were degrees from the Universities of Dublin, Glasgow, Yale and Chicago. He was a member of the Royal Dutch Academy of Science, and a Fellow of the Royal Society of Edinburgh.

Ariëns Kappers was a tall, well-built man, courteous and dignified in bearing, with a genial twinkle in his eye, and a friendliness which could be relied on. He welcomed students at the Institute without regard to race or creed, and gave them freedom not only to work but also to think. His contacts with students and colleagues at the Institute, on numerous lecture tours, and as visiting professor at the Peiping Union Medical School and the American University at Beirut, developed in them a sound interest in and respect for comparative neuroanatomy.

In his researches, which covered all parts of the nervous system, he clearly demonstrated the usefulness of the comparative method for elucidating the complexity of the structure and functions of the brains of the higher mammals and of man. His concepts were presented in an encyclopedic treatise published in German in 1920[3] and reissued in a much enlarged English edition in collaboration with G. Carl Huber and Elizabeth Caroline Crosby in 1936.[4] A second treatise, in French, prepared in collaboration with E. H. Strasburger, was published posthumously.[5] In the latter he included a summary of his more recent interests on the fissuration of the cortex in modern and prehistoric man and its anthropologic bearing. These interests were stimulated by his visit to China in 1924 and intensified while in Syria in 1929 and led him naturally into the field of anthropology during his later years.

During World War II he worked for his country with intense patriotism and lived to see peace and freedom again established. His end came suddenly while working in his garden on July 28, 1946.

ROCKVILLE, MARYLAND   DAVID MCK. RIOCH

References

[1]Neur. Cbl., 1907, 26: 834–840.   [2]Acta psychiat. neur., Kbh., 1927, 2: 118–145.   [3]Die vergleichende Anatomie des Nervensystems der Wirbeltiere und des Menschen. 2 vol. Haarlem, Bohn, 1920–21 (with Fortuyn).   [4]The comparative anatomy of the nervous system of vertebrates, including man. 2 vol. New York, Macmillan, 1936.   [5]Anatomie comparée du système nerveux, particulièrement de celui des mammifères et de l'homme. Haarlem, Bohn, 1947.

References to Biography: 1) J. Comp. Neur., 1946, 85: 309–311 (Crosby). 2) Med. tschr. geneesk., 1946, 90: 1917–1927 (van Valkenburg).   3) Yearb. R. Soc. Edin., 1947; p. 19–21 (Dott).

JULES GABRIEL FRANÇOIS BAILLARGER (1809–1890)

*B*aillarger was born of a middle-class family, in Montbazan, Indre-et-Loire, France. His education was entrusted to an old priest who was, however, a better apiarist than scholar. Baillarger studied medicine at Paris under Esquirol and devoted his professional career to the management of the mentally ill, first at Charenton and later at Ivry. To him Trélat and Magnan owed their deliverance from cholera, for it was he who personally nursed them back to health.

An energetic, sociable individual, noted as a teacher and given to philanthropy, he founded with Longet and Cerise in 1843 the *Annales médico-psychologiques* in which he published many of his papers, and later he was the moving spirit in establishing the *Société médico-pyschologique* and the *Association mutuelle des médecins aliénistes*. He was vitally interested in hospital administration, the care of prisoners, deficiency disorders and cretinism, and made the usual run of mental hospital observations. In 1865, according to André Ombredane,[1] Baillarger pointed out that patients with aphasia had lost the power of voluntary speech but nevertheless retained certain automatic expressions that were not always employed correctly. This contribution was recognized by Hughlings Jackson, who called it "Baillarger's Principle."

Jules Gabriel François Baillarger

Baillarger's interests were mainly clinical, and his descriptions of behavior in various types of mania, melancholia and general paralysis were true to form but not really enlightening. He described the manic-depressive cycle and the stupor of melancholia, and he noted

Portrait, courtesy of the Library of the New York Academy of Medicine.

the unequal pupils in dementia paralytica and its occasional association with locomotor ataxia. From his description of these disorders, however, it must be concluded that as a clinican he was working in etiologic darkness.

Outstanding among his works on psychiatry was that on hallucinations—which brought him the Prix de l'Académie (1842). According to Zilboorg and Henry,[2] Baillarger "was the first to sense that hallucinations are what we would call today spontaneous results of a psychological reaction; he called them 'involuntary.' He also studied the role of the state which is intermediary between that of being asleep and that of being awake, at which time normal people have hallucinatory experiences, now called 'hypnagogic.' "

Baillarger's name endures like that of Gratiolet because of a minor incident in his career when, at the age of 30, while still engaged in clinicopathologic correlations, he presented in 1840 a paper before the Académie Royale de Médecine on the structure of the gray matter of the cortex.[3] Gennari, Vicq d'Azyr and Soemmering had noted white lines in the cortex with the naked eye by gross dissection; Baillarger, on the other hand, made his advance by cutting thin slices of fresh cortex, placing them between two pieces of glass, and observing them with the aid of a light held behind them. By this means he divided the cortex into six layers of alternate white and gray laminae. He was able to satisfy himself that the white lines seen by Gennari in the occipital area could be traced in all parts of the cortex, although they were far less conspicuous anteriorly than posteriorly. This continuation of Gennari's line has therefore come to be known as the "external line or white stripe of Baillarger" (Fulton).[4] Baillarger's stripes attracted much attention and as late as 1907, Elliot Smith—who at that time was in Cairo—examined freshly cut slices of brain with a hand lens, and taking the stripes as landmarks, was able to distinguish some 40 sharply delimited cortical areas.[5]

After 1840, Baillarger was drawn more fully to the clinic, from which he made one more sally into the field of anatomic research. This netted him in 1845 the credit of having first shown that the surface of the human brain, in comparison to its volume, is less than that in smaller animals and that as a compensatory measure larger brains undergo greater fissuration than smaller ones—in short that the difference in external form of lissencephalic and gyrencephalic brains is explicable on the basis of the geometric law of volumes, namely, that the volume increases as the cube of the diameter while the surface increases as the square.[6,7] This observation has stood the test of time.

WASHINGTON, D. C. WALTER FREEMAN

References

[1]*Études de psychologie médicale. I. Perception et langage.* Rio de Janeiro, Atlantica, 1944. [2]*A history of medical psychology.* New York, Norton, 1941; p. 396. [3]Mém. Acad. K. Méd., 1840, 8: 143–183. [4]Bull. Inst. Hist. M., Balt., 1937, 5: 895–913. [5]J. Anat. Physiol., 1907, 41: 237–254. [6]Gaz. hôp., 1945, 18: 179. [7]Bull. Acad. méd., Par., 1845, 10: 558.

References to Biography and Works: 1) France méd., 1902, 49: 473–475 et seq. (Magnan). 2) Ann. méd.-psychol., Par., 1892, 7.sér., 16: 5–58 (contains bibliography; Ritti, Dureau). 3) *External morphology of the primate brain.* Springfield, Ill., Thomas, 1950 (Connolly). 4) *The comparative anatomy of the nervous system of vertebrates, including man.* 2 vol. New York, Macmillan, 1936 (Kappers, Huber and Crosby).

KORBINIAN BRODMANN (1868–1918)

*K*orbinian Brodmann was born in Liggersdorf, Hohenzollern. He studied medicine in Munich, Würzburg, Berlin and Freiburg i.B. and received his license to practice medicine in 1895. For a year thereafter he worked in the Universitäts-Kinderklinik und Poliklinik in Munich with the intention of settling down, eventually, as a general practitioner in the Schwarzwald. He contracted diphtheria, however, and in order to recuperate from its sequelae took a position as assistant in a sanitarium for nervous diseases in Alexanderbad im Fichtelgebirge (northern Bavaria), which was directed at that time by Oskar Vogt. This contact with Vogt, in the summer of 1896, induced Brodmann to devote himself to the study of neurology and psychiatry. In 1898 he received the M.D. at Leipzig.

During the period 1900–01 Brodmann worked at the Städtische Irrenanstalt at Frankfurt-am-Main, where he came in contact with Alzheimer; it was under his influence that he became interested in the anatomical problems which were to occupy him exclusively for the remainder of his life. In 1901, he accepted a position with Vogt at the Neurobiologisches Institut in Berlin. Here he remained until

1910. During this period Brodmann accomplished virtually everything for which he later became known.

In a series of papers,[1-9] Brodmann established the basis upon
which the present-day science of comparative cytoarchitectonics of
the mammalian cortex rests. His famous map of the human cortex
appeared in 1908.[6,7] Brodmann's broad comparative-anatomic approach, his recognition that the cortex is organized anatomically
along the same basic principles in all mammals, and his idea of
utilizing the morphogenesis of the cortex as a basis for the classification of cortical types and for the nomenclature of the layers, were

Portrait, courtesy of Prof. Hugo Spatz, Giessen, Germany.

all instrumental in dispelling the almost hopeless confusion which existed before Brodmann entered the field. His studies culminated in his famous book, *Vergleichende Lokalisationslehre der Grosshirnrinde* (Leipzig, Barth, 1909; reprinted 1925) which remains the only comprehensive work ever published on this subject. After Brodmann left Berlin he began a series of investigations dealing with the size and development of mammalian cortical fields. However, the lack of adequate laboratory facilities curtailed greatly his productivity, and the outbreak of World War I interrupted his research altogether.

Despite the fact that the significance of his work was recognized early by leading German scientists, Brodmann faced great obstacles in his academic career. The opposition to his work was so strong that the medical faculty of the University of Berlin refused to admit him as a Privatdozent. His personal relations at the Neurobiologisches Institut were also strained.

The economic insecurity of his position at the Neurobiologisches Institut induced him to leave Berlin in 1910 and to accept a position with R. Gaupp at Tübingen, where he was made titular professor in 1913. Gaupp, now 82, was one of his staunchest friends. Only in 1916, when he became Prosector at the Irrenanstalt Nietleben near Halle, did Brodmann achieve for the first time in his life an economically secure position which offered him at the same time an opportunity for research. When, in Munich, the Deutsche Forschungsanstalt für Psychiatrie was established, an institution where Kraepelin, Nissl and Spielmeyer had taken up their abode, Brodmann was appointed head of its topographic-histologic division. W. Scholz relates that Spielmeyer spoke of Brodmann as an intense and earnest man who was reserved almost to the point of timidity, but who could flare, on occasion, into a temper. A few months after the appointment, Brodmann died of acute sepsis. He was survived by his wife, whom he had married less than two years previously, and by a baby daughter, Ilse, who was taken into the home of her maternal grandmother. His daughter is now in Western Germany.

BALTIMORE, MARYLAND   JERZY E. ROSE

References

[1] J. Psychol. Neur., Lpz., 1903, 2: 79–107.   [2] *Ibid.*, 1903, 2: 133–159. [3] *Ibid.*, 1905, 4: 177–226.   [4] *Ibid.*, 1905, 6: 108–120.   [5] *Ibid.*, 1906,

6: 275–400.   [6]*Ibid.*, 1908, *10:* 231–246.   [7]*Ibid.*, 1908, *10:* 287–334. [8]Verh. anat. Ges., 1912, *26:* 157–216.   [9]Verh. Ges. deut. Naturforsch., 1913, *85:* I.Teil: 200–240.

References to Biography: 1) J. Psychol. Neur., Lpz., 1918, *24:* I–X (O. Vogt).   2) Münch. med. Wschr., 1920, *67:* 75–78 (Kraepelin). 3) Zschr. ges. Neur. Psychiat., 1919, *45:* 329–349 (Nissl).

ALFRED WALTER CAMPBELL (1868–1937)

*A*lfred Walter Campbell was born in his father's "station" at Cunningham Plains, near Harden, in the hills of New South Wales, Australia. He studied medicine in Edinburgh, receiving the degrees of M.B. and Ch.M. in 1889. Here he showed athletic prowess which won him the captaincy of the cricket and soccer teams. He then went to Vienna as assistant to Krafft-Ebing, and later studied in Prague. In 1892 he obtained his doctorate in medicine with a thesis *On the pathology of alcoholic insanity*, for which the University of Edinburgh accorded him a gold medal.

He spent the next 13 years as resident medical officer and director of the laboratory of pathology at Rainhill Asylum near Liverpool, and it was in that laboratory that he conducted the studies for which he is famous. Campbell owed much to Sir Charles Sherrington who gave him—as he stated—"not only valuable specimens, but counsel and encouragement when energy flagged."

In 1905 Campbell returned to Sydney, N.S.W. where he took up the practice of neurology and psychiatry, which he carried on with great distinction until he retired in 1937.

Those who knew him say he was a fine speaker. In private life he was reserved but not hard to know. He had a keen and "pleasantly sardonic" sense of humor. He was reticent about his scientific accomplishments but ready to talk more freely when it came to sporting achievements.

Although some spadework had been done, "it is safe to say that architectonics of the cerebral cortex started with Campbell in England and Brodmann in Germany." Campbell's magnum opus, *Histological studies on the localization of cerebral function* (Cambridge, University Press, 1905), has become a classic, and his map of the human brain has been reproduced in virtually every textbook on neuroanatomy.

Alfred Walter Campbell

While Brodmann thought mainly as a comparative morphologist and evolutionist, Campbell thought fundamentally in terms of function. "Not until the ground is prospected and prepared by the physiologist and clinician can the histologist hope to step in and work with any real measure of success" (*Histological studies* etc., p. xix). He worked up three normal human hemispheres, a tremendous task in itself, and studied with the same thoroughness the hemispheres of the chimpanzee, the orang (he later described the brain of a gorilla[1]), and the dog, cat and pig. Fifteen other brains, with pathological changes, were studied for special purposes, such as to clarify the finer organization of the motor cortex and the visual area. Most

Portrait, courtesy of the Armed Forces Institute of Pathology, Washington, D. C. (From portrait in *Med. J. Australia*, 1: 182, 1938.)

brains were examined for both cells and fibers. Campbell's subdivisions of the primate cortex were not as fine as those of the
German school, but modern architectonics has time and again decided in favor of his sober views.

Other works which have earned for him the respect of the scientific world were those on radicular fields in herpes zoster (with
Henry Head)[2] and cerebral sclerosis.[3]

Among his later contributions, his address on *Dr. John Hughlings
Jackson*[4] was a model of charm and clarity.

CHICAGO, ILLINOIS   GERHARDT VON BONIN

References

[1]Rep. Path. Lab. Lunacy Dep., N. S. Wales, 1916, *3:* 19–36.   [2]Brain,
Lond., 1900, *23:* 353–523.   [3]*Ibid.,* 1905, *28:* 367–437.   [4]Med. J.
Australia, 1935, *2:* 344–347.

References to Biography: 1) Med. J. Australia, 1938, *1:* 181–185 (contains bibliography; Parker, Dawson, Wallace).   2) Arch. Neur.
Psychiat., Chic., 1938, *40:* 566–568 (Fulton).

JACOB AUGUSTUS LOCKHART CLARKE (1817–1880)

*T*he English neurologist, Lockhart Clarke, was born in London.
While he was still a small boy, his father died; and his mother,
who had been left with adequate financial means, took her family of
seven to France for their education. As a student in France, Clarke
is said to have shown no unusual ability and to have been regarded
by his family as rather indolent. But after returning to England in
1830, he displayed more interest in intellectual pursuits and later
chose a career in medicine, a profession which had already claimed
his grandfather and one of his elder brothers. After receiving his
medical training at Guy's and St. Thomas' Hospitals, he was licensed
by the Apothecaries Society and went to live with his mother at Pim-
lico where he entered into the general practice of medicine.

It was during the period of his life from 1851–68, while engaged in
general practice, that Clarke carried on those detailed investigations which have given his name to posterity. In addition to fundamental investigations on the anatomy and histology of the central
nervous sysem, he published a number of papers on various clinical

Jacob Augustus Lockhart Clarke

subjects, stressing the view that much could be learned of the function of the nervous system in man by carefully correlating the clinical and pathological data.

Clarke's investigations, carried out with great skill and characterized by extreme thoroughness, were illustrated with excellent drawings from his own hand. He is best known for his researches on the spinal cord, especially those establishing the presence of the nucleus dorsalis, called by him the " posterior vesicular column" ("column of Clarke"), and the nucleus intermediolateralis.[1,2] Furthermore, he introduced the method of mounting cleared sections in Canada bal-

Portrait, courtesy of the Army Medical Library, Washington, D. C.

sam,[1] a procedure that constituted a major advance in histological technique. Several of his most important publications on anatomy are to be found in the *Philosophical Transactions of the Royal Society of London* from 1851 to 1868. It was in 1868[3] that Clarke described syringomyelia more or less as it is known today, being preceded in this respect only by Gull.[4] A further understanding of this disorder was soon to appear in the contributions of Hallopean,[5] Charcot and Joffroy,[6] and that by Th. Simon,[7] who distinguished it from hydromyelia. In the late 1880's the clinical descriptions by Fr. Schultze,[8] Kohler,[9] and Bäumler[10] brought more light to the subject, and the turn of the 20th century saw the great monograph of Hermann Schlesinger (1866–1934), of Bohemia (Austria), who became professor of medicine at the Allgemeines Krankenhaus in Vienna. In this monograph Schlesinger discussed 260 cases of the disorder.[11] The masterpiece on syringobulbia by Jonesco-Sisesti appeared in 1932.[12]

Although little appreciated by his own profession, Clarke's research was given recognition by the Royal Society, which elected him Fellow in 1854, and ten years later awarded him its Gold Medal for his scientific achievements. He was also made an Honorary Fellow of the King and Queen's College of Physicians of Ireland in 1867. After obtaining his medical degree from St. Andrews in 1869, he became a member of the College of Physicians of London and left general practice, limiting himself thenceforth to consultations in diseases of the nervous system. Two years later he was appointed physician to the Hospital for Epilepsy and Paralysis at Regent's Park, a position held by him until his death from tuberculosis at the age of 63.

Clarke's contemporaries have described him as a man of the highest character, "with a singleness of purpose, of noble independence, honest and just, conscientious and intellectually keen," but with a singularly retiring and reserved disposition. He never acquired a large practice and is reputed not to have been well off financially. The major satisfaction which he received in life came from his research accomplishments, which brought him world-wide recognition. It is these achievements which give his name a permanent place in neurology.

ROCHESTER, NEW YORK   WILBUR K. SMITH

References

[1]Philos. Tr. R. Soc. London, 1851, *141:* 607–621.   [2]*Ibid.,* 1859, *149:* 437–467.   [3]Med.-Chir. Trans., Lond., 1868, *51:* 249–262 (with Z. Johnson.)   [4]Guy's Hosp. Rep., Lond., 1862, 8: 244–258.   [5]Gaz. méd., Par., 1870, 3.sér., *25:* 183.   [6]Arch. Physiol., Par., 1869, 2: 354–367 *et seq.* [7]Arch. Psychiat., Berl., 1875, *5:* 108–163.   [8]Zschr. klin. Med., 1888, *13:* 523–557.   [9]Prag. med. Wschr., 1888, *13:* 45–47 *et seq.*   [10]Deut. Arch. klin. Med., 1887, *40:* 443–543.   [11]*Die Syringomyelie.* Leipzig u. Wien, Deuticke, 1895.   [12]*La syringobulbie. Contribution à la physiopathologie du tronc cérébral.* Paris, Masson, 1932.

References to Biography: 1) *Dictionary of national biography.* London, Smith, Elder & Co., 1885, *10:* 428 (Bettany).   2) Brit. M. J., 1880, *1:* 170–171 (not signed).

GEORGE ELLETT COGHILL (1872–1941)

*B*orn and reared on a farm near Beaucoup, Illinois, where incessant toil and even hardship were his lot, Coghill early developed a seasoned character, honesty, tenacity of purpose, and inflexibility when it came to dealing with persons of less lofty standards. His education was received at Shurtleff College (Illinois), the University of New Mexico, and Brown University (Rhode Island). In the summer of 1902 he studied with Th. Boveri at Würzburg. After teaching zoology in Oregon at Pacific University and Willamette University, and in Ohio at Denison University, he became, in 1913, Professor of Anatomy at the University of Kansas, and was head of the department from 1918 to 1925. During the next 10 years he was research professor of comparative anatomy at the Wistar Institute of Philadelphia. He was a member of the editorial board of the *Journal of Comparative Neurology* from 1904 until his death, and managing editor from 1927 to 1933.

Coghill's most important contribution was the secure foundation he laid for study of the embryology of behavior. Anatomy did not reach maturity as a science until the origins and relationships of adult structures were revealed by embryology. So also the data of animal and human behavior were not knit together into a consistent fabric of firm texture until certain basic principles were discovered by Coghill and validated by him through a rigorous program of embryologic research. For intensive study he chose the

salamanders, because their patterns of behavior and their bodily structure are generalized and yet comparable with those of man.

Coghill's objective was a record of the exact sequence of changes in patterns of behavior from first motility to the adult, based on statistically adequate numbers of specimens, and a description of the correlated stages in the growth of the nervous system. This inquiry was the first, and so far the most complete, account of the relationships between the progressive differentiation of bodily structure and the operation of that structure as manifest in overt behavior. His most fundamental principle was the demonstration of the primacy of an integrated "total pattern" of organization and the progressive individuation of local "partial patterns" within and under the dominance of the integrated whole. This was validated by detailed

Portrait, courtesy of Dr. O. Larsell, Portland, Oregon.

descriptions of the growth of the mechanisms of both the total and the partial patterns.[1-6] Up to Coghill's time it was generally believed that the reflex constituted the unit of behavior, but Coghill showed that efficient movement occurs prior to the development of reflex mechanisms. In the larvae of Amblystoma, he demonstrated repeatedly that the first movements are adaptive ones (such as those used in swimming), the coordination of which is governed by tegmental and other motor centers,[6-8] that coordinated movements occur before the sensory fibers reach the periphery, and that only later, when the sensory fibers have spanned the gap between periphery and central motor fields, do partial patterns or reflexes come into being. An epitome of his views and a detailed historical background of neuro-embryology, in which are discussed the contributions of some of the founders of neurology with which this volume deals (Vulpian, Remak, His, Schilder, Pavlov), were presented in his presidential address before the American Association of Anatomists in 1933.[3]

The impact of Coghill's views, which undermined the current assumptions of behaviorism, not only profoundly influenced subsequent research in biology and psychology, but also awakened much controversy. Studies of behavior patterns in mammalian and human embryos undertaken by several of Coghill's students and others led to divergent interpretations but left his own results on salamanders intact.

An ambitious program for carrying on his investigations on pouch young of the opossum, unimpeded by the difficulties in maintaining an adequate oxygen supply to which experimental work on living non-marsupial mammalian embryos are subject, failed to develop at the Biological Farm of the Wistar Institute, established in 1929 near Fallsington, Pennsylvania. Difficulties arose and frictions developed which caused him to move back to the Institute laboratory in Philadelphia, where he continued his work on Amblystoma. In December, 1935, his connection with the Institute was severed and Coghill, in poor health and facing an uncertain future, saw the collapse of his program.

From 1936 until his death, Coghill lived in retirement at Gainesville, Florida, where, although partially disabled, he established a private laboratory and opossum colony, supported by a small farm. Here his program was revived and he continued his studies on individuation of limb movements in Ablystoma and the opossum. Sev-

eral younger investigators came to his laboratory from time to time
to work with him on various aspects of development of behavior,
and a number of papers resulted. Coghill himself published a translation of part of W. Preyer's *Specielle Physiologie des Embryo*, a
critical review of the literature on early somatic movements in birds
and mammals other than man, and several briefer papers. While
handicapped by physical infirmity and the necessity of providing for
his immediate needs and for old age from his farm, he continued his
investigations almost to the end, which came on July 23, 1941.

PORTLAND, OREGON   O. LARSELL

References

[1]Correlated anatomical and physiological studies of the growth of the
nervous system (Papers I-XII). J. Comp. Neur., 1914–36, vol. 24–64.
[2]*Anatomy and the problem of behavior*. Cambridge, Univ. Press,
1929.   [3]Science, 1933, 78: 131–138.   [4]J. Genet. Psychol., 1936, 48:
3–19.   [5]*Early embryonic somatic movements in birds and in mammals
other than man*. Monogr. Soc. Res. Child Development, National Research Council, Washington, D. C. Vol. 5, No. 2, 1940.   [6]J. Comp.
Neur. 1943, 79: 463–486.   [7]*Ibid.*, 1926, 40: 47–94; 41: 95–152;
42: 1–16; 1931, 53: 147–168.   [8]Arch. Neur. Psychiat., Chic., 1929, 21:
989–1009.

*Reference to Biography: George Ellett Coghill, naturalist and phi-
losopher.* Chicago, Univ. Chicago Press, 1949 (C. J. Herrick).

ALEXANDER STANISLAVOVICH DOGIEL (1852–1922)

D ogiel was born in Panevezys, district of Kaunas, Lithuania. He
studied medicine at the University of Kazan where in 1883 he
obtained the M.D., and two years later became instructor in embryology. In 1888 he was appointed lecturer in histology at the
University of Tomsk, and in 1892, professor of histology at the
Women's Medical Institute in St. Petersburg, where he remained
for the rest of his life. Here he succeeded in organizing a laboratory
of histology, the products of which attracted world-wide admiration.

Of the Russian investigators who distinguished themselves for
their neurohistologic work (Babukin, Yakulovich, Oviasnikov, Doini-
kov, Bekhterev) from 1850 to the turn of the century, Dogiel was
probably the most outstanding. Boeke regarded him as a "master

Portrait, courtesy of Dr. Leon Roizin, New York City.

of the technique of staining the elements of the nervous system."
He was extraordinarily versatile and prolific, and throughout his
life was inspired by a strong conviction to "réunir des faits pour se
donner des idées" (Buffon). Having exceptional linguistic ability,
he published his scientific papers not only in Russian, but also in
German and French. He had the highest esteem for Cajal, Golgi
and Retzius, to all three of whom he dedicated his classical monograph on the structure of the spinal ganglia of man and animals.[1]
The magnificent illustrations in this volume are from his own hand.

Besides his contributions to various medical fields, Dogiel excelled particularly in his studies on the histologic structure of nerve
fibers, their somatic distribution, and the functional correlations
of motor, and especially sensory, nerve endings. Important also
were his papers on the histology of the sympathetic nervous system,
the neuroglia of the retina, and the sensory end corpuscles in skeletal
muscle, external genital organs, salivary gland, and conjunctiva and
cornea.[2,3]

Dogiel's classification of the neuron types in the spinal, sympathetic, cardiac and intestinal ganglia (in 1899[4]) has been confirmed
by many leading neurohistologists (Marinesco, L. R. Müller, de
Castro, Ranson and Billingsley, Terni, Harting), and is still regarded
as a classical contribution to the knowledge of the cytology of the
nervous tissue. His demonstration of the presence of sensory fibers
in the three extraocular nerves, based on animal experiment,[5] has
been widely quoted.

Due to his unlimited interest and enthusiasm for scientific investigations he was not discouraged by the many obstacles he en-
countered. After frequent delays he succeeded, in 1915, in founding the *Russian Archives of Anatomy, Histology and Embryology*.
As editor-in-chief, he was regarded by his collaborators (Kolossov,
Mislavsky, Severtsov, Tonkov, Zavarin, Deineka) as the most critical and the most accurate of them all. Even during the political
and social upheaval resulting from the Russian revolution, he did
not relax his efforts until stricken by fatal cerebral hemorrhage, which
occurred while he was preparing a manuscript on a favorite subject
in histology.

Papers on the spinal ganglia of man and mammals[1] and on the
sensory apparatus[6] were the most outstanding works among Dogiel's
93 published papers. He will always be known for his works on

histology, distinguished by their precise and rich documentation, their superb drawings, and their lucid thought.

NEW YORK CITY   LEON ROIZIN

References

[1]*Der Bau der Spinalganglien des Menschen und der Säugetiere.* Jena, Fischer, 1908.   [2]Arch. mikr. Anat., 1890, *35:* 305–320; 1893, *41:* 585–612; 1893, *41:* 612–623; 1894, *44:* 15–26; 1895, *46:* 305–344.   [3]Anat. Anz., 1890, *5:* 483–494.   [4]Arch. Anat. Physiol., Anat. Abt., 1899; p. 130–158.   [5]Arch. mikr. Anat., 1906, *68:* 501–526.   [6]Arch. russes d'anat., d'hist. et d'embr., 1917, *1:* 3.

Reference to Biography: Bolshaia meditsinskaia entsiklopediia. Vol 9. Moscow, 1929 (Semashko).

LUDWIG EDINGER (1855–1918)

*E*dinger was born in Worms on the Rhine. He studied in Heidelberg under Carl Gegenbaur (1826–1903) and in Strassburg with Wilhelm Waldeyer (1837–1921). The former stimulated his interest in comparative anatomy and phylogenetic development, and the latter impressed him with his frequent reiteration that clinical and pathological neurology could not be developed successfully without better knowledge of neuroanatomy than was available at the time. Under Waldeyer's guidance, Edinger finished in 1877 his first neurological paper, *Die Endigung der Hautnerven bei Pterotrachea,* which was published in the *Archiv für mikroskopische Anatomie* the same year. During that year he was assistant to Kussmaul.

Edinger's academic career began in Giessen in 1880. Two years later he settled down as a practising neurologist in Frankfurt-am-Main, where he came under the influence of Carl Weigert, who had just perfected his method of staining the myelin sheath. Edinger applied this technique so successfully to the central nervous system of lower vertebrates that he became the founder of modern comparative anatomy of the nervous system. From a work desk in Weigert's Senckenbergisches Pathologisches Institut he built up a Neurological Institute of his own, financed by himself. He was made Ordinarius in neurology at the newly founded University of Frankfurt in 1914, and from that time on his institute was part of the University and was financed by a "Ludwig Edinger Stiftung."

Ludwig Edinger

Early in his career he established his reputation as the foremost teacher of the functional anatomy of the nervous system. His much translated textbook on the structure of the central nervous system[1]

Portrait, courtesy of Mrs. Dora L. Lindley, Pearl River, New York.

grew out of lectures before the medical society in Frankfurt during
the winter of 1883–84. Its success lay in Edinger's endeavors to in-
terconnect structure, function and clinical experience. His attitude
toward comparative neurology was expressed as follows: "There
must be a number of anatomic arrangements which are present alike
in all vertebrates . . . we have only to find . . . that developmental stage of an animal in which this or that mechanism can be
discovered so clearly that it can be fully understood. Once the
configuration of a given structure has been studied in detail in some
forms, one can generally easily discover it in other forms even when
it is more or less obscured by new additions" (translation by Gerhardt von Bonin). He was the first to describe the syndrome
of thalamic pain (1891), which he verified post mortem.[2] This was
a splendid contribution, not overshadowed by that of Roussy and
Dejerine which was published 15 years later. Edinger proposed in
1911[3] that hormones of the anterior lobe of the pituitary are trans-
ported up the pituitary stalk to the hypothalamus, a view recently
amplified by Spatz, Diepen and Gaupp.[4] In 1909 appeared Edinger's volume on the clinical application of neuroanatomy: *Einfüh-
rung in die Lehre vom Bau und den Verrichtungen des Nervensystems* (Leipzig, Vogel).

Distinguished scientists of many countries joined him in his work.
Van Gehuchten and Streeter cooperated in demonstrating the
phylogenetic development of the forebrain, while Ariëns Kappers
did the same for the striatum, and Franz, Goldstein and Röthig for
the diencephalon. With Gordon Holmes and Wallenberg he described the avian brain. Comolli and Shimazono were his co-workers
in formulating the modern concept of the cerebellum, while Wallenberg and Ariëns Kappers collaborated in expanding the idea that
the olfactory system is related to an oral sense, operative in the
recognition, assessment and ingestion of food. It was Edinger who
laid the main groundwork for Ariëns Kappers' later contributions,
although Th. Ziehen and A. Bethe assisted materially. The Edinger
brain collection and library are still intact at the Edinger Institut in
Frankfurt.

No higher praise can be given any scientist than that the discoveries he made and the terms he coined became within one generation household words. The Edinger-Westphal nucleus (identified
in fetal human material by Edinger in 1885[5] and in the adult by

Carl F. O. Westphal in 1887[6]) is well known to every student of neurology. He was the first to describe the ventral and dorsal spinocerebellar tracts and to distinguish between paleo-encephalon and neo-encephalon, and between paleo-cerebellum and neo-cerebellum. He coined and introduced the terms "gnosis" and "praxis," which were later adopted by Freud and by Liepmann in their anatomical and psychological descriptions of agnosia and apraxia. As Critchley has pointed out, the term agnosia was an outgrowth of Finkelnburg's "asymboly," a disorder previously recognized by Hughlings Jackson as an "imperception" and "a defect as special as aphasia."

Edinger was a rare combination of profound scientist, brilliant teacher, fine artist, and able organizer. Also he was noted as a hypnotist. Avellis, of Frankfurt, brought his now famous patient to Edinger, who hypnotized away the patient's weakness and sensory disorders, but the paralysis of the vocal cord and palate was still present six weeks later.[7] Edinger would delight his students by simultaneously drawing the intricate structures of the brain with his left hand while writing their legend with his right. In a moment of relaxation he designed a brain in which the sulci formed the outlines of a host of well concealed cherubs; subsequently a drawing of it was made by R. von Gudden. His daughter, Dr. Tilly Edinger, relates that while he was sitting for his portrait, with shelves of specimens as the background, he noticed that the artist, Lovis Corinth, had difficulty in portraying the brain he was dissecting, and forthwith he came to the canvas and painted it himself. He was as devoted to art as he was to science, and always had on his desk some exquisite small figures, sculptured in ancient Greece.

While still at the very height of his powers, full of plans and ideas for the future, he underwent an operation and died a few hours later of a heart attack. A study of his brain, which he often said he hoped someone would undertake, has recently been reported by Riese and Goldstein.[8]

Edinger's place in history was no better indicated than in a remark by Ariëns Kappers (1915): "So sind auch mir meine Frankfurter Jahre in der Erinnerung geblieben als die schönste Zeit meines Lebens—und nie werde ich den Meister vergessen, der mir das Gebiet der vergleichenden Faseranatomie des Gehirns—*sein* Gebiet—eröffnete."

PHILADELPHIA, PENNSYLVANIA   F. H. LEWEY

References

[1]*Zehn Vorlesungen über den Bau der nervösen Centralorgane des Menschen und der Thiere.* Leipzig, Vogel, 1885 (ed. 8, 1911).   [2]Zschr. Nervenh., 1891, *1:* 262–282.   [3]Arch. mikr. Anat., 1911, *78:* 496–505. [4]Deut. Zschr. Nervenh., 1948, *159:* 229–268.   [5]Neur. Cbl., 1885, *4:* 309.   [6]Arch. Psychiat., Berl., 1887, *18:* 846–871.   [7]Berl. Klinik, 1891, *40:* 1–26.   [8]J. Comp. Neur., 1950, *92:* 133–168.

References to Biography: 1) Fol. neurobiol., Lpz., 1915, *9:* 343–366 (contains bibliography; Ariëns Kappers).   2) Deut. Zschr. Nervenh., 1918, *59:* I–XXXV (contains bibliography; Wallenberg).   3) *Ibid.,* 1915, *53:* 425–448 (Ariëns Kappers).   4) Klin. Wschr., 1925, *4:* 841–842 (not signed).   5) Deut. med. Wschr., 1918, *44:* 302–303 (Oppenheim).   6) Münch. med. Wschr., 1918, *65:* 272–275 (Dreyfus).   7) Zschr. ges. Neur. Psychiat., 1918, *44:* 114–149 (Goldstein).

PAUL EMIL FLECHSIG (1847–1929)

*P*aul Flechsig was born in Zwickau, Saxony, the son of a Protestant clergyman, and was educated in his native city. In 1865 he began the study of medicine in Leipzig, where he came under the influence of the brothers Ernst and Eduard Weber in anatomy, Schweigger-Seidel in histology, and Carl Ludwig in physiology. In 1870, when he was only 23, he received the M.D., his inaugural dissertation being *Bemerkungen über Meningitis luetica* . . . (Leipzig, Fr. Andrae's Nachfolger, 1870); and with the outbreak of the Franco-Prussian War he was pressed into service as surgeon. On demobilization two years later, he returned to the University of Leipzig, where he was appointed assistant at the Institute of Pathology and at the Medical Polyclinic.

Impressed by Meynert's contribution on structure of the mammalian brain which had just appeared in Stricker's *Handbuch* (1872), Flechsig prepared a set of brain sections from the human newborn, and in studying them was struck by the presence of white streaks formed by early myelinating tracts. Here was Flechsig's cue; and by following it he was to show that "we may learn as much of the course of fibers by studying them in their birth as in their death—in their development as in their decay" (Gowers). Already in 1872 a report of his preliminary findings[1] at a national meeting in Leipzig brought him encouragement from von Helmholtz and Ludwig. He

Paul Emil Flechsig

concentrated at first on myelogenesis of the spinal cord, both in man
and experimental animals, amplifying the work of Türck and Bouchard, which had been based on secondary degeneration. The emphasis was on the course of the dorsal spinocerebellar tract, which became known as "Flechsig's tract," and on the pyramidal tract, which
he traced from the precentral and postcentral parts of the cortex.[2]
Flechsig came to the conclusion that complete function of a tract
is assumed only when its fibers have become myelinated, a view
still considered, in general, correct.

In 1873 he was made chief of the histological section in the Institute of Physiology under Carl Ludwig, and in 1875 became Privatdozent. During the next few years he studied primary systemic disorders of the spinal cord, the course of the medial lemniscus, and the

Portrait, courtesy of the Army Medical Library, Washington, D. C.

myelogenesis of the internal capsule, which he subdivided into anterior limb, posterior limb, and knee.[3-5] In 1877 he was promoted to Extraordinarius and soon thereafter became Ordinarius of psychiatry. Having, however, rather scanty knowledge of psychiatry, he obtained several years' leave of absence so that he could study at the most progressive institutions in Germany and abroad. On these travels he spent some time in Paris, visiting Charcot at the Salpêtrière.

In 1882 Flechsig opened his new Irrenklinik and soon visitors and students from all corners of the earth gathered around him—Beevor, Bekhterev, Darkschewitsch, Schütz, Tschirch, Yakowenko, Popov, Blumēnau, Klimov, Donaldson, O. Vogt, Martinotti and Held. Flechsig was at first preoccupied with the therapy of epilepsy and general paralysis and the pathology of tabes dorsalis. Bekhterev and Held collaborated with him on myelogenetic studies. Flechsig's assistant, H. Schütz, wrote, in 1891, a memorable treatise on the dorsal longitudinal fasciculus,[6] to which relatively little has been added. Another pupil was Richard Arwed Pfeifer, whose work on cerebral vascularization was technically perfect—there are no finer plates on capillary distribution in the brain than in his *Die Angioarchitektonik der Grosshirnrinde* (Berlin, Springer, 1928)—but by oversight, presumably, he failed to publish his method.

In 1893 Flechsig embarked on the study of myelogenesis in the hemispheres. He discovered the auditory radiation and on the basis of myeloarchitecture distinguished 36 cortical areas. During the ensuing years he developed, step by step, his theory of projection and association centers.[7] The cortex was divided by him into 1) primary and secondary projection areas—motor and sensory—and 2) association, or cognition, areas. His view that the parietal lobe is a primary sensory area which transmits the impulses it receives to a parietal association area for elaboration was long-lived, but fell by the wayside when others recognized that thalamic fibers reach all parts of the parietal lobe and that the "association area" is also a projection area.

In Flechsig's opinion the region of the brain most important for mental life was the parietotemporo-occipital association "zone" bounded inferiorly by the hippocampal gyrus. Lesions in this region, he felt, led to the development of dementia, whereas lesions in the frontal associative zone had no such effect. These views were epitomized in the address which he delivered at his inauguration as rector of the University of Leipzig for the year 1894–95, an address published in 1896 under the title, *Gehirn und Seele* (Leipzig, Veit) and subsequently reprinted several times. Bianchi, in 1903[8] acknowledged that while Flechsig's myelogenetic method had furnished "une grand impulsion" to the knowledge of the anatomy and development of the brain, his conclusions in regard to the functional significance of the frontal lobe were erroneous, and in these words stated his own belief: "Il existe une seule zone dont les lésions ne produisent jamais de troubles sensoriels ou moteurs et provoquent au contraire la perte des facultés mentales supérieures, et c'est celle des lobes frontaux . . . Les recherches expérimentales, les maladies de cette zone et l'anatomie concourent à démontrer que la zone frontale est le siège de la synthèse intellective et émotive de la personnalité. Voilà la seule conclusion légitime." Flechsig's myelogenetic method was also submitted to a searching analysis by C. and O. Vogt,[9,10] who disagreed with Flechsig on some points, particularly in regard to the time of myelination of certain projection systems.

In 1901 Flechsig became one of the founders of the International Brain Commission, and in 1904 received an honorary D.Sc. from Oxford University.

A typical Voigtländer, Flechsig was a big, broad, bulky individual with a tendency to be abrupt and dogmatic. He frequently declared that it is the duty of a Professor to think "other than others." His students did not consider him their friend, but conceded that he was extraordinarily erudite. In a case of severe vertigo, Flechsig once found at autopsy a parasitic cyst in the IVth ventricle, and thereafter, in discussing the differential diagnosis of vertigo, laid such stress on the importance of parasitic cysts as a cause of vertigo that his dissertations on the subject became legendary. He tended to have a poor memory for the discoveries of others: Oscar Vogt tells the story that back in 1894 he showed a newly-found group of fibers (in the corpus callosum) to Flechsig and that three weeks later Flechsig demonstrated them to him as his (Flechsig's) discovery. According to Folke Henschen, Flechsig had an aversion to socialism, so much so that on one occasion, on peering at the brain of a well-known socialist which had just been removed by him at autopsy, he remarked: "My! what dysharmonic convolutions!" At the age of 74, Flechsig retired from his official duties at the University of Leipzig where he had spent more than 50 years. Oskar Vogt relates that he had grown so accustomed to his cottage in the garden behind the clinic, forgetting that it belonged to the University, that he refused to budge from it and had to be evicted. Nonetheless he continued to work as "ein Forscher aus Leidenschaft,' stimulating those around him to the very end.

WASHINGTON, D. C.   WEBB HAYMAKER

References

[1]Tagebl. 45.Versamml. Deut. Naturforsch. u. Aerzte. Leipzig, Reusche, 1872; p. 75.   [2]*Die Leitungsbahnen im Gehirn und Rückenmark des Menschen.* Leipzig, Engelmann, 1876.   [3]Arch. Heilk., Lpz., 1877, *18*: 101–141 *et seq.*   [4]Arch. Anat. Entw., 1881; p. 12–75.   [5]*Plan des menschlichen Gehirns.* Leipzig, Veit, 1883.   [6]Arch. Psychiat., Berl., 1891, *22*: 527–587.   [7]*Anatomie des menschlichen Gehirns und Rückenmarks auf myelogenetischer Grundlage.* Leipzig, Thieme, 1920.   [8]C. rend. XIVe Congr. Internat. de Méd., Madrid, 1903. Vol. 5. Sect. Neuropath. Madrid, Sastre, 1904; p. 468–485.   [9]Allg. Zschr. Psychiat., 1901, *58*: 707–709.   [10]J. Psychol. Neur., Lpz., 1903, *2*: 160–180.

References to Biography: 1) *Meine myelogenetische Hirnlehre. Mit biographischer Einleitung.* Berlin, Springer, 1927 (Flechsig).   2) Arch. Psychiat., Berl., 1930, *91:* 1–8 (Schröder).

AUGUST FOREL (1848–1931)

*A*ugust Forel was born on a country estate near Morges, Switzerland, on the shore of Lake Geneva. At the early age of seven he found interest in observing insects, especially ants, and at eleven years Huber's famous work on the behavior of ants literally became his Bible. When 14 he was sent to Lausanne to pursue secondary studies at the Collège Cantonal and later he attended the Academy. In 1866 he began to study medicine in Zürich, at the same time continuing his investigations on ants, publishing papers and becoming a member of the Swiss Entomological Society. His teacher, von Gudden, made such a deep impression on him that he resolved to become a psychiatrist.

After completing courses in Zürich in 1871, he took the cantonal medical examination in Lausanne but because of local medical poli-

August Forel

tics failed to pass. For the next few months he traveled through
Switzerland, working on a monograph dealing with the ants indige-
nous to that country. The winter of 1871–72 was spent in Vienna,
studying neuroanatomy under Meynert and preparing his doctoral
dissertation on the thalamus opticus of mammals.[1] Although in disagreement with many of Meynert's fundamental teachings, Meynert
nevertheless accepted the thesis and had it published in the Proceedings of the Vienna Academy of Sciences. Forel passed the cantonal
medical examination in Lausanne in 1872, but did not succeed in obtaining the position in a psychiatric institution of his native canton
for which he had applied. In 1873 he went to the Ludwig-Maxi-
milians-Universität in Munich as one of von Gudden's assistants,
becoming Privatdozent in 1877 after completing his important paper

Portrait, courtesy of the Army Medical Library, Washington, D. C.

on the tegmental region in which he described the tegmental fields, the zona incerta, and various other hitherto unknown structures.[2] He also had a significant part in devising the first usable brain microtome.

Forel started on a myrmecological expedition to Colombia in 1878, but had to abandon it at St. Thomas in the Virgin Islands because of the sudden death of his companion and friend, Steinheil. The following year he was appointed director of the Burghölzli Asylum and professor of psychiatry at the University of Zürich. His predecessor was Hitzig and his successors Bleuler, Maier and Bleuler, Jr. In 1882 Forel married Emma Steinheil, the young daughter of his deceased friend.

Forel's fundamental paper, in which the neuron theory was unequivocally stated, was published in 1887.[3] This work, based on pathologic and functional evidence, appeared about two months after that of W. His, in which similar conclusions had been reached on the basis of histogenetic studies. Thus, His and Forel must be credited with the independent formulation of the concept of cellular and functional units for which some years later Cajal furnished the strongest support and for which Waldeyer coined in 1891[4,5] the term, "neuron." In addition to his research in brain anatomy, recorded in his collected neuroanatomic papers,[6] Forel studied the therapeutic value of hypnotism and worked on many other problems of psychiatry. Oskar Vogt was a worker in his laboratory in the summer of 1894, and in 1902 they collaborated in founding the *Journal für Psychologie und Neurologie.*

In 1898 Forel retired from his duties as director and professor to return to his native Canton de Vaud, spending the rest of his life in travel, doing research on ants, writing on philosophy, studying sexual problems,[7] and enthusiastically crusading for alcoholic abstinence, monism, pacifism, and later, socialism. He had always been known as a fearless crusader and indefatigable worker of great intellectual honesty and strong convictions. In 1912 he suffered a cerebral vascular accident resulting in right hemiplegia. Courageously he overcame this condition and at 64 years of age learned to write with his left hand. He remained active in his fields of interest until his death at the age of 83.

PHILADELPHIA, PENNSYLVANIA   HARTWIG KUHLENBECK

References

[1]Sitzber. Akad. Wiss. Wien, Physiol. Abt., 1872, 66: 25–58.   [2]Arch. Psychiat., Berl., 1877, 7: 393–495.   [3]Ibid., 1887, 18: 162–198.   [4]Deut. med. Wschr., 1891, 17: 1213–1218 et seq.   [5]Berl. klin. Wschr., 1891, 28: 691.   [6]Gesammelte hirnanatomische Abhandlungen mit einem Aufsatz über die Aufgaben der Neurobiologie. München, Reinhardt, 1907.   [7]Die sexuelle Frage. München, Reinhardt, 1905. (Engl. trans. by Marshall: The sexual question. New York, Rebman, 1909.) (Review by Collins in J. Nerv. Ment. Dis., 1909, 36: 255–256.)

References to Biography: 1) Rückblick auf mein Leben. Mit einem Nachwort von O. L. Forel. Zürich, Europa, 1935 (Forel). (Review by Maier in Schweiz. Arch. Neur. Psychiat., 1935, 35: 383.) (Engl. trans.: Out of my life and work. New York, Norton, 1937. French trans.: Auguste Forel mémoires. Neuchatel, Baconniére, 1941).   2) Deut. Zschr. Nervenh., 1931, 122: 117–118 (Veraguth).   3) Schweiz. med. Wschr., 1948, 78: 838–839 (O. L. Forel).   4) Schweiz. Arch. Neur. Psychiat., 1950, 65: 421–425 (Steck).   5) Med. Welt, 1928, 2: 1–5 (O. Vogt).   6) Arch. Neur. Psychiat., Chic., 1931, 26: 1303–1305 (Adolf Meyer).   7) J. Comp. Neur., 1893, 3: 1–6 et seq. (Adolf Meyer).

ARTHUR VAN GEHUCHTEN (1861–1914)

*V*an Gehuchten was born in Antwerp. As a student, he was trained in the Laboratory Jean-Baptiste Carnoy in Louvain. After studying in Berlin and Frankfurt-am-Main, he returned, at the age of 26, to the Catholic University of Louvain to take charge of descriptive anatomy.

In 1890 appeared his first paper, which dealt with the olfactory mucosa of mammals as revealed by the Golgi method. This was the beginning of years of research on the olfactory bulb, optic lobes, cerebellum, spinal cord, innervation of the hair follicles, etc., an account of which is to be found in Lewellys F. Barker's classic volume on *The nervous system and its constituent neurons* (New York, Stechert, 1909). Van Gehuchten's work on the structure of nerve cells and his promulgation of the theory of dynamic polarization in 1891[1] helped to establish the neuron doctrine.

In 1900 he began the publication of his journal, *Le Névraxe,* in which many of his papers appeared. His early work had laid the foundations for his first textbook, *Anatomie du système nerveux de*

l'homme (Lierre, In, 1893), which went to several editions; the second edition, published in 1897, ranks with the greatest anatomic works of our time. The journal and textbook had a lasting influence

Portrait, courtesy of the Army Medical Library, Washington, D. C.

on neurological teaching and research in other countries, as did also his *Les centres nerveux cérébro-spinaux* (Louvain, Uystpruyst-Dieudonné, 1908). These were fruitful years in the delineation of nerve tracts: Probst[2-5] carried out monumental studies on the course of tracts from the brain stem to the thalamus, including the termination there of the medial lemniscus and brachium conjunctivum; Wallenberg[6] elucidated the trigeminal lemniscus; von Monakow,[7] Held[8] and Lewy[9] traced the course of auditory pathways through the brain stem; and Mott,[10] Choroschko,[11] Goldstein[12] and Collier and Buzzard[13] charted the course of the lateral spinothalamic tract to its termination. Van Gehuchten worked in all these fields, providing new facets here, dissenting there, always evaluating what was new and giving it proper perspective.

As time went on, van Gehuchten became more preoccupied with clinical neurology, contributing papers on a variety of subjects, including poliomyelitis, syringomyelia, and aphasia, which culminated in 1941 in a textbook of neurology.[14] His interest in clinical neurology had, indeed, always been keen. In 1897 he entered the controversy on the nature of the motor disturbances in cerebral palsy.[15] but he added nothing substantially new to the knowledge of the disorder which the pioneer English orthopedist William John Little (1810–94)[16] had described in 1862 under the term "spastic rigidity." and which he considered to be due to asphyxia neonatorum. In 1884 von Strümpell attempted to distinguish acquired from congenital forms,[17] and in 1893[18,19] and 1897[20] Sigmund Freud's important works on the subject appeared.

Van Gehuchten's habits were those of an ascetic and as regular as clockwork: he would lecture in the early morning hours, work in his laboratory until late afternoon—singing all the while—then take a long walk with his dog, after which he would return to the laboratory. His friendliness and diligence in research made him a favored scholar and attracted many investigators to his laboratory. The anniversary of his 25th year of service to the University, on December 1, 1912, was the occasion for a great ceremony in Louvain, at which scientists from every quarter of the globe gathered to do him honor. But the homage paid him was not the usual two-edged weapon, for he continued to find full support for his work.

Van Gehuchten's work and his journal came to an untimely end in 1914 when World War I broke out. His laboratory, country home and manuscripts destroyed, he sought refuge in England. He was received at Cambridge, where he was given a position and the use of laboratory facilities in the Research Hospital. There, with a hopeful spirit, he set himself the task of repeating the work on which he had been engaged at Louvain, but the sudden development of volvulus interrupted his studies as they were recommencing. He died of a heart attack shortly after an operation. He had done an immense amount of pioneer work in his 53 years.

COLUMBUS, OHIO   JAMES W. PAPEZ

References

[1]Cellule, Louvain, 1891, 7: 81–122.   [2]Mschr. Psychiat., 1900, 7: 387–404.   [3]Arch. Psychiat., Berl., 1900, 33: 1–57.   [4]Ibid., p. 721–817. [5]Mschr. Psychiat., 1901, 10: 288–309.   [6]Anat. Anz., 1900, 18: 81–105. [7]Arch. Psychiat., Berl., 1891, 22: 1–26.   [8]Arch. Anat. Physiol., Anat. Abt., 1891; p. 279–299.   [9]Folia neurobiol., Lpz., 1909, 2: 471–518. [10]Brain, Lond., 1895, 18: 1–20.   [11]Mschr. Psychiat., 1909, 26: 534–545. [12]Neur. Cbl., 1910, 29: 898–911.   [13]Brain, Lond., 1903, 26: 559–591. [14]Les maladies nerveuses. Louvain, Librairie Universitaire, 1914 (ed. 4, 1936).   [15]Rev. neur., Par., 1897, 5: 558–559.   [16]Tr. Obst. Soc. London, 1862, 3: 293–344.   [17]Jahrb. Kinderh., 1884, 22: 173–178. [18]Rev. neur., Par., 1893, 1: 177–183.   [19]Neur. Cbl., 1893, 12: 512–515 et seq.   [20] Die infantile Cerebrallähmung. Wien, Hölder, 1897.

References to Biography: 1) Bull. Acad. méd. Belgique, 1920, 4.sér., 30: 961–978 (Henrijean).   2) Med. tschr. geneesk., 1914, 50: 2071–2075 (Winkler).

CAMILLO GOLGI (1843–1926)

Golgi was born in the small Alpine town of Córtena, in Lombardy, Italy, the son of a distinguished medical practitioner. He studied at the University of Pavia, from which he graduated in medicine in 1865. From 1865 to 1872, he was resident in the Ospedale di San Matteo in Pavia, frequently working in the Instituto di Patologia Generale, directed by Giulio Bizzozero. The influence of his great friend, Bizzozero, the work he had done on pellagra under the direction of Cesare Lombroso (1868), and the reading of Virchow's Die Cellularpathologie were the factors which led Golgi to dedicate himself to the study of the structure of the nervous sys-

Prof⟮ Camillo Golgi

tem. His work on psammomata appeared in 1869, and his initial
studies on the neuroglia of the cerebral gray and white matter in
1870 and 1871.

His financial needs compelled him to accept a position as chief

Portrait, courtesy of Dr. J. R. M. Innes, Washington, D. C.

resident physician in the Ospizio-Cronici in Abbiategrasso. In this small town, away from all forms of scientific academic activity, with a laboratory consisting only of a microscope and a few instruments set up in the kitchen of his home, Golgi, working mostly at night by candlelight, discovered a chromate of silver method, *la reazione nera*, for staining the nervous tissue, with which he was to revolutionize the concept of the histologic structure of the nervous system. He described this method in 1873[1] and again in 1875[2] in connection with a study of cerebral gliomas. In 1874 he made the first clinico-pathologic application of his method, selecting a case of chorea for the purpose.

He was called in 1875 to the University of Pavia as Extraordinarius in histology. Here he spent virtually the remainder of his academic life (until 1918), at first under conditions which would have discouraged less determined men. In time, pupils and scholars, many of them from abroad, flocked to his laboratory, among them Marchi, Monti, Sala, Negri, von Kölliker, and his nephew and adopted son, and later his successor, Perroncito. Fridtjof Nansen, the Norwegian explorer, was also a pupil of his, and is credited with having introduced Golgi's method to the rest of Europe and with having been a co-founder of the neuron theory (with Forel and His) through a study entitled *Nerve-elementerne, deres struktur og sammenhäng i centralnervesystemet,* which he published in 1887.[3]

Golgi's monumental work, *Sulla fina anatomia degli organi centrali del sistema nervoso* (Milano; Hoepli), appeared in 1885–86. Here is to be found among a wealth of new data his description of type I and type II nerve cells of the cerebral cortex, the former sending their axons down through the white matter to subcortical centers and the latter—some short, some long—taking their course entirely within the cortex. His 3-volume *Opera omnia* (Milano; Hoepli), which illustrate the formal elegance of his drawings, were published in 1903. Descriptions of the musculo-tendinous end organ and of peripheral and central nerve fibers[4] were made in 1880. The cytoplasmic reticular substance of nerve and other cells has been called the Golgi apparatus since his clear portrayal of it in 1898.[5,7] Von La Valette Saint George described the apparatus in the sexual cells of snails in 1867.[6]

Golgi's interest in the nervous system was on the wane during the 1890's. He turned to other subjects and made particularly outstanding contributions to the field of malarial research. In 1886 he related the fever curve to the stages of development of the malarial parasite in the blood, and in 1892 demonstrated that whereas in the pernicious type of malaria the parasite develops in the organs, in typical intermittent malaria it passes through its life cycle while in the blood.

Golgi's observations led him to postulate that nerve fibers within the central nervous system, both efferent and afferent, lose their individuality, breaking up into many secondary branches which anastomose to form a network. He persistently refuted the neuron theory, and in 1906, in Stockholm, where he was awarded jointly with Cajal the Nobel Prize for Physiology and Medicine, he reiterated his views on this subject. Tello, in his splendid Valdecilla Lectures on *Cajal y su labor histológica* (Madrid, Tipografía Artistica, 1935) has provided details by which one can judge the stature of Golgi and Cajal so far as the discovery of fundamental structures of the nervous system is concerned.

Golgi was twice elected rector of the University of Pavia and he was a member of the Royal Senate for a few years. His rich endowment as a scientist was matched by the excellence of his character: he was modest, reserved and a tenacious defender of the scientific faith that he had professed, even against such stout adversaries as Cajal on the question of the neuron theory. The tenor of his criticism of Cajal over the years reveals, however, that he was not a man without foibles. When he died in Pavia, at the age of 83, Ottorino Rossi pronounced the benediction, *Gloria gloria a Te, o immune della morte* . . .

NEW YORK CITY   ARMANDO FERRARO

References

[1]Gazz. med. Ital. lombarda, 1873, *33:* 244–246.   [2]Riv. sper. freniat., 1875, *1:* 66–78.   [3]Nord. med. ark., 1887, *19:* Nr. 24, p. 1–23.   [4]Arch. ac. med., Tor., 1880, *4:* 221–246.   [5]Arch. ital. biol., 1898, *30:* 60–71. [6]J. R. Micr. Soc., Lond., 1935, *55:* 28–31 (Douglas).   [7]Rev. sudamer. morf., B. Air., 1948, *6:* 115–133 (history of Golgi apparatus; Sosa).

References to Biography: 1) J. Path. Bact., Lond., 1926, *29:* 500–514 (Da Fano).   2) Arch. Neur. Psychiat., Chic., 1926, *15:* 623–627 (Viets).   3) Penfield (ed.), *Neurological biographies and addresses.* London, Oxford Univ. Press, 1936 (Chorobski); p. 121–127.

BERNHARD ALOYS VON GUDDEN (1824–1886)

*V*on Gudden was born in Kleve, Germany, near the Dutch fron-
tier. He studied in Bonn, Berlin, and then in Halle, where he
received the M.D. in 1848. His career was marked by successive appointments to positions of eminence in psychiatry: he became director of the Unterfränkische Landes-Irrenanstalt in Werneck in 1855,
was associated with mental institutions at Siegburg, Illenau and
Würzburg, was appointed professor of psychiatry at Zürich in 1869,
and then at the University of Munich, in 1872, where he was also
director of the Kreis-Irrenanstalt. For many years he was editor
of the *Archiv für Psychiatrie und Nervenkrankheiten.*

Von Gudden appeared on the scene at a time when a considerable
number of highly useful technical tools and methods had been made
available. Alcohol as a tissue fixative had been introduced by Reil
in 1809[1] (the same year that the insular cortex named after him
was described) and chromic acid and its salts by Hannover in
1840[2] (formaldehyde fixation came much later; it was first employed
by Blum in 1893)[3]; a method for serial sectioning of the brain by
hand had been devised by Stilling in 1842[4]; paraffin embedding had
been introduced by Edwin Klebs in 1869[5]; and carmine as a staining
agent for nerve cells had been popularized by Gerlach in 1858.[6]
Carmine as a cell stain, dependent on fixation in potassium bichro-
mate, continued in use for a considerable time, even after Nissl had
introduced his methylene blue method in 1885. Thus, Forel[7] used
it for the cellular changes in retrograde phenomena, von Monakow[8]
for similar purposes, and even as late as 1911, Winkler and Potter[9]
preferred the Gerlach method because it gave such an excellent contrast to the structure of the gray matter as compared to that of the
white.

Taking full advantage of the crude methods available at the
time, von Gudden embarked on a series of epochal experiments. He
is best known for his studies on the partial decussation of optic
paths,[10–12] a subject which occupied him for some 30 years. His
method of producing secondary atrophy of central structures following removal of sense organs or cranial nerves in young animals
ushered in a fresh advance in experimental neurology. In full

Bernhard Aloys von Gudden

grown animals from which eyes had been removed when they were young, he demonstrated not only crossed and uncrossed optic fibers, but also a supraoptic commissure and the transverse peduncular tract,[10–12] both of which now bear his name. He also was the first to describe the interpeduncular and deep tegmental nuclei. The observation that lesions of the cerebral cortex do not cause atrophy of peripheral nerves came to be known as Gudden's Law. But one of von Gudden's greatest contributions was his observation in 1870[10] that destruction of certain areas of the cerebral cortex leads to atrophy of specific thalamic nuclei. Here, again, very young animals were used and they were allowed to live as long as ten months before

Portrait, courtesy of Dr. W. Krücke, Frankfurt-am-Main, Germany.

the effects of decortication on the thalamus were determined. Nowadays the study of the thalamocortical projections is generally carried out on adult animals which are sacrificed within one or two months after the cortical extirpations. This is the retrograde cell degeneration method of Nissl, which should be distinguished from the atrophy method of von Gudden: in the one the degenerative changes are in cells, and in the other the cells have completely disappeared. This pioneer work of von Gudden initiated the modern study of the thalamus. Von Monakow, of Zürich, learned this technique from von Gudden, and was thus enabled to make important contributions to experimental neurology from 1882 onward, beginning in that year with his work on thalamocortical connections.[13]

In 1875 von Gudden devised a microtome for sectioning the whole human brain. His student, Forel, relates that he (Forel) was able to make the first complete section.[16] When collodion for embedding was introduced by Duval in 1879,[14] von Gudden immediately took advantage of the method. He later tried his hand at defining certain areas of the cortex by Golgi's chromate of silver method. His many papers, including posthumous ones, were brought together by his friend, H. Grashey in 1889.[15] His slide collection is still to be found in the Deutsche Forschungsanstalt für Psychiatrie in Munich, an institution undamaged in the late war.

Von Gudden enjoyed great prestige and made a powerful impression on the scientific world of his day. His laboratory was the mecca for anatomists and psychiatrists, among them Forel, who came to von Gudden in 1874. In his autobiography,[16] Forel relates that von Gudden was an unpredictable genius. "If one could make an ensemble of all the contrasts and the contradictions possible," he wrote, "one would obtain a Gudden." Now and again von Gudden showed no regard for anyone or anything, defects of which he was conscious, for he often said in a vexed tone: "Every one of my errors revenges itself bitterly." He was free from all pedantry and in discussions permitted his assistants the greatest liberty: he was interested in their scientific growth, but was completely unconcerned for their future. Although his conversation was punctuated by flashes of brilliance, he would let fall most artless remarks, for instance, that he disbelieved that somnamulism existed, for he (von Gudden) always slept well without dreaming. "I learned enormously while with Gudden," wrote Forel, "but above all how not to direct an asylum, for," as he added, "his tendency to let everything drift resulted in indescribable disorder."

In 1875 Gudden was made a noble and was appointed physician-in-charge of the mad king, Ludwig II of Bavaria, who was confined to one of his castles on Starnbergersee. At intervals, von Gudden's young pupil, Franz Nissl, attended the king. On a fateful Sunday afternoon in June, 1886, von Gudden took the king for a walk. The subsequent events, as reconstructed by Grashey, were as follows: Near the shore of the lake the king dashed away and jumped into the water with suicidal intent. Von Gudden rushed after him and managed to seize him, but the king slipped loose. In the ensuing struggle the king, a large, powerful man, stunned von Gudden with a blow to the head, and held him under the water until he was drowned. The king then walked deeper into the lake and drowned himself.

COLUMBUS, OHIO   JAMES W. PAPEZ

References

[1]Arch. Physiol., Halle a.S., 1809, 9: 136–208.   [2]Arch. Anat., Physiol., wissensch. Med., 1840; p. 549–558.   [3]Zschr. wissensch. Mikr., 1893, 10: 314–315.   [4]Untersuchungen über die Functionen des Rückenmarks und der Nerven. Leipzig, Wigand, 1842.   [5]Arch. micr. Anat., 1869, 5: 164–166.   [6]Mikroskopische Studien aus dem Gebiete der menschlichen Morphologie. Erlangen, Enke, 1858.   [7]Arch. Path., Berl., 1887, 18: 162–198.   [8]Ibid., 1898, 31: 1–73 et seq.   [9]An anatomical guide to experimental researches on the rabbit's brain. Amsterdam, Versluys, 1914. [10]Arch. Psychiat., Berl., 1870, 2: 693–723.   [11]Arch. Ophth., Berl., 1874, 2.Abth., 20: 249–268.   [12]Ibid., 1879, 1.Abth., 25: 1–56.   [13]Arch. Psychiat., Berl., 1882, 12: 141–156.   [14]J. de l'anat., physiol., 1879, 15: 185–188.   [15]Grashey (ed.), Bernhard von Gudden's gesammelte und hinterlassene Abhandlungen. Wiesbaden, Bergmann, 1889.   [16]Auguste Forel mémoires. Neuchatel, Baconnière, 1941.

References to Biography and Works: 1) Münch. med. Wschr., 1886, 33: 577–580 et seq. (Kraepelin).   2) Wien. med. Bl., 1886, 9: 729–731 (Meynert).   3) Arch. Psychiat., Berl., 1925, 76: 21–46 (Wallenberg). 4) The primate thalamus. Chicago, Univ. Chicago Press, 1938 (Walker).

WILHELM HIS (1831–1904)

*H*is came of an old patrician Swiss family whose wealth enabled him to finish at the best schools of Europe the medical studies which he had begun at Basle (1849) and Bern (1850). In Berlin, the venerable Johannes Müller instilled in him the inquiring attitude, and Remak's lectures (1850–52) on the theory of the germ layers had a determining influence on his later work. At Würzburg (1852–53), Virchow gave him the right start in research, and although he had no formal instruction from von Kölliker, he owed much to this great microscopist. After passing his examination in medicine *summa cum laude* (Basle, 1854), he journeyed to Paris where he worked in the laboratories of Brown-Séquard and Claude Bernard.

He returned to Basle as Privatdozent under Meissner (1856) whom he soon succeeded, becoming Ordinarius (1857); and after 15 fruitful years there he accepted the chair of anatomy at the University of Leipzig (1872) vacated by the retirement of Ernst Weber. He remained at Leipzig for the rest of his life. Keibel and Mall were among his most distinguished students.

Rather early in his career, His announced a new classification of tissues based on histogenesis,[1] and with this as a guide formulated an extensive research program in developmental anatomy, centering largely on the nervous system. Although one of the greatest students of histogenesis, he never lost sight of the embryo as a whole, as evidenced by an epochal 3-volume work on the subject.[2] In 1887 he established that axons are outgrowths from primitive nerve cells,[3] and by 1889 demonstrated the individuality of nerve cells. Dendrite, neurite, neuropil, neuroblast and spongioblast are familiar neurological terms which he introduced. Moreover, he established proof of Hensen's hypothesis that the neural parts of the nervous system originate in the ectoderm, while the blood vessels arise in the mesoderm. After His's lucid explanations, the ectodermal origin of Virchow's neuroglia was no longer contested. The very end of his life saw him still actively engaged in this major field of his interest, his last work being *Die Entwickelung des menschlichen Gehirns während der ersten Monate* (Leipzig, Hirzel, 1904). Many of His's embryologic findings were disputed by Hochstetter, of Vienna, but the fact re-

mains that though his embryologic material was of poor quality he was able to make fundamental discoveries, whereas others with perfect material could not match it with ideas.

His was one of the founders of the *Anatomische Gesellschaft* (1886), and by drafting the final report of the international commission on anatomic nomenclature he was largely responsible for the B.N.A.[4] He founded the *Zeitschrift für Anatomie und Entwicke-*

Portrait, courtesy of the Army Medical Library, Washington, D. C.

lungsgeschichte (1876) and helped to found the *Archiv für Anthropologie* (1876). He was the guiding spirit (from 1886) in the organization of the Brain Commission which established the Central Institute for Brain Research at Amsterdam (1908), with Ariëns Kappers as director.

Science is also indebted to him for new or improved methods. He devised the best microtome of the time (1866). The embryograph, a device for the drawing of sections on wax plates and then setting the plates in juxtaposition, was invented by him, and the His-Steger models (F. J. Steger was his assistant) are to be found in anatomical museums the world over.

His's interests were exceedingly broad: he took his stand—one of reasoned scepticism—on the much disputed question of Darwinism; Rütimeyer and he made an important contribution to anthropology through their *Crania Helvetica* (Basle, Georg, 1864); he wrote a detailed review (1870) of *Microcosmos*, by Lotze, with whose realistic idealism he concurred heartily; and he sharply attacked Haeckel's *biogenetisches Grundgesetz*. An interesting sidelight is that he identified the remains of Johann Sebastian Bach, unearthed from the yard of the Johanneskirche in Leipzig after lying buried there for almost a century and a half; his account of this investigation appeared in 1895.

His's way of life was Spartan in its simplicity and in its serious devotion to duty. Abhorring trite and conventional expression, he became a master of the art of terseness in speaking and in writing. Almost every vacation found him at Basle, for his Swiss homeland was close to his heart. A sociable individual, his home in Leipzig was frequented by his colleagues and was open at all times to students from Switzerland. Much of His's microscopic work was done in his home, where usually there was a congregation of students. As an avocation he experimented for years with daguerrotypes. His son, Wilhelm His, Jr., was also a distinguished anatomist, whose name is linked with the cardiac atrioventricular bundle which he first described (1893).

MINNEAPOLIS, MINNESOTA   A. T. RASMUSSEN

References

[1]*Die Häute und Höhlen des Körpers.* Basle, Schweighauser, 1865 (reprinted 1903).   [2]*Anatomie menschlicher Embryonen.* 3 vol. Leipzig,

Vogel, 1880–85.   [3]Abh. Math.-Physisch. Cl. k. Säch. Gesellsch. Wis. sensch., 1887, *13:* 477–514.   [4]*Die anatomische Nomenclatur. Nomina anatomica.* Leipzig, Veit, 1895.

References to Biography: 1) *Lebenserinnerungen.* Leipzig, als Manuskript gedruckt, 1904 (His).   2) Deut. med. Wschr., 1904, *30:* 1438–1441 *et seq.* (Waldeyer).   3) Am. J. Anat., 1905, *4:* 139–161 (Mall). 4) Anat. Anz., 1904, *25:* 161–208 (contains bibliography; Fick).   5) *Wilhelm His der Anatom. Ein Lebensbild.* Berlin u. Wien, Urban & Schwarzenberg, 1931 (contains selected bibliography; W. His, Jr.). 6) Q. Phi Beta Pi M., 1942, *39:* 19–38 (contains bibliography; Bast).

RUDOLF ALBERT VON KÖLLIKER (1817–1905)

*V*on Kölliker was born in Zürich, Switzerland, and spent most of his early life there.   His medical training was begun in his native city and continued in Bonn and then Berlin (1839–41), where Johannes Müller and Jakob Henle exerted a particularly strong influence on him.   Summer vacations were spent in Helgoland and Föhr in work on zoological problems, which culminated in a paper on sexual physiology of invertebrates,[1] for which the University of Zürich awarded him the Ph.D. in 1842.   After receiving the M.D. at Heidelberg (1843) he returned to Zürich.

As Prosector under Henle, he soon became Privatdozent, then Extraordinarius of physiology and comparative anatomy (1844). In 1847 he accepted the chair of comparative anatomy at Würzburg, and two years later also became Ordinarius in human anatomy.   In 1864 he relinquished the chair of physiology, continuing as head of the Institute of Anatomy and the Institute of Comparative Anatomy, Microscopy and Embryology.   He retired from the former post in 1897, from the latter in 1902, at the age of 85 years!   His mental acumen was such that he published 20 papers in the last eight years of his life.   Von Kölliker's most outstanding pupil was Gegenbaur.

One of the leading biologists of the 19th century, he devoted prodigious effort to the study of the finer structure of the nervous system.   The second volume of his *Handbuch der Gewebelehre des Menschen,* 6th edition (Leipzig, Engelmann, 1889–96), is as much a classic as any of Cajal's great works.   In that edition appeared the results of his study of Golgi preparations, undertaken after he had

seen Cajal's sections in 1889. In a paper published in 1845, von Kölliker anticipated by almost fifty years Waldeyer's formulation of the neuron theory, by stating that nerve fibers are secondary to nerve cells, and at least some of them are processes of nerve cells, and later he provided proof that nerve fibers are continuous with nerve cells. In the concluding chapter of his *Handbuch* (ed. 6, vol. 2, p. 810) appeared an epitome of his belief, which may be translated as follows: "All nerve cells must have essentially the same function and their functional dignity depends solely upon the different extraneous stimuli which might impinge upon them or upon the many possibilities of answers to a stimulus." From his pen came the first work on comparative embryology,[2] in which are included his important observations on the relation of the vertebrate notochord to the adult spine and skull. His 3-volume *Mikroskopische Anatomie*

Portrait, courtesy of Dr. W. Krücke, Frankfurt-am-Main, Germany.

(Leipzig, Engelmann, 1850–54) and his contributions to the developmental anatomy of the eye and ear[3] are also celebrated works.

Von Kölliker had the astuteness to recognize immediately the genius of Cajal. As a stranger from Spain and scientifically almost unknown even in his own country, Cajal came, in 1889, to a meeting of the German Anatomical Society at the University of Berlin, of which von Kölliker was chairman, and demonstrated his preparations to a group he knew well to be a little arrogant and very critical. But Cajal won the esteem of the members of the Society not only by the beauty of his preparations but also through the energetic support given him by von Kölliker. Subsequently Cajal wrote: "A noble exception among great investigators, Kölliker united a great talent for observation . . . with enchanting modesty and exceptional rectitude and calmness of judgment."

Von Kölliker "was a dignified figure, a veteran of pure science" (Garrison). His geniality brought him many friends. His lifelong passion for hunting and mountain climbing was exercised to the full. He was a yodeler of rare ability. Widely traveled, he was most fascinated by England, where he acquired the enduring friendship of William Sharpey. He received many honors, among them the order *Pour le merité*—the highest ranking in Germany, which made him *Seine Excellenz*—but they never spoiled his personal charm.

CHICAGO, ILLINOIS   GERHARDT VON BONIN

References

[1]*Beiträge zur Kenntnis der Geschlechtsverhältnisse und der Samenflüssigkeit wirbelloser Thiere.* . . . .Berlin, Logier, 1841.   [2]*Entwicklungsgeschichte des Menschen und der höheren Thiere.* Leipzig, Engelmann, 1861.   [3]Verhandl. d. phys.-med. Gesellsch. in Würzb., n.F., 1833; p. 2–16.

References to Biography: 1) *Erinnerungen aus meinem Leben.* Leipzig, Engelmann, 1899 (Koelliker).   2) Anat. Anz., 1906, *28:* 539–552 (contains selected bibliography; Waldeyer).   3) Zschr. wiss. Zool., 1906, *84:* I–XXVI (contains bibliography; Ehlers).

JULES BERNARD LUYS (1828–1897)

*P*arisian by birth, Luys spent most of his life in his native city or its environs. His doctorate in medicine in 1857 was obtained on the basis of a thesis on the microscopic pathology of tuberculosis. In 1862 he became médecin des hôpitaux and chef de service at the Salpêtrière and the Charité, and two years later succeeded Marcé as director of the Maison de Santé Esquirol at Ivry-sur-Seine.

Luys soon found his metier in the problems of the structure and connections of the brain. He was the first to portray the internal nuclei and tracts of the brain in three-dimensional visualizations. He was an excellent draughtsman, and his reconstructions were founded on carefully made drawings of sections through all parts of the brain. These were all portrayed in his first and most important book, completed when he was 37: *Recherches sur le système nerveux cérébro-spinal: sa structure, ses fonctions, et ses maladies* (Paris, Baillière, 1865). Here were depicted the two structures which bear his name: the subthalamic nucleus and the centre médian of the thalamus. He referred to the subthalamic nucleus as the "bandelette accessoire de l'olive supérieure" and recognized its spatial relation to the red nucleus, which he called the "olive supérieure." Meynert, in 1872,[1] considered it to be a subdivision of the substantia nigra, and in 1884[2] called it the "discus lentiformis." Forel, in 1877,[3] provided the term "corpus Luysi." More of the story of this nucleus is to be found in a paper by Denkhaus.[4] Many years were to pass before the clinical import of Luys' subthalamic nucleus was to be determined: in 1927, Martin[5] and in 1934 Martin and Alcock[6] presented convincing evidence that lesions affecting this nucleus result in hemiballismus (a term coined by Kussmaul,[7] though some have given the credit to von Economo).[8] As to the centre médian nucleus, its functional significance is still unknown.

Before 1865 there was some inkling in the writings of Türck (1859) and Hughlings Jackson (1864) that the thalamus is concerned with sensibility, but the publication of Luys' book in that year marks the beginning of knowledge of thalamic function. He recognized four centers, each mediating one of the senses. They were the anterior or olfactory center, the middle or optic center, the median or somesthetic center, and the posterior or acoustic center.

Jules Bernard Luys

He was intensely interested in the arrangements of the fibers within the white matter and depicted them with spirit. He came, however, to the mistaken conclusion that all cortical connections are interrupted in the basal ganglia and hence divided the long tracts into superior and inferior groups of converging fibers, recognizing, however, that some afferent fibers were reflex and that they did not reach the thalamus. The thalamus, then, was the *sensorium communale*, while the corpus striatum was the subcortical motor center.

In his physiological studies he attempted to show that destruction within the thalamus leads to specific sensory loss, while damage to

Portrait from *Prog. méd., Par.*, 3 sér., 6: 141, 1897.

the corpus striatum produces alterations of motility. The cerebral cortex was considered the organic substratum of motor and sensory functions, its gradual destruction leading to paralysis and finally to dementia. In 1874 his book on reflex cerebral activity appeared,[9] and soon thereafter his *Le cerveau et ses fonctions* (Paris; Baillière) (ed. 2, 1876), which was translated into English.[10] In them, as in his first book, he attempted to integrate neuroanatomy, neuropathology and physiologic psychology. Among his accomplishments was the effective use of photography in the illustration of brain anatomy; a large volume[11] testifies to his pre-eminence in this field in which he was the pioneer.

The major part of Luys' career was spent in clinical work, especially in the study of insanity, hysteria and hypnotism. He wrote many articles and two books on hypnotism, and he was one of the founders of the Société d'Hypnologie et de Psychologie. Little came from his work in this field for he allowed himself to be deluded by his patients; for instance, he was responsible for perpetuating the folly that patients may profit therapeutically from drugs placed at a distance from them. In his latter days the quality of his scientific work sharply declined as he shifted his emphasis more and more from the objective to the subjective.

Luys was a vigorous, active and industrious man. Of ingratiating personality, he was revered by his colleagues. His later years were marred by increasing deafness. He continued to attend the meetings of the Académie de Médecine and the Société de Biologie when he could no longer hear the proceedings, smiling recognition to his many friends. He had just retired to the country when, at the age of 69, he was fatally stricken.

CHICAGO, ILLINOIS   WENDELL J. S. KRIEG

References

[1]In Stricker, S., *Handbuch der Lehre von den Geweben.* Vol. 2. Leipzig, Engelmann, 1872. [2]*Psychiatry. A clinical treatise on diseases of the forebrain.* London, Putnam's Sons, 1885 (trans. by B. Sachs). [3]Arch. Psychiat., Berl., 1877, 7: 393–495. [4]*Ibid.*, 1942, 115: 61–81. [5]Brain, Lond., 1927, 50: 637–650. [6]*Ibid.*, 1934, 57: 504–516. [7]Neur. Cbl., 1898, 17: 603–604. [8]Wien. klin. Wschr., 1910, 23: 429–431. [9]*Études de physiologie et de pathologie cérébrales. Des actions réflexes du*

cerveau dans les conditions normales et morbides de leurs manifestations.
Paris, Baillière, 1874.   [10]*The brain and its functions.* New York, Appleton, 1882.   [11]*Iconographie photographique des centres nerveux.* 2
vol. in 1. Paris, Baillière, 1873.

References to Biography and Works: 1) Rev. hypnot., Par., 1898, *12:*
185–186 (Dumont-Pallier).   2) Ann. méd. psychol., Par., 1897, 8.sér.,
6: 321–323 (Ritti).   3) Chron. méd., Par., 1897, *3:* 589–591 (not
signed).   4) Rev. hypnot., Par., 1898, *12:* 91–93 (not signed).   5)
Progr. méd., Par., 1897, 3.sér., *6:* 141–142 (M.B.).   6) *The primate
thalamus.* Chicago, Ill., Univ. Chicago Press, 1938 (Walker).

OTTO MARBURG (1874–1948)

Shortly before his death, already resigned to the inevitable end
of his distressing terminal illness, Marburg wrote: "Though it
may be unusual to write one's own obituary, yet I do so in order to
save time for my friends, and to give just the bare facts of my
modest achievements." This pathetic document served well in the
task of reconstructing the work and life of a figure which linked
several generations in neurology and its two mainstays: neuroanatomy and neuropathology.

Marburg was born in Roemerstadt (now Raymariv), Moravia.
His premedical education was received in Olmütz, Silesia (then
Prussian). On graduation he entered the medical faculty at the University of Vienna. During his last year as a medical student, he
worked in Obersteiner's laboratory. On receiving the M.D., with the
highest honors, in 1899, he was appointed assistant to Obersteiner,
then director of the Neurological Institute of Vienna.

His clinical experience in psychiatry and neurology was acquired
under the guidance of Wagner von Jauregg (Vienna) and Oppenheim (Berlin). Later he came under the tutelage of Pierre Marie
(Paris), a significant event that determined his subsequent works
on neuroanatomy.

The University of Vienna recognized his great abilities and enthusiastic devotion to his chosen field by advancing him to Extraordinarius and by appointing him director of the Neurological
Institute on the death of his friend and chief, Obersteiner.

As associate of Obersteiner, and later as director of the Neurological Institute, he attracted multitudes of postgraduate students from

Otto Marburg

all corners of the earth. With his encouragement and driven by his inexhaustible energy, they produced some 300 original articles. This happy and highly productive activity was brought to a sudden close by the advent of tyranny preceding the recent war, which forced him to leave Vienna.

With the sympathetic aid of his staunch friend, Bernard Sachs, a corner for his scientific activity was created for him in my laboratory at the Mount Sinai Hospital, New York. On the second day after his arrival, he was already hard at work. Here I came to know this very kind man and to watch him in action as the great investiga-

Portrait, courtesy of Mrs. Malvine Marburg, New York City.

tor and the teacher, eager to advise, guide and instruct, though his somewhat unrelenting views undermined his good intent. To his younger colleagues he also served as an inexhaustible, ever-ready source of well ordered bibliographic information.

After some six months he was appointed clinical professor of neurology at Columbia University, and laboratory space was provided for him at the Montefiore Hospital and the Neurological Institute of New York.

He was most grateful for the consideration which was shown him in the United States, particularly by the Rockefeller Foundation. This he demonstrated on many occasions; even his own obituary concluded with the exclamation: "God bless America!"

Among his contributions to neurology, neurophysiology, and neuropathology, he listed, rightfully, as his major one, his *Mikroskopisch-topographischer Atlas des menschlichen Zentralnervensystems* (Wien, Deuticke, 1910)—a volume on which many an important neuroanatomist was raised. Altogether he published some 200 original papers and several books. He pointed to his work on acute multiple sclerosis[1-4] as an important step in the study of this disease and considered significant his views on malformations of the nervous system, discounting heredodegenerative forces as factors. He never abandoned his claim that the pineal body is an endocrine gland.[5] Much of the success of the Alexander and Marburg *Handbuch der Neurologie des Ohres* (1924–29) was due to his efforts. His grasp of medical literature is apparent in his splendid review article on topographic diagnosis of lesions of the pons and medulla oblongata, which brought up to date (1911)[6] the essential symptomatology of the various lesions to which these parts of the brain stem fall heir.[7]

No subject in neuropathology escaped his attention. He wrote on amaurotic family idiocy,[8] injuries of the nervous system, internal hydrocephalus, cerebral neoplasms, and particularly on trauma in relation to brain tumor.[9,10] He even tried his hand at experimental production of brain tumors.

NEW YORK CITY   JOSEPH H. GLOBUS

References

[1]Jahrb. Psychiat. Neur., Wien, 1906, 27: 213–312.   [2]Wien. med. Wschr., 1909, 37: 2147–2153.   [3]Zschr. Augenh., 1920, 44: 125–132.   [4]Bumke,

O., and Foerster, O., *Handbuch der Neurologie.* Berlin, 1936, *13:* 546–
693. [5]Bethe, A., *et al., Handbuch der normalen und pathologischen
Physiologie.* Berlin, 1930, *16:* 493–509. [6]Deut. Zschr. Nervenh., 1911,
41: 41–91. [7]Am. J. Ment. Defic., 1942, *46:* 312–322. [8]*Injuries of the
nervous system including poisonings.* New York, Veritas, 1939 (with Hel-
fand). [9]*Unfall und Hirngeschwulst; ein Beitrag zur Ätiologie der
Hirngeschwülste.* Wien, Springer, 1934. [10]Virchows Arch., 1935, *294:*
759–773.

References to Biography: 1) J. Mount Sinai Hosp., New York, 1942, *9:*
213–248 (Meyer). 2) Schweiz. Arch. Neur. Psychiat., 1950, *65:* 415–
420 (Minkowski).

VITTORIO MARCHI (1851–1908)

*M*archi was born in Novellara (Reggio Emilia), Italy. He
studied at the University of Modena where, in 1873, he obtained the Ph.D. in chemistry and pharmacology, and in 1882 the
M.D. Soon thereafter he was appointed assistant in anatomy at
the University of Modena and prosector at the Mental Hospital of
San Lazzaro in Reggio Emilia. In 1883 he obtained a fellowship
under Golgi (in Pavia), and after the completion of a year's work
he stayed on as Golgi's assistant.

In 1885, Marchi became assistant to Luciani, who at that time
was directing the Instituto di Fisiologia at the University of Florence. Although Luciani encouraged him to concentrate on cerebellar physiology, Marchi's heart was in histological problems. Consequently, in 1887, he competed for the chair of histology at the
University of Palermo, and was placed third among the elegible
candidates. This hurt him deeply; he renounced the academic
career and decided to become a country doctor in San Benedetto
del Tronto. In 1890 he was appointed chief of the Hospital of Jesi,
where he was successful in organizing a neurological clinic and a histological laboratory.

There Marchi finally made his permanent residence and continued
to work until his premature death, which occurred under tragic
conditions: he had just returned from a visit to his old master,
Luciani, with whom he had made arrangements to do some experimental investigations, when his middle ear became infected; symptoms of meningitis ensued, and in agonizing pain he correctly diag·

Vittorio Marchi

nosed his condition, called in a friend to whom he accurately predicted the time of his death—which came three days later.

Marchi's name became internationally known in connection with
his and Algieri's observation in 1885[1] and 1886[2] that the products
formed in degenerating myelin sheaths could be stained specifically
by osmic acid after mordanting with a chromic salt. The year 1885
was an auspicious one in neurohistologic research, for it marked the
discovery of the aniline staining method by Nissl. As Rasmussen

Portrait, courtesy of the Army Medical Library, Washington, D. C.

reminds us, osmic acid as a staining agent was used first by Fr. Schultze in 1849 and was popularized by Max Schultze in 1864, who employed it in the staining of myelin sheaths, as did Rudneff in 1865. But the method as devised by Marchi was immediately recognized as a new approach for histopathologic studies, for it now became possible to follow myelinated fibers from their source almost to their termination; his method "set the stamp of final approval." Through its use, investigators of many countries have been able to determine accurately the anatomo-topographic distribution of various degenerative processes involving the central and peripheral nervous pathways. The Swank-Davenport modification of the Marchi method is one of the most widely used today.[3]

Marchi's most outstanding contributions to neuroanatomy were those based on descending degeneration following experimentally induced lesions of the various regions of the cerebral cortex[2] and the origin and destination of fibers in the cerebellar peduncles.[4,5] He published, in all, 21 papers.

Marchi was a modest and persevering investigator who, due to ill-fated circumstances, was unable to use to full extent the staining technique he discovered; but it served other investigators in making fundamental contributions to the normal and pathologic histology of the central and peripheral nervous systems.

NEW YORK CITY   LEON ROIZIN

References

[1]Riv. sper. freniat., 1885, *11:* 492–494.   [2]*Ibid.,* 1886, *12:* 208–252. [3]Stain Techn., 1934, 9: 129–135.   [4]*Sull'origine e decorso dei peduncoli e sui loro rapporti cogli altri centri nerviosi.* Firenze, LeMonnier, 1891. (Publicazioni del R. Ist. studi sup. pratici. Sez. scienze fisiche e naturali. No. 18.)   [5]Nota prev. lab. fisiol. R. Ist. studi sup. Firenze, 1886.

References to Biography and Works: 1) Arch. ital. biol., 1908, *49:* 149–152 (contains bibliography; Luciani).   2) *Some trends in neuroanatomy.* Dubuque, Iowa, Brown, 1947 (Rasmussen).

THEODOR MEYNERT (1833–1892)
Erst seit Meynert ist das Gehirn beseelt

*I*n the history of neurology and psychiatry, Theodor Meynert stands out as a prophet of things to come. He inspired the work of Flechsig, Wernicke and Forel, and he was Freud's teacher. To Meynert we owe some of the current dynamic concepts in neurology and psychiatry.

Meynert was born in Dresden. He had his medical training in Vienna, where he received the M.D. in 1861. He became Dozent at the University of Vienna in 1865, Prosector of the Wiener Landes-Irrenanstalt in 1866, director of the psychiatric clinic in 1870, and Ordentlicher Professor of nervous diseases at the University of Vienna in 1873. Meynert's successor to the chair of psychiatry was Krafft-Ebing, and after him came Leidesdorf; subsequent holders of the chair, which came to include neurology, were Wagner-Jauregg, Poetzl, Kauders, and at present Hoff.

Meynert began his studies of the nervous system early in his medical career. At that time precise microtomes were not yet known. Employing the methods of B. Stilling (1810–79), he acquired an excellent command of histologic technique which enabled him to cut serial sections. From these he obtained a masterful grasp of the structural plan of the central nervous system. It was in 1867 that Meynert first called attention to regional differences in the cerebral cortex,[1] and in the following year appeared his masterpiece: *Der Bau der Grosshirnrinde und seine örtlichen Verschiedenheiten, nebst einem pathologisch-anatomischen Corollarium* (Leipzig, Engelmann). He set out avowedly to prove or refute certain theories about the brain. "The main function of the central organ," he stated, "is to transmit the fact of existence to an ego gradually shaping itself in the stream of the brain . . . If we look upon the cortex as an organ functioning as a whole then the information that it subserves the processes of the mind is all that can be said . . . To think further about the cortex is impossible and unnecessary . . . But our hope to understand eventually the function of the hemispheres is raised again by the opposite assumption which leads us straight to an organology of the central surface . . . Between these two theoretical possibilities the facts have to decide" (translation by

Theodor Meynert

Gerhardt von Bonin). Meynert then gave a detailed account of the structure of the cerebral cortex, of the differences in what is now known as the visual area—where he described the solitary cells which still bear his name—and analyzed minutely the hippocampal formation, the olfactory lobe, and the septum pellucidum. In concluding, Meynert distinguished between cortex with white surface (allocortex) and cortex with gray surface (neocortex). These two types of cortex were subsequently referred to as "heterogenetic" and "homogenetic" by Brodmann,[2] and as the "allocortex" and "isocortex" by O. Vogt.[3]

Meynert's formulation of the problem of brain structure was of historic importance. He coined the term, "organology of the cor-

Portrait, courtesy of the Army Medical Library, Washington, D. C.

tex." His anatomic studies led him to new ideas concerning the mode of function of the brain as an organ. He considered the cerebral cortex as a retentive recording tissue surmounting the radial bundles, on which the sensory and other impulses were projected by afferent paths, each registered image being the product of a special group (pattern) of simultaneously perceived sensations. He was the first to show that central integration was dependent on this association process.[4,5] His views on the projection of motor paths from the cerebral cortex downward were also dynamic concepts. He did not realize the importance of the short cortical connections to the thalamus in internalized cerebral activity, but he was the first to elaborate the sensory feedbacks from muscular movement to the cortex as the sense of innervation. His brilliantly written book on psychiatry, translated into English by Bernard Sachs,[6] was the epitome of his fundamental concepts. Edinger remarked to Sachs in 1888: "You have managed to translate Meynert into English; it is difficult for us to understand his German." Meynert's *Klinische Vorlesungen über Psychiatrie auf wissenschaftlichen Grundlagen* (Wien; Braumüller) appeared in 1890.

In offering a classification of mental diseases on a purely anatomic basis, Meynert went too far—he even objected to the use of the term "psychiatry"—and although his views on mental diseases have been referred to as "brain mythology" (by Gruhle), time has decided in favor of many of them. The supraoptic commissure which now bears his name was described by him in 1872.[7]

Meynert's novel point of view made a deep impression on his contemporaries. His ideas drew many visitors to Vienna even though he had the reputation of being a poor teacher. August Forel, who spent seven months (1871–72) with Meynert at the old insane asylum on Lazarettgasse, had to hold back his great disappointment in Meynert's lectures and laboratory. His department, Forel relates, was disorderly and filthy, not unlike the Oriental Quarter of Vienna, and through it all romped Meynert's two children. In peering at crudely-cut brain sections together, Forel could seldom follow Meynert—"his imagination played around me 10 times more than my own"—and thus Forel—who was then only 23—came to discount more and more the value of Meynert's anatomical schemes and his conception of the plexus of communication between different parts of the brain. Bernard Sachs, as a novice attempting to learn neuroanatomy in Meynert's laboratory some years later (1882), found it disconcerting that he had to struggle alone with a series of brain sections for a month before the Master would show the least interest in him. "A very stormy day," said Sachs to Meynert on greeting him one morning. "I have not yet had time to think about it," was the reply; and Sachs remarked to himself, "That settled that." Meynert tried to be amiable to his assistants but was seldom cordial. To this man with a massive head surmounting a short body, a sprawling bushy beard, and mane-like hair which had the habit of falling down into his eyes, urbanity was a luxury in which his brilliant mind would not allow him to indulge. There was robustness also about his poetry, regarded highly by the critics of that day. The same may be said of his drawings of the brain, to be found at the Neurological Institute of Vienna to this day.

COLUMBUS, OHIO   JAMES W. PAPEZ

References

[1]Vjschr. Psychiat., 1867, *1*: 77–93 *et seq.*   [2]*Vergleichende Lokalisationslehre der Grosshirnrinde in ihren Principien, dargestellt auf Grund des Zellbaues.* Leipzig, Barth, 1909; reprinted 1925.   [3]Congrès 20e des médecins alién. et neurol. de France; 8 août 1910. Brussels, 1911; p. 3–11.   [4]Sitzber. Akad. Wiss. Wien, 1870, *60*, Abth. 2: 547–566. [5]Leidesdorf, M., *Lehrbuch der psychischen Krankheiten.* Erlangen, Enke, 1865; p. 45–73.   [6]*Psychiatry. A clinical treatise on diseases of the forebrain.* London, Putnam's Sons, 1885.   [7]Stricker, S., *Handbuch der Lehre von den Geweben des Menschen und der Thiere.* Leipzig, Engelmann, 1872, *2*: 694–808.

References to Biography: 1) J. Psychol. Neur., Lpz., 1930, *40*: 256–281 (contains bibliography; Anton).   2) Jahrb. Psychiat., Lpz. u. Wien, 1892, 11: 3–11 (Fritsch).   3) *Barney Sachs, 1858–1944. An autobiography.* New York, privately printed, 1949 (with biographic notes by Nathan Straus and Foster Kennedy).   4) Zschr. ges. Neur. Psychiat., 1939, *165*: 17–38 (de Crinis).   5) *Auguste Forel mémoires.* Neuchatel, Baconnière, 1941.

JEAN NAGEOTTE (1866–1948)

Nageotte was born in the picturesque old French city of Dijon. His medical studies, undertaken in Besançon, were completed in Paris, where in 1889 he became interne des hôpitaux. He received his medical degree in 1893, and was appointed physician to the Bicêtre in 1898. After more than a decade there, he joined (in 1912) the staff of the Salpêtrière and succeeded Ranvier in what then became the chair of comparative histology in the Collège de France. His training as a physician and his study of pathological anatomy, carried on as opportunity offered, provided splendid training for the field of normal histology.

Nageotte was highly productive in research and had many publications to his credit. His doctoral thesis and some later contributions dealt with tabes dorsalis.[1-5,9] From the study of the nervous system of tabetics he concluded that the initial lesion occurs in the dorsal root component of the mixed spinal (or radicular) nerve, called since his time the "radicular nerve of Nageotte." His masterly technique also brought out the boutons terminaux of the spinal cord in great profusion.[6] With Babinski, he formulated a clinical syndrome resulting from lesions of the medulla oblongata (the syndrome of Babinski-Nageotte),[7] and the two of them also collaborated in writing a book on the cerebrospinal fluid.[8]

As his interest in normal histology increased, Nageotte, employing what were then new techniques, undertook a most comprehensive study of the structure of the nerve fiber, particularly the myelin sheath.[6,9-11] Like many modern observers he believed that this sheath is a derivative of the axis cylinder, that it consists of living protoplasm teeming with mitochondria, and that it has a vegetative function. As to the sheath of Schwann (the neurolemma of modern terminology), he felt that it is composed of neuroglia which had migrated peripherally and taken on a syncytial form, and that it is concerned with nutrition of the axis cylinder. Subsequently he studied the various stages of degeneration following injury of the peripheral nerves, and then turned his attention to the problem of nerve regeneration; in this field he was successful in grafting into dogs heteroplastic nerves previously fixed in alcohol.[12] On the basis of these results, Nageotte advocated the use of alcohol-fixed hetero-

Jean Nageotte

plastic transplants for human nerve repair, believing them to be superior to fresh autoplastic transplants. This was during World War I. Most workers today do not share this opinion.

Nageotte's interest in the nerve fiber, and particularly in the myelin sheath, continued throughout his academic career. He became absorbed in the chemical constitution of myelin and presented an interesting theory of its molecular structure.[13] It was his belief that the anatomic characteristics of this sheath, for instance, its discontinuity at the nodes of Ranvier, are manifestations of its chemical composition. He devoted a great amount of energy also to a study of connective tissue.

From Thiébaut we learn that Nageotte was not only a talented, conscientious physician and investigator, but that he was also a de-

Portrait, courtesy of the Armed Forces Institute of Pathology, Washington, D. C. (From portrait in *Presse méd., 69:* 837, 1948.)

votee of classical literature. The pleasures which Paris so liberally provides did not seem to interest him. Though inclined to be sarcastic and slow to make friends, he deeply admired such prominent men of his day as Ramón y Cajal, Ross Harrison, Gombault, Babinski, Raymond, Chaslin, and Caullery. He greatly valued the assistance and counsel of his wife, a distinguished pediatrician, who, for a time, presided over the Société de Pédiatrie. Together they reached as lofty a pinnacle as did the Dejerines and the Vogts. In 1923, as the result of an accident, Nageotte became paralyzed and thereafter was seldom free from pain. Gradually he became deaf. The occupation of his country by the German Army during World War II brought him much sorrow, for his wife died during this period, one of his daughters was imprisoned, and his son-in-law was deported by the Germans. However, he lived to see his country liberated.

ANN ARBOR, MICHIGAN   ELIZABETH C. CROSBY

References

[1]*Tabès et paralysie générale.* Paris, Steinheil, 1893.   [2]Bull. Soc. anat. Paris, 1894, *69:* 808–820.   [3]C. rend. Soc. Biol., 1900, 2.sér., *52:* 354–356. [4]*Ibid.,* 1902, 4.sér., *54:* 1226–1228.   [5]*Pathogénie du tabès dorsal.* Paris, Naud, 1903.   [6]*La structure fine du système nerveux.* Paris, Maloine, 1905.   [7]Rev. neur., Par., 1902, *10:* 358–365.   [8]*Contribution à l'étude du cytodiagnostic du liquide céphalo-rachidien dans les affections nerveuses.* Tours, Maretheux, 1901.   [9]Nouv. Iconog. Salpêtrière, 1906, *19:* 217–238.   [10]C. rend. Soc. biol., 1910, *68:* 39–42.   [11]Arch. mikr. Anat., 1911, 77: 245–279.   [12]C. rend. Soc. biol., 1918, *81:* 761–764.   [13]*Morphologie des gels lipoïdes, myéline, cristaux liquides, vacuoles.* Paris, Hermann, 1937.

References to Biography: 1) Presse méd., 1948, *69:* 837–838 (Thiébaut). 2) Bull. Soc. méd. hôp. Paris, 1948, 4.sér., *64:* 1264–1266 (not signed).

JOHANNES EVANGELISTA PURKINJE (1787–1869)

*T*his great pioneer in physiology, histology and embryology was born at Libochovice in Bohemia. When he was 10 years old, his father died and he was then educated by the Piarist monks. As a novice he taught school for three years, but in 1808, shortly before he was to have been ordained, he went to Prague to study philosophy.

JAN PURKYNĚ
Profesor w léčitelstwj na uniwersitě Wratislawské (Breslau).
Narozen 1787, 17 prosince w Libochowjejch.

Od ěcho etjjelu.

*Dokud i kde Buh žjli powelj,
Buď wěren wlasti, wjře, přjteli.*
Jan Purkyně

Portrait, courtesy of the Army Medical Library, Washington, D. C.

In 1810 he became tutor in the home of Baron Hildprandt, at Blatná, who enabled him to begin the study of medicine.

As a medical student, Purkinje observed the effects of drugs upon himself and, having "eine starke Natur," continued to do so for years. His descriptions of acute poisoning with ipecac, belladonna, camphor, etc. are classics. Stimulated by Goethe's *Farbenlehre*, he wrote his doctoral dissertation (1818) on the subjective aspects of vision,[1] a study which was to occupy him for many years and to gain him the friendship of Goethe. The second volume on entoptic phenomena (1825) included the celebrated chapter on after-images and the different thresholds of various colors. His inaugural dissertation (1823) dealt with visual and cutaneous sensibility and with differences in the diopric media, establishing a basis for objective optometry and the ophthalmoscope. It included the earliest data on the individuality of finger prints. His appointment as professor of physiology at Breslau was arranged by Geheimrat Rust, who had met him in 1817, and by K. A. Rudolphi, professor of anatomy at Berlin, whose daughter he married in 1825; it was Goethe, however, who had introduced him to Rudolphi and to many other notables in Berlin, such as Hegel, Freiherr von Stein, Varnhagen von Ense and the Humbolt brothers. The faculty at Breslau was opposed to the appointment of a Czech, and for years picayune jealousy prevented any effective cooperation from his colleagues. When he introduced demonstrations and laboratory work into his teaching, procedures new to biology, the faculty recommended that he be demoted. The Ministry of Education replied by commending his methods.

Important discoveries in histology came after Purkinje obtained his compound microscope (1832). The development of technical methods helped materially in the analyses which made his laboratory the "cradle of histology." In 1835 the "pest" carried off his devoted wife and two of his children, and the laboratory was moved to his home. The detailed histologic studies were all published under the names of his students, except for the monograph on ciliary epithelium and its function in mammals, which appeared in 1834[2] under co-authorship with the highly gifted Gabriel Gustav Valentin (1810–83), Purkinje's favorite pupil, who in 1835 received the Grand Prix des Sciences Physiques of the Institut de France for his work on a comparison of the development of tissues in animals and plants, and who, later, at Bern, was acknowledged as "the most prominent physiologist of his time."[3]

In 1837 Purkinje presented to the German Men of Science and Physicians in Prag a brief resumé of his microscopic survey of the human brain.[4] It included the first adequate description and illustrations of myelinated fibers, nerve cells (Körnchen) with their nuclei and dendrites, and the layers of a cerebellar folium, including a row of "flask-shaped ganglionic bodies." These, he said, usually have two branches extending almost to the pia.[5]

These observations contributed basic facts for the development of the cell theory. In 1839 he introduced the term "protoplasma." This was a significant advance, for prior to that time botanical terms had been used in describing the cells observed in animals. In the same year appeared his work on the cardiac fibers which were to be named after him. His pioneering autognostic studies on vertigo, begun in 1820, enabled him to distinguish the ocular from other factors involved. In 1846 he wrote on the value of dreams as an index to personality.

In 1850 Purkinje was called to the chair of physiology at Prag and was provided with a good laboratory, but nationalistic interests greatly reduced the scope of his scientific work. When we consider the acclaim and confirmation that greeted the discoveries for which the time was ripe, it would seem that many of the leading biologists of the day were Purkinje's followers. His enduring monuments are the cells, the fibers and the phenomenon which bear his name. At Breslau his home was a mecca for visiting Czech and Polish students. After his return to Prag he labored constantly to raise the cultural level of his countrymen. His translations from Schiller, Shakespeare and Tasso, and his many popular essays on science, enthroned him in the hearts of al Czechs.

What the great cosmopolitan Goethe thought of him is whimsically expressed in the following quatrain:

"Im eigenen Auge schau mit Lust
Was Plato von Anbeginn gewusst!
Und will Dir's nicht von selbst gelingen
So wird Purkinje Dir es bringen."
. . . .
"Let your delighted eye behold
All things that Plato knew of old!
And if yourself you can't quite do it,
Purkinje'll come and help you to it."
(Trans. by W. J. Wilson.) Quoted by K. A. Baer.[6]

CHICAGO, ILLINOIS   G. W. BARTELMEZ

References

[1]*Beiträge zur Kenntniss des Sehens in subjectiver Hinsicht.* Prag, Calve, 1819. (ed. 2, 1823). [2]Müller's Arch., 1834, *1:* 391–400. [3]Kagan (ed.), *Victor Robinson memorial volume. Essays on the history of medicine.* New York, Froben, 1948 (Kisch); p. 193–212. [4]Ber. ü. d. Versamml. deut. Naturf. u. Aerzte, Prag, Hasse, 1838, *15:* 174–175 *et seq.* [5]Bull. Hist. M., 1940, *8:* 1397–1398 (Viets and Garrison). [6]Bull. Hist. M., 1951, *25:* 159–168.

References to Biography: 1) Vierteljahresschr. f. d. prakt. Heilk., Prag, 1859, *63* (Beilage): 1–20 (contains bibliography; Eiselt). 2) Osiris, 1936, *2:* 464–483 (Hykeš and Studnička). 3) J. Am. M. Ass., 1899, *32:* 812–814 (Opitz). 4) Presse méd., 1938, *1:* 681–682 (Karasek).

SANTIAGO RAMÓN Y CAJAL (1852–1934)

*T*his eminent Spanish neurohistologist was born in the little pueblo of Petilla in the Pyrenees of northern Spain. His father was a struggling country physician, who, by his own tireless efforts, had succeeded in obtaining an academic degree from the medical faculty of the University of Zaragoza. The father long feared that his artistically inclined son would never earn his salt. A wandering artist said that he had no talent; his teachers declared him a dolt; a barber and shoemaker, to whom he was finally apprenticed, said he was lazy. Salvation came through his love of drawing which first led him to anatomy and thence to medicine.

Once through medical school (1873), he served as regimental surgeon in Cuba. In his short military service he acquired a breadth of experience, a deeper love for his own soil, but also a mixture of pulmonary tuberculosis and malaria which almost cut short his medical career. On his return to Spain he was appointed assistant, then professor of anatomy at the University of Zaragoza (1877), where he began the histologic studies which were destined to make him famous. A professorship of anatomy at Valencia (1884), then at Barcelona (1887), and finally an assignment on the medical faculty at the University of Madrid (1892), where the greater part of his life's work was accomplished, mark the steps of his scholastic career.

Once he had received recognition through a demonstration of silver-impregnated brain sections before a meeting of the German Anatomical Society at the University of Berlin (1889) (of which

von Kölliker was chairman), other honors soon came to him. He
delivered the Croonian Lecture (1894), received honorary degrees
from Oxford and Cambridge, and then gave a series of lectures at
Clark University in the United States, only a year after the Spanish-
American War. As a climax, he received the Nobel Prize jointly
with Golgi in 1906.

Portrait, courtesy of the Army Medical Library, Washington, D. C.

Meanwhile he had established his Laboratorio de investigaciones biológicas at the University and a school of followers had begun to form. Much of his work and that of his illustrious pupils was published first in the *Revista trimestral de histologia normal y patológica* and then in the *Trabajos del Laboratorio de investigaciones biológicas de la Universidad de Madrid,* a publication begun in 1901 and continuing until terminated by the Spanish Civil War.

In addition to well over 250 articles concerned largely with the normal and pathologic histology of the nervous system in animals and man, he published a number of monographs on the cerebral cortex, the retina, and on degeneration and regeneration of the nervous system. His manual of pathologic anatomy[1] went through seven editions. His textbook on histology of the nervous system, with its 25 original illustrations,[2] still remains the outstanding classic on the subject. His autobiography,[3] his philosophic cogitations,[4] and his observations on the development of the spirit of research[5] reveal the breadth of his thinking; his work on color photography[6] portrays something of the catholicity of his interests.

Cajal has been characterized as a man of "furious enthusiasm," of intense industry, and of deep philosophical reflection. He was also in the best sense a national zealot—a patriot jealous for his nation's reputation. He inspired a number of pupils who achieved an international reputation. He was the personal source of a renaissance of the scientific spirit in Spain.

LOS ANGELES, CALIFORNIA   CYRIL B. COURVILLE

References

[1]*Manual de anatomía patológica general.* Barcelona, 1890. (ed. 7. Madrid, Moya, 1922.)   [2]*Textura del sistema nervioso del hombre y de los vertebrados.* 2 vol. Madrid, Moya, 1899–1904.   [3]*Recuerdos de mi vida.* ed. 3. Madrid, Pueyo, 1923.   [4]*Charlas de café.* ed. 4. Madrid, Tipografía Artística, 1932.   [5]*Reglas y consejos sobre investigación científica.* ed. 6. Madrid, Pueyo, 1923. (Engl. trans. by Sanchez-Perez and Courville: *Precepts and counsels on scientific investigation. Stimulants of the spirit.* Mountain View, Cal., Pacific Press, 1951).   [6]*La fotografía de los colores: fundamentos científicos y reglas prácticas.* Madrid, 1912.

References to Biography: 1) *Recuerdos de mi vida.* ed. 3. Madrid, Pueyo, 1923 (contains bibliography; Cajal). (Engl. trans. by Craigie: *Recollections of my life.* American Philosophical Society Memoirs VIII.

Phila., Univ. Penna. Press, 1937).   2) Grote (ed.), *Die Medizin der Gegenwart in Selbstdarstellungen.* Vol. 5. Leipzig, Meiner, 1925 (autobiography).   3) Arch. Neur. Psychiat., Chic., 1926, *16:* 213–220 (Penfield).   4) Anat. Anz., 1935, *80:* 46–75 (contains *bibliography;* Tello). 5) Tr. Lab. invest. biol. Univ. Madrid, 1935, *30:* 1–210 (contains annotated bibliography; Tello).   6) *Explorer of the human brain. The life of Santiago Ramón y Cajal (1852–1934).* New York, Schuman, 1949 (Cannon).

STEPHEN WALTER RANSON (1880–1942)

Stephen Ranson, the son of a physician in a small community in Minnesota, was one of the foremost of a generation responsible for the flowering of contemporary neurological investigation in the United States. His career as professor of anatomy at Northwestern University Medical School, and later as director of its Institute of Neurology, was marked for some forty years by a continuing series of basic contributions, initially anatomical in nature but gradually becoming more concerned with the functional significance of neural structures.

Ranson's interest in neurology was developed by his association with Johnston and with Donaldson during his student years at the Universities of Minnesota and Chicago. In his doctoral investigation, Ranson began a long-term study which revealed the prevalence of nonmyelinated afferent fibers in peripheral nerves.[1] In orderly succession, the distribution of these fibers, their origin from the small cells of sensory ganglia and their central course in Lissauer's and the spinal trigeminal tracts were determined, and their importance for pain conduction indicated.

His growing interest in neurological function was next responsible for research on visceral and somatic reflexes, and his attention then became directed to brain stem centers involved in spinal integration. The chance observation that a "hypothalamic cat" could walk began a second major program of investigation, occupying the latter part of his career, in which he revived the use of the Horsley-Clarke instrument to reach, with facility, this hitherto inaccessible part of the brain.

With closely knit teams of associates, he clarified the hypothalamic innervation of the pituitary gland and established its importance

Stephen Walter Ranson

for the regulation of water exchange and for gonadotrophic control. The role of the hypothalamus in initiating the objective features of emotional excitement and in preserving a constant body temperature was elucidated,[2] and the profound hypokinesia and somnolence resulting from basal diencephalic injury were described.[3] Thus, Ranson, through his many contributions—well over 200— was one of the most distinguished of a long line of pioneers whose efforts were

Portrait, courtesy of Dr. H. W. Magoun, Chicago, Illinois

directed in one way or another toward clarifying the problem of hypothalamic function.

In 1933 and again in 1936 Ranson sought the anatomical explanation of the Argyll Robertson pupil and found that an important part of the neural mechanism concerned is the pretectile region.[4,5]

Toward the end of his career, in collaboration with his son and daughter, Ranson began investigations of the corpus striatum which led to a disclosure of the structural basis of recurrent striatal influences exerted on the cerebral cortex.[6]

At Northwestern University, Ranson was director of an institute created to provide him full time opportunity for research, with his only teaching responsibility that of training numerous graduate students, in whose subsequent independent progress he took a personal interest. Edition after edition of his unsurpassed textbook on *The anatomy of the nervous system* (1st ed., 1920; Philadelphia, Saunders) engaged his careful attention. Merited honors came to him—invitations to lectureships, the dedication of a volume of contributions on the hypothalamus by the Association for Research in Nervous and Mental Disease (1940), membership in the National Academy of Sciences, and the presidency of the American Association of Anatomists. Nevertheless, he remained to the end an unremitting worker, of keen mind and quiet dignity, who vastly preferred the satisfaction of investigative accomplishments in his laboratory and the enjoyment of his charming family, to the pursuit of recognition and acclaim. A duodenal ulcer plagued him for years, but a heart attack caused his death.

LOS ANGELES, CALIFORNIA

H. W. MAGOUN

References

[1]Am. J. Anat., 1911, *12:* 67–87.   [2]Bull. N. York Acad. M., 1937, *13:* 241–271 (Harvey Lecture).   [3]Arch. Neur. Psychiat., Chic., 1939, *41:* 1–23. [4]Arch. Neur. Psychiat., Chic., 1933, *30:* 1193–1204 (with Magoun). [5]Brain, Lond., 1936, *59:* 234–239 (with Magoun, Atlas and Hare). [6]Arch. Neur. Psychiat., Chic., 1941, *46:* 230–249 (with S. W. Ranson, Jr., and M. Ranson).

References to Biography and Works: 1) Q. Bull. Northwest. Univ. M. School, 1942, *16:* 302–310 (contains bibliography; Magoun and M. R.). 2) Anat. Rec., 1943, *86:* 3–10 (Arey).   3) List of Ranson's graduate students, research assistants, fellows and colleagues: vol. 15 of Publ. Inst. Neurol., Northwestern Univ. Med. School, 1943.

ROBERT REMAK (1815–1865)

Remak was born in Poznan, Poland. He studied medicine in Berlin under Schönlein and Johannes Müller, and, after graduating, became Müller's assistant at the Charité. The position brought no stipend, which made it necessary for Remak to spend most of his time in general practice. His doctoral dissertation, in 1838, entitled *Observationes anatomicae et microscopicae de systematis nervosi structura,* included an account of his discovery of nonmyelinated fibers, since called "Remak's fibers." From 1843 to 1847 he was clinical assistant to Schönlein, and was occupied with pathological and especially embryological investigations. He became Ausserordentlicher Professor to the University of Berlin rather late in life (1859).

Among the early cytologists of the nervous system, Remak was foremost. Most of his publications were epoch-making. His works were in three fields: microscopic anatomy of nervous tissues, embryology, and electrotherapy. As early as 1836, when a compound microscope came into his possession, he published treatises on the histologic structure of the nervous system,[1,2] and in 1838 recognized that the sympathetic fibers were gray because they were nonmyelinated.[3] He discovered that axons of nerves were continuous with cells in the spinal cord. His name became linked with the intrinsic ganglia of the heart, which he was the first to describe.[4] It was he who first mentioned the myelin sheath, which soon thereafter (1838) was described by Schwann. (Another year was to pass before Schwann published his observations of the neurolemmal sheath.) The earliest description of neurofibrils in nerve cells was Remak's.[4] After Baillarger's demonstration of the white bands in the cortex of the gross brain, Remak was the first to recognize histologically the six cortical cell layers.[4]

In the early 1850's, Remak's attention was turned to embryology of the nervous system. He defined for the first time the three germ layers and their significance for the development of the main tissue systems of the human body, and was a pioneer in the study of the

Robert Remak

Portrait, courtesy of the Army Medical Library, Washington, D. C.

formation of the neural tube.[5,6]   Indeed he shared with von Baer (1792–1876) the credit for founding the science of the germ layers. Among those who attended Remak's lectures on embryology was Wilhelm His, who later was to become the master in the field. Another student, von Kölliker, also owed much to the novel ideas Remak imparted.

Remak's substitution of the induced for the galvanic current in the treatment of nervous diseases, culminating in a book on the subject,[7] provoked much professional jealousy, but was later acknowledged by such an authority as His as "epoch making." In this field he ranks with Addison and Duchenne de Boulogne. Among his works in clinical neurology, the most outstanding was that on ascending neuritis (1861). Other contributions are indicated in Garrison's invaluable check-list of texts illustrating the history of medicine[8] and in Soury's *Le système nerveux central* . . . (2 vol., Paris, Naud, 1899), which remains today one of the most detailed and reliable accounts of the history of neurology.

Remak was not only unusually gifted and indefatigable, but also impulsive in word and deed, riding roughshod over the traditions held sacred by his contemporaries. His sensitive temperament made life difficult for him and often tempestuous. In the earlier part of his career it was only after the intercession of those who recognized his worth that the cabinet of Friedrich Wilhelm IV granted him permission to join the faculty of Berlin as Privatdozent.

While still at the height of his power and apparently in the best of health he took a trip from Berlin to Kissingen. Here he suddenly died. The obituary notes were peculiarly reticent concerning his personal characteristics.

COLUMBUS, OHIO   JAMES W. PAPEZ

References

[1]Arch. Anat. Physiol., Lpz., 1836; p. 145–161.   [2]Froriep's Notizen, 1837: No. 47, 54, 58.   [3]*Observationes anatomicae et microscopicae de systematis nervosi structura.* Berolini, Reimerianis, 1838.   [4]Arch. Anat. Physiol., Lpz., 1844; p. 463–472.   [5]*Untersuchungen über die Entwickelung des Wirbelthieres.* Berlin, Reimer, 1851.   [6]*Arch. Anat. Physiol., Lpz., 1862;* p. 230–241.   [7]*Galvanotherapie der Nerven- und Muskelkrankheiten.* Berlin, Hirschwald, 1858.   [8]Bull. Inst. Hist. M., Balt., 1933, 53: 333–434.

References to Biography: 1) Berl. klin. Wschr., 1865, *2:* 372 (not signed). 2) Deut. Klinik, 1865, *17:* 413–414 (not signed). 3) Wien. med. Presse, 1865, *6:* 915–917 (Benedikt). 4) Berl. klin. Wschr., 1865, *2:* 372 (His).

GUSTAF MAGNUS RETZIUS (1842–1919)

*O*ne of the leaders in research during the classical period of neuro-anatomy was Gustaf Retzius, whose amazing industry and versatility resulted in a series of princely monographs without parallel in the history of anatomy. His studies of nerve cells and their processes in a wide variety of invertebrates and vertebrates helped establish the foundation upon which the neuron doctrine was based, and his investigations in prehistoric craniology were among the major contributions to physical anthropology.[1] Comparative studies of a large series of subprimate, simian and human brains, fetal and adult, clarified many of the more difficult problems of brain morphology.[2,3] In addition, he made outstanding contributions to the knowledge of the sensory organs, nerve terminations, and the supporting tissues and ependyma of the central nervous system.

Born in Stockholm, Retzius entered the University of Uppsala in 1860. On the death of his father, Anders Retzius, professor of anatomy at the Caroline Institute (Karolinska mediko-kirurgiska Institutet), in 1864, he edited and published his father's fundamental researches in ethnology and began his own comprehensive studies on prehistoric crania. After receiving his medical degree in 1871, Retzius became Docent in anatomy at the Caroline Institute, where, with Axel Key, in 1869, he had begun researches on the membranes and cavities of the nervous system. In 1875–76 appeared their monumental work in this field, in which they affirmed through injection experiments and dissections the existence of the foramina of Magendie (discovered in 1825) and Luschka (1859), and presented the view that the cerebrospinal fluid escapes from the subarachnoid space through the Pacchionian bodies into the subdural space, then into the venous sinuses, and that some of it reached the cervical lymphatics.[4] Many years were to pass before Weed (1914) advanced the opinion, now generally accepted, that most of the fluid is absorbed by the arachnoidal villi. Retzius and Key's view that the fluid in the Virchow-Robin space flows into the subarachnoid

Portrait, courtesy of Prof. Folke Henschen, Stockholm, Sweden.

space was adopted by Weed, and a diagram by him illustrating this point is still to be found in most textbooks on neuroanatomy. It has since been demonstrated that true perivascular spaces extend from the subarachnoid space to the beginnings of the capillaries, where their contents become continuous with the tissue fluid of the central nervous system.[5]

Retzius' studies on the labyrinth were equally impressive.[6] Other papers of this period were published as annual volumes.[7]

In recognition of his attainments, Retzius was made *personligt* professor of anatomy at the Caroline Institute in 1877. From 1884 to 1887 he served as chief editor of the *Aftonbladet*, a leading Stockholm newspaper owned by his wife's father, but in 1888 he returned to the Institute as professor of anatomy, resigning the following year. Commanding ample means he thenceforth devoted himself to research.

The well-known *Biologische Untersuchungen*, printed on the press of the *Aftonbladet*, includes most of his contributions from this time on. Nineteen folio volumes, handsomely illustrated, and including only his own work, appeared from 1890 to 1920.[8] A wide range of subjects was covered, but the finer anatomy and the comparative morphology of the nervous system were the predominant themes. Most of the hundreds of figures were indicated as drawn by his own hand. His descriptions were accurate and his interpretations have stood the test of time.

His publications numbered 333 scientific titles,[9] to which should be added numerous sketches of scientists and several volumes of poems. He also wrote several cantatas. The extraordinary volume of his labors was partially due to his private means for financing his publications and in part to his ability to inspire assistance from others.

Retzius received widespread recognition. In 1908 he delivered the Croonian Lecture before the Royal Society of London, choosing as his subject, *The principles of the minute structure of the nervous system*,[10] and in the following year he gave the Huxley Lecture on *The so-called North European race of mankind* before the Royal Anthropological Institute.[11] He was not only one of "De Aderton" of the Swedish Academy, the group of 18 men which decides on the bestowal of the Nobel Prize for Literature, etc., but he was also a member of the Swedish Academy of Science, which chooses Nobel laureates in physiology and medicine. A man of gracious charm and courtesy, he numbered among his friends the prominent scientists of the day.

Retzius belonged to a club whose members bequeathed their brains to scientific research. At the request of his wife, who also belonged to the club, Retzius' brain was removed by Prof. Folke Henschen. It is now in the collection of élite brains in the Museum of Pathology of the Caroline Institute.

PORTLAND, OREGON   O. LARSELL

References

[1]*Crania suecica antiqua.* Stockholm, Aftonbladetsdruckerei, 1900. [2]*Das Menschenhirn.* 2 vol. Stockholm, Norstedt, 1896. [3]*Cerebra simiarum illustrata. Das Affenhirn in bildlicher Darstellung.* Jena, Fischer, 1906. [4]*Studien in der Anatomie des Nervensystems und des Bindegewebes* (with Key). 2 parts. Stockholm, Samson & Wallin, 1875–76. [5]Anat. Rec., 1944, 88: 1–12 (Patek). [6]*Das Gehörorgan der Wirbelthiere.* 2 vol. Stockholm, Samson & Wallin, 1881–84. [7]Biol. Untersuch., Stockh. vol. 1–2, 1881–82. [8]*Ibid.,* N.F., vol. 1–19, 1890–1920. [9]*Ibid.,* 1920, 19: 81–100. [10]Proc. R. Soc., Lond., 1908, ser.B, 80: 414–443. [11]J. R. Anthrop. Inst., Gr. Britain, 1909, 39: 277–313.

References to Biography and Works: 1) Man, Lond., 1919, 19: 149–150 (Keith). 2) Sc. Month., 1920, 10: 559–569 (Larsell). 3) *Biografiska anteckningar och minnen* (autobiographic notes and recollections). 2 vol. Upsala, 1933, 1948 (Retzius). 4) *Observations on the pathology of hydrocephalus.* Medical Research Council Special Report Series No. 265. London, His Majesty's Stationery Office, 1949 (Russell).

PÍO DEL RÍO HORTEGA (1882–1945)

*H*ortega was born in Portillo, Spain. He received his medical education at Valladolid, graduating in 1908. After practising medicine for two years and finding it not to be his vocation, he accepted a position as auxiliary professor of anatomy and histology at his alma mater. The outstanding gifts of the young histologist were soon recognized, and he was awarded a fellowship by the Spanish Cancer Committee for study in France, England and Germany.

On his return to the laboratories of Achúcarro and Cajal in Madrid, he initiated an era of brilliant research. After improving some

of the techniques of Achúcarro, he introduced in 1918 his silver sodium carbonate method. With this he succeeded in staining cells which he called "microglia" and "oligodendroglia," but withheld publication for a year because his discoveries ran counter to the views of his master, Cajal, who regarded such cells as in the category of "polar neuroglia." Persuaded by his colleagues to publish his observations, Hortega finally yielded (1919),[1,2] with the result that it

Portrait, courtesy of Dr. William C. Gibson, Vancouver, Canada.

became necessary for him to leave Cajal's laboratory—or, to be more explicit, Cajal requested his resignation.

Through his friend, Negrín, he obtained a position in a small laboratory in Madrid. Here he demonstrated that microglia and cells of the reticuloendothelial system are identical. In 1932 he was appointed director of the Instituto de Oncologia. During these years, he worked under high tension. Uninterrupted development of the silver carbonate method permitted deep inroads into virgin soil. Although the nervous tissue remained one of the main subjects of investigation, he found time to study tumors of the nervous system, publishing epochal monographs in 1932, 1934 and 1945.[3]

At the height of his activity, the Civil War broke out in Spain. His Institute destroyed by shell fire, he was forced to leave his country, the culture of which was his very life. The Republican Government sent him to Paris (1936), where he worked in the laboratory of Clovis Vincent. Later on, he went to Hugh Cairns' laboratory at Oxford (1937). Here, according to McMenemey, "he would learn to be 'very English' in time and with grim determination would request a tea of fish and chips . . . The rooks' nest in the elms reminded him of senile plaques . . . The conferment of an honorary degree at the Sheldonian theatre was to him a real joy, but who will forget that nervous, lonely little man, his eyelids blinking faster even than their wont, swamped in scarlet robes, as he listened to the memorial of the Public Orator . . . 'In England,' he said, 'I love you all but, oh God, not your draughts and your everlasting mutton . . .' His English was shocking though surprisingly adequate. 'My section, good,' he would say, 'your section, not good.' If you poured too much solution into your pocillo he would cry 'Not convenient!' and hastily decant away the excess. He would bend over his little dishes and with consummate skill and patience order the cells of the brain to deliver up to him their secrets. The microglia danced to him and revealed their graceful limbs. The astrocytes scintillated in their peculiar firmament of the ground substance. A faint exclamation of surprise would greet the appearance of a globoid and almost limbless gitter zelle. 'Look,' he would say, 'this one eat so much arroz he want not to move.' And under the microscope he found a world of beauty which pleased his artistic soul and fed his inquisitive mind, for at heart he was a physiologist."

In 1940, Hortega left the gray skies of England to accept an invitation from the Institución Cultural Española to work in Buenos Aires, where he went with his faithful lifelong friend, Nicolás Gomez del Moral.

During his five years there, he succeeded in discovering (with Prado and Polak) the glia of the sympathetic nervous system and the perispinal ganglia, and thus introduced new concepts into our knowledge of the glia. In a series of papers on brain tumors, he announced new techniques which still are largely unknown outside of the Argentine. It was on these techniques that he was working when he was forced to bed by cancer. Gomez del Moral's attendance upon him to the end, during which he performed even the most menial tasks of nursing, is a story of devotion hard to equal.

Hortega was a sensitive, shy, modest person, simple in his tastes, very meticulous, rapid in his actions, extraordinarily gifted not only as a scientist but also as an artist. His profession of faith is to be found in his essay, *Arte y artificio de la ciencia histológica.*[4]

ANN ARBOR, MICHIGAN   K. SCHARENBERG

References

[1]Arch. neurob., Madr., 1921, 2: 212–255.   [2]*Ibid.*, p. 16–43.   [3]*Nomenclatura y clasificación de los tumores del sistema nervioso.* Buenos Aires, López y Etchegoyen, 1945.   [4]Residencia, Madr., 1933, 4:191–206. (Engl. trans.: Texas Rep. Biol. M., 1949, 7: 363–390).

References to Biography: 1) Arch. histol. norm. patol., B. Aires, 1947, 3: 377–421 (contains bibliography; Polak). 2) J. Neurosurg., 1946, 3: 275–284 (Prados and Gibson). 3) Arch. Neur. Psychiat., Chic., 1945, 54: 413–416 (Penfield). 4) Lancet, 1945, 2: 222 (McMenemey). 5) Tr. Lab. invest. biol. Univ. Madrid, 1945, 37: VII–XVIII (de Castro).

SIR GRAFTON ELLIOT SMITH (1871–1937)

*E*lliot Smith was born at Grafton, New South Wales. He attended the newly founded medical school in the University of Sydney, and graduated in 1892. Stimulated by Anderson Stuart, professor of physiology, and by J. T. Wilson, professor of anatomy, he studied the morphology and histology of the cerebrum of non-placental mammals, writing his doctoral thesis on this subject. In 1896, he obtained a travelling fellowship from the University of Sydney and came to the British Isles to continue his research. Because Oxford

demanded proficiency in Latin and Greek, he entered Cambridge
University. Under the stimulus of Macalister, and stirred by contact with Gaskell, Horsley, Langley, Mott, E. A. Schäfer (later
Sharpey Schaffer), all of whom were intensively engaged in studies
of neurophysiology, Elliot Smith continued his work on cerebral
morphology.

   In 1900 he was invited to the chair of anatomy in the new Govern-

Portrait, courtesy of Lady Elliot Smith, Oxford, England. (Photographer: F. W.
Schmidt, Manchester.)

ment Medical School at Cairo, a post which profoundly influenced his future course. The unusual opportunities for study of ancient Egyptian life, mummies and paleopathology fascinated him. With his characteristic energy, he set about to study the remains of the old civilization, and ended by preparing some 20,000 anatomic reports of burials in Nubia. The careful analysis of this material was presented in several books,[1-4] and his conclusion that culture had been spread from Egypt startled the thinking world. The story goes that Elliot Smith, on finding advanced calcific arteriosclerosis of the heart in a mummy he was dissecting, turned to his assistant and remarked: "Do you remember the old Biblical passage, 'And the Lord hardened the heart of Pharaoh'?"

In 1909 he returned to England to the chair of anatomy at Manchester, where he continued his studies on ethnology, anthropology and the evolution of the brain, the last of which formed the basis of his Arris and Gale Lectures in 1910.[5] World War I forced his attention to subjects of more immediate importance, especially shell shock.[6] At the conclusion of the War, he delivered the Croonian Lectures on the cerebral cortex.[7] In 1919 he was invited to the chair of anatomy at University College, London. Here he had another unique opportunity, for the Rockefeller Foundation made possible the founding of an Institute of Anatomy. Elliot Smith developed the teaching of anatomy to new heights, and by making that specialty attractive, encouraged a succession of brilliant pupils to vivify that discipline in the medical school curriculum.

In 1932 he was partially incapacitated by a stroke and in 1936 retired from the chair of anatomy. He continued to work, however, until his death.

Elliot Smith's main contributions were in the field of comparative anatomy and evolution of the nervous system. His comparative analyses of the fissural pattern of the brain have been the basis of our homologies of cerebral configuration. He gave meaning to the phylogenetic changes in the surface topography of the brain by his studies of the subcortical and cortical factors which influence the elaboration and modification of the convolutions of the pallium,[5,7] and he was an important contributor to the understanding of the development of speech and of binocular vision.[8] An outline of Elliot Smith's contributions to neurology has been provided by Woollard.[9]

In spite of the many honors heaped upon him, he remained a simple, charming man, delighted with a yarn and ready to discuss biblical prophecies or the University rugger match. His genial qualities and stimulating personality attracted to him a host of young men, many of whom now hold important university posts.

BALTIMORE, MARYLAND   A. EARL WALKER

References

[1]*The migration of early culture.* Manchester, Univ. Press, 1915. [2]*Human history.* New York, Norton, 1929.   [3]*Egyptian mummies.* London, Allen & Unwin, 1924 (with Dawson).   [4]*The ancient Egyptians and the origin of civilization.* New York, Harper, 1923.   [5]Lancet, 1910, *1*: 1–6 *et seq.*   [6]*Shell shock and its lessons.* Manchester, Univ. Press, 1917 (with Pear).   [7]Brit. M. J., 1919, *1*: 758 (abstract of Croonian Lecture).   [8]*Essays on the evolution of man.* London, Oxford Univ. Press, 1927.   [9]J. Anat., Lond., 1938, *72*: 280–294.

References to Biography: 1) J. Anat., Lond., 1936, *71*: 1–6 (J.T.W.) 2) Man, Lond., 1937, *37*: 51–53 (Young).   3) Brit. M. J., 1937, *1*: 99–101 (not signed).

LUDWIG TÜRCK (1810–1868)

*T*ürck, a native of Vienna, attended the University there and obtained his degree in medicine in 1837. Three years later, he was appointed physician in the Allgemeines Krankenhaus, where in 1846 a department of neurology was created, with him as its chief in 1847. Partly because of his modest and retiring disposition, Türck did not receive recognition for a long time and was given academic rank only toward the end of his life.

Türck's interest in neurology manifested itself soon after his graduation, when he published several articles on neurosyphilis and cerebral apoplexy. During this period, neurology in Vienna was largely of a speculative character, and was dominated by the theories of Benedikt Stilling (1810–79), of Cassel, on "spinal irritation." This point of view also attracted Türck who, in 1843, published a book on the subject, but even at that time he showed his independent and scientific approach. In 1844 he went to Paris, where he was influenced mostly by Ricord, whose lectures on syphilis he translated into German. There followed a relatively quiet period of five

years devoted largely to clinical observation. Vienna at that time was still in neuroanatomical darkness, as reflected by the remark of the distinguished Josef Hyrtl (1810–94) in his well-known *Lehrbuch* (1846): "Die Anatomie des inneren Baues des Gehirns ist und

Portrait, courtesy of Library of College of Physicians of Philadelphia, Pennsylvania. (Photographer: Schultz, Vienna.)

bleibt wahrscheinlich für immer ein mit sieben Siegeln verschlossenes und überdies noch in Hieroglyphen geschriebenes Buch."

From 1849 onward, Türck made his chief contributions to neurology. His most important original investigations were concerned with secondary degeneration in the central nervous system.[1-3]   In this work he was influenced by the studies of Sir Charles Bell (1774–1842) on the physiology of nerve conduction, and by the observation made by his close friend and associate, C. Wedl, that compound granular corpuscles develop in the region of injury of the central nervous system. Based on neuropathological observations in cases of hemiplegia and compression of the spinal cord,[1] and confirmed by experimental investigations, Türck established the principle that the direction of tract degeneration corresponds to the direction of conduction. Thus, focal capsular lesions in the brain produce degeneration of the corticospinal tract, and transverse lesions of the spinal cord result in degeneration of the centripetal tracts above the level injured and of the centrifugal tracts below. In this way, he was able to outline six tracts in the spinal cord, one of which, the anterior corticospinal tract, bears his name.[4] He did not recognize this tract as such—he called it the "Hülsen-Vorderstrangbahn"—but he knew that it emanated from the region of the pyramidal decussation. In regard to the lateral corticospinal tract, it was he who discovered a century ago that it passed through the internal capsule and the middle third of the basis pedunculi in its course downward.[2,3] He felt that the secondary degeneration was due probably to an interruption of conduction.

Türck was an originator of the concept of system disease of the spinal cord, and he described the syndrome of hemisection of the cord now-a-days attributed to Brown-Séquard.[5] His work on spinal tract degeneration, although it proved to be one of the major medical discoveries of the 19th century, was ignored by the scientific world for more than a decade. In 1866 Bouchard took up the subject where Türck had left off, and some 10 years later Türck's studies served as the foundation for the study of myelogenesis by Flechsig.

Türck made many other contributions to neurology. Most significant were his neuro-ophthalmologic investigations in cases of Bright's disease and brain tumor. He was one of the first to describe the mechanism of choked disc. His studies on the cutaneous distribution of individual spinal nerve roots (1858–68) are classics.

He was a pioneer also in the study of sensory localization in the cerebral cortex, the course of the optic pathways, trigeminal neuralgia, tabes dorsalis,[6] and multiple sclerosis.

In the last ten years of his life, Türck abandoned the field of neurology and became interested in laryngology. It is still disputed whether he or Czermak first invented the laryngoscope. His contribution to this field[7] received at that time much greater attention than his previous studies, so much so that in the Memorial Address by Sigmund at the unveiling of his bust in the Allgemeines Krankenhaus following his sudden death from typhus in 1868, Türck's researches in neurology were scarcely mentioned.

SAN FRANCISCO, CALIFORNIA   N. MALAMUD

References

[1]Zschr. k. k. Gesellsch. Ärzte zu Wien (Med. Jahrb.), 1849, 1: 173–176. [2]Ibid., 1852, 2: 511–534.   [3]Ibid., 1853, 2: 289–317.   [4]Sitzber. math. naturw. Klasse Akad. Wiss., Wien, 1853, 11: 93.   [5]Rev. thérap. méd.-chir., Par., 1857; p. 309–316.   [6]Zschr. k. k. Gesellsch. Ärzte zu Wien (Med. Jahrb.), 1855, 16: 517–532.   [7]Praktische Anleitung zur Laryngoskopie. Wien, Braumüller, 1860. (Review by Semeleder in Med. Jahrb., 1861, 17: 1–8.)

References to Biography: 1) Jahrb. Psychiat. Neur., Wien, 1910, 31: 1–21 (contains collected works, p. 23–194; Neuburger).   2) Wien. Klinik, 1889, 15: 165–192 (Heitler).

AUGUSTUS VOLNEY WALLER (1816–1870)

Waller was born on a farm in Kent, England. His childhood was spent in the south of France, but he returned to school in his native country at the age of 14. Later, when a student in Paris, he became interested in the histologic structure of the tongue of the frog, and his first and most notable observations were made on such preparations. After graduating in Paris (1840), he practiced medicine in Kensington in London for 10 years (1842–51), during which period he continued indefatigable microscopic observations whenever he could spare time from attendance upon patients. In this period two of his papers were published in the *Philosophical Transactions of the Royal Society*. The first of these was an account of diapedesis of the white cells of the blood, already noted by Addison.

Augustus Volney Waller

The second dealt with the effects of transection of the glossopharyn-geal and hypoglossal nerves of the frog,[1] a study in which Waller established the nature of degeneration of the peripheral part of the nerve.

In 1851 Waller decided to give up medical practice and devote himself entirely to physiologic studies. He went to Bonn, where, with the ophthalmologist Julius Ludwig Budge (1811–84), he be-

Portrait, courtesy of Dr. D. Denny-Brown, Boston, Massachusetts.

gan experiments on the pathway of the pupillary dilator fibers.[2] Together, they noted that when the vagosympathetic trunk of the dog was severed the degeneration of the peripheral end of the nerve was incomplete. The remaining intact fibers were identified with the sympathetic trunk and were traced to the Ist and IId thoracic segments of the spinal cord. When, in the intact animal, this region was stimulated, the pupils enlarged, but when the cervical part of the sympathetic trunk was sectioned unilaterally the electrical stimulation no longer caused pupillary dilatation on that side. They named these segments the "ciliospinal center." For this work, Budge and Waller were awarded the Monthyon Prize of the Académie des Sciences for 1852. In 1852[3] and 1853[4] Budge and Waller described the vasoconstrictor action of the cervical sympathetic, which was in confirmation of the discoveries of Claude Bernard in 1851 and Brown-Séquard in 1852. Not long afterward the vasoconstrictor action of the sympathetic supply to the upper limbs was described by Claude Bernard (1862), Schiff (1862)[5] and Cyon (1868),[6] and that to the lower limbs by Claude Bernard (1854) and Ostroumoff (1876).[7] This period was the dawn of knowledge of the function of the autonomic system.[10]

Waller is best known for his study of trophic degeneration of nerve fibers as a method of investigating the anatomy of the nervous system. This was described in a series of memoirs communicated to the Académie des Sciences, the most important of which was his first, which appeared in 1851: *Nouvelle méthode pour l'étude du système nerveux applicable à l'investigation de la distribution anatomique des cordons nerveux.*[8] His approach gained immediate recognition as the "Wallerian method," and in 1856 he was awarded the Monthyon Prize for the second time.

Waller moved from Bonn to Paris in 1856, but almost immediately became seriously ill with what appears to have been rheumatic fever. During the next two years he recuperated in England, and had just taken up a new appointment as professor of physiology in Birmingham when further illness forced him to retire to Bruges, then to the Pays de Vaud, in search of health. By 1868 he was well enough to begin a quiet medical practice in Geneva, where he again briefly renewed his physiologic studies. He was, however, greatly troubled by angina pectoris, to which he succumbed not long after he had given his last paper on Wallerian degeneration.[9] His son,

Augustus D. Waller, was also a distinguished physiologist. Bartel-mez relates how, on one occasion, with the mention of his father's name, the younger Waller said, "I am *the* Wallerian degeneration!"

BOSTON, MASSACHUSETTS   D. DENNY-BROWN

References

[1]Philos. Tr. R. Soc. London, 1850; p. 423–429.   [2]C. rend. Acad. sc., 1851, *33:* 370–374 *et seq.*   [3]Med. Zeitung, Berl., 1852, *21:* 161–162 (Budge).   [4]C. rend. Acad. sc., 1853, *36:* 378–382.   [5]*Ibid.,* 1862, *55:* 425–427.   [6]Arb. a. d. physiol. Inst. Leipzig, 1868, *3:* 62–77. [7]Pflügers Arch., 1876, *12:* 219–277.   [8]C. rend. Acad. sc., 1851, *33:* 606–611.   [9]Proc. R. Soc., Lond., 1870, *18:* 339–343 (abstract of the Croonian Lecture).   [10]Arch. Neur. Psychiat., Chic., 1936, *35:* 1081–1115 (Sheehan).

References to Biography and Works: 1) Proc. R. Soc., Lond., 1871, *20:* xi–xiii (not signed).   2) *Some apostles of physiology.* London, privately printed, 1902; p. 123–126 (Stirling).

CORNELIS WINKLER (1855–1941)

W inkler was born in the old walled town of Vianen (not far from Utrecht), the son of a physician. He was graduated in medicine at the University of Utrecht in 1879. After a few years in internal medicine, first at The Hague, then under Talma at Utrecht, he became fascinated by the experiments of Fritsch and Hitzig and began working on neurological subjects in the physiological laboratory of Pekelharing. He studied with Meynert in Vienna in 1882 and again in 1885; then went on to Heidelberg for further instruction in psychiatry and to Munich for work in anatomy with von Gudden. Leidesdorf (1818–89) influenced him greatly, and Leidesdorf's young assistant, Wagner von Jauregg, became one of his close friends. With Pekelharing, in 1887, he journeyed to the Dutch East Indies to study beriberi at first hand, and our knowledge of the nature of this disease dates from that trip.[1,2]

Influenced by the experiments of von Gudden (atrophy method) he began his far-reaching experimentation on the anatomy of the nervous system of laboratory animals, which he continued the rest of his life. His laboratory atlases with Ada Potter on the brain of

Cornelis Winkler

the rabbit[3] and cat[4] became standard equipment in all laboratories of experimental neuropathology.

But his interests were much broader than that. He collaborated with the surgeon van Guldenarm in the first brain tumor removals done in Holland.[5] Stimulated by the work of Lombroso in forensic medicine, he contributed much to this field, becoming, in fact, an outstanding criminologist. In neurology he was considerably influenced by Charcot, whom he knew well, and by Pierre Marie.

He became professor of neurology and psychiatry at Utrecht in 1893, but soon resigned (1895) to accept a similar chair at the Uni-

Portrait, courtesy of Dr. L. Raymond Morrison, Boston, Massachusetts.

versity of Amsterdam (1896). When, in 1908, the Central Institute for Brain Research was established in Amsterdam, Winkler was elected president-curator, a position which he held for more than three decades. In 1915 he returned to Utrecht, succeeding Heilbronner.

His publications in the field of neurology and psychiatry were numerous: over 200 works, among them the famous 5-volume *Manuel de neurologie* (Haarlem, Bohn, 1933). He published not only in Dutch but also in German, French and English, all of which he could read, write, and speak with facility and charm. His subject matter extended from the simplest reflex abnormalities to that borderland of science where neurophysiology becomes philosophy; but his greatest contributions were in anatomy. The School of Neuroanatomy that he founded produced many famous pupils, outstanding among them, Brouwer, Ariëns Kappers, and van Valkenburg. His own contributions were prodigious; typical of them were the papers on the connections of the tractus centralis tegmenti and the central pathways of the VIIIth nerve,[6] his work on the latter being considered by Spiller (1925) the best in the field. With Magnus and with Rademaker he set new standards for anatomic research by the atrophy method.

His devotion as a father was shown by an abiding interest in the education of his children. Though beloved by his patients, he kept his practice small to find time for scientific work. He was warmly regarded and greatly respected by his colleagues, and at medical meetings served constantly as catalyst. As a teacher and in the privacy of his laboratory, he was patient, gentle and lucid. After becoming Emeritus, in spite of his age—which he carried well—he still walked back and forth each day to his laboratory. The fragrance from the excellent, small cigars he was accustomed to smoke, the fine level gaze of his steady blue eyes, so much younger than his years would indicate, and the wisdom of his words, all combined to give one the feeling of being in highly civilized company. And this impression was in no way diminished as one watched him sketch with a pencil on the white, starched cuff of his immaculate shirt how the pallidoreticular fibers proceed around the thalamus.

BOSTON, MASSACHUSETTS   L. RAYMOND MORRISON

References

[1]Deut. med. Wschr., 1887, *13:* 845–848.   [2]*Recherches sur la nature et la cause du béri-béri et sur les moyens de le combattre.* Utrecht, Kemink & Zoon, 1888 (with Pekelharing).   [3]*An anatomical guide to experimental researches on the rabbit's brain.* Amsterdam, Versluys, 1914. [4]*An anatomical guide to experimental researches on the cat's brain.* Amsterdam, Versluys, 1914.   [5]Ned. tschr, geneesk., 1886, *22:* 526–529. [6]Verh. Akad. wet. Amsterdam, 1907, *14:* 1–202.

References to Biography: 1) *Herinneringen van Cornelis Winkler, 1855– 1941.* Arnheim, van Loghum Slaterus, 1947.   2) Encéphale, 1946–47, *36:* 97–109 (Lhermitte and Mourgue).

II

NEUROPHYSIOLOGISTS

HANS BERGER (1873–1941)

With a physician father, a poet grandfather (Rückert), and a literary mother (who read books on the relationship of mind and body), "Hans" Berger—as he preferred to call himself, although he was christened "Johannes"—seems to have been oriented by heredity toward the study of that strange alchemy by which the brain turns physical energy into psychic function.

Although born in Neuses near Doburg (Thuringia), he was usually referred to as Hans Berger of Jena, because Jena was the geographic center of his life work. In 1900 he joined the psychiatric clinic, was made Ausserordentlicher Professor in 1906, and physician-in-chief of the clinic in 1912. In spite of objections that he was not a "true" psychiatrist, he succeeded Otto Binswanger in 1919 as Ordinarius and head of the department of psychiatry. He served as Rector of the University in 1927 and 1928 and as Prorector from 1935 to 1938, when he became Professor Emeritus.

His publications show how sharply he focused on what he considered the central problem of psychiatry—the physical basis of psychic function. Among his more important contributions were those on intracranial blood circulation,[1] bodily manifestations of psychic states,[2] temperature of the brain[3] and psychophysiology[4]; but the studies which crowned his career and marked him as one of the great innovators of all time were those on the electroencephalogram of man. The forerunner in this field was Richard Caton (1842–1926), a Liverpool surgeon who had succeeded in 1875 in leading off action potentials from the brains of animals.[5] Berger's paper announcing that such variations in voltage could be recorded through the intact cranium appeared in 1929.[6] The others that followed were all epoch-making.[7,8]

Although at first the importance of his work went generally unrecognized and was even ridiculed, he was undismayed. He thought he was right and believed his critics were piling up confusion for themselves. He was greatly pleased when in 1937 he was invited to preside with Adrian at the symposium on electrical activity in the nervous system held by the Congress of Psychology in Paris. Baudouin hailed Berger as the most distinguished of all the visitors to his laboratory. Berger was overwhelmed and tears came to his eyes

as he said: "In Germany I am not so famous." Plans were made to have him visit the United States to inspect laboratories where electrical studies on the brain were in progress and to lecture on his work. He was delighted at the prospect and began to polish his English. He wrote: "I will come as soon as the international situation permits."

As a front-row witness of the rise of Hitler and World War II, Berger saw not only the destruction of lives and property, but also the dissipation of man's slowly accumulated treasures of benevolence and reason. Prescient of irreparable losses, both social and personal, yet to come, and forced by old age merely to wait and watch, he decided in a fit of melancholia—to which he was subject—that he had seen enough and on June 1, 1941, ended his life.

Like Osler's good physician he was imperturbable in outward manner, but he was a warm-hearted friend. To his psychodynamically

Portrait, courtesy of Dr. Frederic A. Gibbs, Chicago, Illinois.

oriented fellow-psychiatrists he seemed unimaginative and plodding; they were inclined to patronize him. To his students he seemed rather dry and aloof, and occasionally he would storm and fume if their knowledge of the fundamentals of neuroanatomy was inadequate.

Hans Berger is called the father of electroencephalography. He was also the founder of psychophysiology.

CHICAGO, ILLINOIS   FREDERIC A. GIBBS

References

[1]*Zur Lehre von der Blutzirkulation in der Schädelhöhle des Menschen, namentlich unter dem Einfluss von Medikamenten.* Jena, Fischer, 1901. [2]*Über die körperlichen Äusserungen psychischer Zustände.* Jena, Fischer, 1904–07. [3]*Untersuchungen über die Temperatur des Gehirns.* Jena, Fischer, 1910. [4]*Psychophysiologie in 12 Vorlesungen.* Jena, Fischer, 1921. [5]Brit. M. J., 1875, *2:* 278. [6]Arch. Psychiat., Berl., 1929, 87: 527–570. [7]*Ibid.*, 1931, *94:* 16–60; 1932, 97: 6–26; 1933, 98: 232–251; 1933, 99: 555–574; 1933, *100:* 301–320; 1933, *101:* 452–469; 1934, *102:* 538–557; 1935, *103:* 444–454; 1936, *104:* 678–689; 1937, *106:* 165–187. [8]Nova Acta Leopoldina, 1938, 6: 173–309.

References to Biography: 1) Arch. Psychiat., Berl., 1941, *114:* 17–24 (contains bibliography; Böning). 2) Nervenarzt, 1941, *14:* 481–484 (Wawrzik and Jung). 3) J. Hist. M., N. Y., 1949, *4:* 361–371 (Ginzberg).

CLAUDE BERNARD (1813–1878)

Claude Bernard's birthplace, the old farmhouse in St. Julien (Rhône, France), is now a carefully preserved monument. It stands on a hill, surrounded now, as then, by vineyards, and in his afterlife it was to this quiet spot that Claude Bernard returned each summer to perform a few additional experiments in an improvised laboratory, but especially to think over the results of the experimental work he had done in Paris, its significance for the science of experimental medicine, and particularly its philosophical implications.

When he had finished his early education in the local schools he went to work for a pharmacist in nearby Lyons. The composition

Cl. Bernard

of a romantic drama in his leisure moments led him to wish to try his hand at authorship in Paris; but when he showed his efforts to a prominent literary critic in the capitol, he was advised to return to a career more nearly related to his experience as a pharmacist's assistant. It was not until he was thirty that he obtained the M.D.

Portrait, courtesy of the Army Medical Museum, Washington, D. C.

The great influence in his life was François Magendie (1783–1855), of Bordeaux, who may be termed the father of experimental physiology in France. Magendie was Claude Bernard's sponsor and patron from the time of the younger man's student days to the older scientist's death, when he bequeathed his chair of medicine at the Collège de France to his assistant who, by that time, was giving the courses for him. Although Claude Bernard held a professorship of general physiology first at the Sorbonne, and later at the Muséum d'Histoire Naturelle concurrently with his professorship at the Collège de France, his heart really belonged to the Collège de France where Magendie and he had worked so long together. In the course of his life he touched with an illuminating hand almost every phase of physiology, so that Pasteur characterized him not as a physiologist but as physiology itself.

His first paper (1843) concerned the origin and functions of the tiny chorda tympani nerve, but after this came the discovery of the fat-splitting enzyme of the pancreas and the glycogenic function of the liver before he returned to the nervous system for the most spectacular of all his discoveries (1849),[1,2] viz. that a slight wound in the floor of the fourth ventricle of the brain would render an animal temporarily diabetic. From his observation (1852)[3] that cutting the cervical sympathetic nerve in the neck of the rabbit causes not only constriction of the pupil of the eye but flushing and rise of temperature in the ear, came the discovery of the possibility of control of blood flow by the nervous system through vasomotor nerves, constrictor and dilator. Johann Friedrich Horner (1831–86), Swiss ophthalmologist, described his famous triad of miosis, ptosis and enophthalmos in 1869,[4] and although Claude Bernard's contribution in this field seems to have escaped the notice of clinical neurologists of this country, the disorder is still referred to in France as the Claude Bernard-Horner syndrome.

The old question whether voluntary muscle can be excited otherwise than by way of its motor nerve was settled in the affirmative by Claude Bernard with the use of curare (1849), and the principles he discovered have lately been applied in the use of this drug in anaesthesia and in the use of artificial stimulation to preserve the functions of denervated skeletal muscle.

Physiology during the middle of the nineteenth century was dominated by Claude Bernard. Pupils came to him from Russia,

Germany and America.   The succeeding generation of French physiologists, d'Arsonval, Paul Bert, Dastre, and a host of others all owe
much to him.   Even today his *Introduction à l'étude de la médecine
expérimentale* (Paris, Baillière, 1865), now available in English,[5] is
an inspiration to laymen as well as to the profession.

Claude Bernard was always rather solitary.   His moments of
greatest happiness came when he had found a neat solution to some
problem arising from his physiological investigations.   The intransi-
gent Paul Bert (1830–86), author of the incomparable *La pression
barométrique* (Paris, Masson, 1878), was his favorite pupil and his
successor at the Sorbonne in 1868.   Bert, acknowledging his debt
to the master, described him as a man of "great kindliness, simplicity
of soul, and possessed of a naive generosity."

BERKELEY, CALIFORNIA   J. M. D. OLMSTED

References

[1]C. rend. Soc. biol., 1849, *1:* 13–15 *et seq.*   [2]*Leçons sur la physiologie
et la pathologie du système nerveux.* 2 vol. Paris, Baillière, 1858.   [3]C.
rend. Acad. sc., 1852, *34:* 472–475.   [4]Klin. Mbl. Augenh., 1869, 7: 193–
198.   [5]*An introduction to the study of experimental medicine.*   New
York, Schuman, 1950 (trans. by Greene).

References to Biography: 1) *Claude Bernard.*   London, Unwin, 1899
(Foster).   2) *Claude Bernard, physiologist.*   New York and London,
Harper, 1938 (Olmsted).

LEONARDO BIANCHI (1848–1927)

*L*eonardo Bianchi was born in San Bartolomeo (Galdo, Bene-
vento).   He studied at the University of Naples where, in 1871,
he graduated in medicine and surgery.   After having become well
grounded in pathology and internal medicine, he received, in 1882,
a position under Buonomo at the newly organized psychiatric institute of Naples.   In 1888 he became Professor Extraordinarius in
psychiatry at the University of Palermo, but in 1890 returned to
Naples to accept the chair of nervous and mental diseases as successor to Buonomo.

For the next 37 years Bianchi worked without surcease toward
the development of research in the fields of psychiatry and neurology.

Leonardo Bianchi

In 1905 his textbook on psychiatry[1] appeared. It was of a magnitude previously unattained, with every observation closely scrutinized in the light of his own experience. Bianchi's approach to the problems of psychiatry was mainly biologic and sociologic, and was antagonistic to the doctrines of Freud. He was outspoken in his view that psychoanalysis is a dangerous form of treatment. This book went through three Italian editions (the last in 1924) and was translated into English[1] and other languages. Bianchi was well versed in neuroanatomy, contributing among other works a superb account of the developmental anatomy of the thalamic nuclei of the rabbit,[2] a study carried out in Ziehen's laboratory in Berlin.

Portrait, courtesy of the Army Medical Library, Washington, D. C.

Bianchi's main experimental work was concerned with the neural mechanisms of the brain as a whole and the functions of the frontal lobes in particular.[3] This great contribution, translated into English and French,[3] was the outcome of 32 years of work on dogs, foxes and monkeys. One of his earlier papers on the functions of the frontal lobes was translated into English by de Watteville.[4] He found that destruction of the frontal association area on one side was without significant effect, but that when the area was destroyed bilaterally, alterations of character became evident. The propensities of the monkeys were exaggerated by this operation; thus, timid animals became withdrawn, affectionate ones more loving, and so on. He referred to the character changes as alterations in the social sense, and understandably so, for he lived with his monkeys, ate with them—allowing them even to choose morsels from his plate —permitted them to run about in his office while he was writing, and made every effort to gain their confidence and friendship. Thus he was able to detect after bilateral destruction of the frontal lobes that they were lacking in perceptive judgement, that their memory was poor and unreliable, that associative power was reduced, that initiative and resourcefulness were lost, and that sociability disappeared. The frontal lobes were considered, then, the organ of intellect.

Bianchi's conclusion that emotional disturbances occur after bilateral destruction of the frontal cortex was contested by Franz,[5] who felt that the disorder was entirely in the realm of intelligence, although he (Bianchi) avoided the use of this term; and Bianchi's view that lesions of the frontal cortex lead to dementia was countered by Franz who showed that recently lost habits following frontal lobe damage could be relearned. The work of Bianchi, now fully substantiated, has found its practical application in psychosurgery—a field opened by Egas Moniz[6] of Portugal, advanced in the United States by Freeman and Watts,[7] and modified by means of the orbital approach by Fiamberti of Italy. Apparently the first lobotomies were performed by a Swiss, named G. Burckhardt.[9]

Bianchi's distinguished career reflected his great versatility. He was senator of the Kingdom of Italy, minister of state, university professor, asylum superintendent, lecturer, and president of the Italian Society of Neurology, which he founded in 1904. It was his high sense of public duty and his disappointment in the results achieved by the professional politicians that caused him to turn to politics as early as 1905 as a means of rectifying the inadequacies of the Italian lunacy laws. As secretary of state for public instruction, he took great pains to promulgate autonomy in the teaching of neurology and psychiatry. Among his acts was the creation of a chair of criminal anthropology for Lombroso. His last publication, on eugenics in mental and neurological diseases,[8] was the pioneer work in this field.

Distinguished in manner, gifted in oratory, inspiring in the lucidity of his teaching, with duty as his deity—"let duty be your altar and your law"—Bianchi was for almost a quarter of a century the dominant figure in Italian psychiatry and neuropathology. During this time he gathered around him a happy family of students, which included D'Abundo, Fragnito, Colucci, Sciuti, Baldi, and Gozzano, most of whom have carried his tradition to other Italian universities. Up to the very last he pursued all of his many interests. While attending a scientific meeting in Rome he died suddenly of a heart attack.

NEW YORK CITY   ARMANDO FERRARO

References

[1]*Trattato di psichiatria ad uso dei medici e degli studenti.* Napoli, Pasquale, 1905. (Engl. trans. by Macdonald: *A text-book on psychiatry for physicians and students.* London, Baillière, Tindall & Cox, 1906). [2]Mschr. Psychiat., Erg. Heft, 1909, *25:* 425–471. [3]*La meccanica del cervello e la funzione dei lobi frontali.* Torino, Bocca, 1920. (Engl. trans. by Macdonald: *The mechanism of the brain and the function of the frontal lobes.* Edinburgh, Livingstone, 1922. French trans. by Collin and Sanguineti: *La mécanique du cerveau et la fonction des lobes frontaux.* Paris, Arnette, 1921.) [4]Brain, Lond., 1895, *18:* 497–522. [5]*On the functions of the cerebrum: the frontal lobes.* Monog. No. 2, Arch. Psychol. New York, Science Press, 1907. [6]Lisboa med., 1936, *13:* 141–151. [7]South. M. J., 1937, *30:* 23–31. [8]*Eugenica igiene mentale e profilassi delle malattie nervose e mentali.* Napoli, Idelson, 1925. [9]*Frontal lobotomy and affective behavior. A neurophysiological analysis.* New York, Norton, 1951; p. 97 (Fulton).

References to Biography and Works: 1) Riv. neur., Nap., 1937, *10:* 180–211 (Donaggio, Fragnito, Sciuti). 2) Ann. nevr., Nap., 1927, *41:* 5–9 (V. Bianchi, Morselli, Tanzi, Mingazzini). 3) J. Ment. Sc., Lond.,

1928, *74:* 381–385 (Lord).   4) *Psychosurgery. Intelligence, emotion and social behavior following prefrontal lobotomy for mental disorders.* Springfield, Ill., Thomas, 1942 (ed. 2, 1950) (Freeman and Watts). 5) *Brain and intelligence. A quantitative study of the frontal lobes.* Chicago, Univ. Chicago Press, 1947 (Halstead).

WALTER BRADFORD CANNON (1871–1945)

Cannon was born in Prairie du Chien, Wisconsin. Both parents belonged to pioneering families that had pushed westward from Massachusetts early in the nineteenth century to settle eventually in the upper Mississippi valley. Cannon's career appears to have been largely determined by this genetic and social background, for throughout his life he displayed those traits which are found in the successful frontiersman and explorer—unusual energy of body and mind, resourcefulness, curiosity motivated by the spirit of adventure but directed by a keen intelligence, and a desire to be of help to one's fellows.

In retrospect the place of Cannon's birth seems most auspicious, for Prairie du Chien had grown up on the site of Fort Crawford where in the 1820's William Beaumont had made those classic observations on the fistulous Alexis St. Martin, that constituted the most important work on gastric digestion before the investigations of Pavlov. In 1896, after he entered medical school, Cannon demonstrated for the first time by means of the newly discovered Roentgen rays the movements of the alimentary tract. Thus began observations and experiments that placed him beside Beaumont and Pavlov as one of the great contributors to our knowledge of digestion. On his graduation in medicine at Harvard (1900) he became an instructor in physiology and six years later he succeeded Bowditch as professor. His studies of the gastrointestinal tract, summarized in *The mechanical factors of digestion* (London, Arnold, 1911), terminated in 1912 with the demonstration that the pangs of hunger are due to cramp-like contractions of the stomach.

It was the observation that the movements of the stomach and intestines ceased whenever his animals became excited that aroused Cannon's interest in the autonomic nervous system. Gaskell and Langley had beautifully detailed the origins, distribution and local effects of autonomic neurons. It remained to determine the condi-

tions of their activity. Over a period of more than twenty years, which began in 1911, Cannon and his many students published a long series of papers in which was set forth evidence that under conditions of physiological stress the sympathetic system and its constituent part, the adrenal medulla, act to produce visceral adjustments which are nicely adapted to the preservation of the individual. The earlier results were reported and interpreted in the first edition of *Bodily changes in pain, hunger, fear and rage* (New York, Appleton, 1915); a second edition (1929) presented much new evidence bearing on the general theme and included an account of notable experiments on thirst and a discussion of the central mechanisms involved in emotional behavior and emotional experience. The validity of the emergency theory of the sympatho-adrenal system was dramatically confirmed in 1929 when Cannon and four collaborators showed that cats from which both chains of ganglia had been removed are capable of normal life under uniformly serene circum-

Portrait, courtesy of Dr. Philip Bard, Baltimore, Maryland.

stances, but exhibit deficiencies when exposed to conditions of physiological stress.[1] A facility for seeing the different facets of a physiological problem led Cannon to a broader interpretation of these experimental facts, namely that the sympatho-adrenal system is important in the maintenance of what he termed "homeostasis," the relatively steady state of the *milieu interne*. His accounts of the bodily organizations for homeostasis, particularly his book, *The wisdom of the body* (New York, Norton, 1932; also 1939), have had a widespread influence.

From the use of the denervated heart as an indicator of medulli-adrenal secretion came the discovery that *sympathin* is produced in the normal animal. This disclosure led Cannon into the territory of the chemical mediation of nerve impulses where he became pioneer. Two stimulating monographs on this subject were written in collaboration with Rosenblueth.[2,3]

In his extraordinary autobiography,[4] Cannon tells us that "It is probable that if, while a first-year student of medicine, I had not undertaken research on the physiology of the digestive tract by use of the then newly discovered x-rays, I would have become a neurologist." The reference is to clinical neurology.

BALTIMORE, MARYLAND   PHILIP BARD

References

[1]Am. J. Physiol., 1929, 89: 84–107 (with Newton, Menkin and Moore). [2]*Autonomic neuro-effector systems.* New York, Macmillan, 1937. [3]*The supersensitivity of denervated structures. A law of denervation.* New York, Macmillan, 1949. [4]*The way of an investigator. A scientist's experiences in medical research.* New York, Norton, 1945.

References to Biography: 1) Psychol. Rev., 1946, 53: 137–146 (Yerkes). 2) Am. Rev. Soviet M., 1946, 4: 155–162 (Leibson).

EMIL DU BOIS-REYMOND (1818-1896)

*W*hether the lines of progress in electrophysiology be traced backward over a century or forward from an earlier time they are found to meet in the work of one great figure. The half century which had elapsed since Galvani's great discovery had been one of expectancy completely frustrated by lack of methods, until

Emil du Bois-Reymond

Portrait courtesy of the Army Medical Library, Washington, D. C.

the impasse was broken in 1819 by Oersted, who demonstrated the connection of electricity and magnetism. Thus galvanometers were made possible, but until their sensitivity could be made equal to that of the rheoscopic frog they were useless. In the competition the two had just begun to come alongside when du Bois-Reymond started his studies. Deflection by the frog current had already been seen. However, the conditions of the experiments were such that no decision could be reached with respect to the famous controversy that arose between Volta and Galvani.

First du Bois-Reymond gave clear descriptions of the resting currents observed in excised muscles and nerves. He postulated electromotive forces pre-existent in the tissues, a view the soundness of which has only been strengthened by its ability to withstand worthy opposition.

Next there followed the observation which is basic to the understanding of the changes taking place during activity. He found by direct galvanometric methods that during a tetanus the current flowing at rest from an intact surface to an injured region is decreased, and proved indirectly that this negative variation must be made up of a series of individual variations. It is the magnitude and time-course of these variations and their sequelae that have occupied the attention of physiologists ever since.

The third contribution of high importance was introduced in connection with the term "electrotonus," which was coined to refer to the potential changes produced by an externally applied current. In recent years the findings have been correlated with the potential changes known to occur during activity. It is quite possible that future historians will attribute a greater significance to electrotonic influences than we can at present.

The difficulties with which du Bois-Reymond had to contend are now hard to realize. That he could work at all was only made possible by his ingenuity in the improvement of methods: notably his astatic galvanometer evolved to a high sensitivity, his introduction of non- polarizable electrodes and potentiometric measurement by the compensation technique, and his appreciation of the need to keep tissues in contact with physiological fluids. For excitation he invented a form of induction coil still in use; and his, the first, law of excitation satisfied physiologists during the long period before the re-evaluation of the time parameter which he introduced.

A native of Berlin, of French forebears, he became one of the brilliant coterie around Johannes Müller; and he succeeded the master in the chair of physiology in 1858. By then the researches for which he is most famous had largely been completed; and, while he continued his investigations, his growing responsibilities came more and more to occupy his time: his teaching, his permanent secretaryship of the Prussian Academy of Sciences, and his duties at the Physical Society (of which he was a co-founder) and at the Physiological Society. In connection with his official positions he became instrumental in the promotion of the welfare of science and the author of numerous occasional lectures. The latter are notable because of his vigorous opposition to vitalism, and for other reasons of interest to the student of epistemology.

From du Bois-Reymond and his friend and contemporary, Helmholtz, our great heritage is the directive influence of their inspired welding of physics with physiology.

NEW YORK CITY   HERBERT S. GASSER

References

Reference to Chief Work: Untersuchungen über thierische Electricität. 2 vol. in 3. Berlin, Reimer, 1848, 1849, 1884.

References to Biography: 1) Rev. sc., Par., 1897, 4.sér., 7: 385–394 (Rosenthal). 2) Emil du Bois-Reymond. Wien, Springer, 1922 (Boruttau). 3) Zwei grosse Naturforscher. Leipzig, Barth, 1927 (Diepgen).

JOHANNES GREGORIUS DUSSER DE BARENNE (1885–1940)

The sudden death of Professor Dusser de Barenne on June 9, 1940 occurred at a time when international communications were seriously disrupted, and many of his colleagues in Europe were therefore long unaware that his brilliant career had been brought to a premature close when he was but 55 years of age and at the height of his powers.

Dusser de Barenne was born in the village of Brielle in The Netherlands. His father was a municipal official of Amsterdam, and Dusser de Barenne, after preliminary education in the public schools, entered Amsterdam University and received his medical qualifica-

Johannes Gregorius Dusser de Barenne

tion in 1909. His professional career began that year as a teaching assistant in the Laboratory of Physiology at Amsterdam where he commenced the work on the action of strychnine on the central nervous system,[1] for which he gained an international reputation. After two years he was appointed psychiatrist to the Meerenberg Lunatic Asylum where he was engaged until the outbreak of World War I in the physiological analysis of decerebrate rigidity and also of tonic neck and labyrinthine reflexes.

During the War he served as a medical officer in the Dutch Army

Portrait, courtesy of Dr. John F. Fulton, New Haven, Connecticut. (Donated to Yale Medical Library by Dr. Paul E. Rekers.)

and found time while stationed at a military establishment at Delft to continue his studies on the tonus of skeletal muscle. In 1918 he became an assistant to Rudolf Magnus at Utrecht and participated actively for twelve years in investigations on the physiology of posture which brought widespread recognition to the Utrecht School. His most important paper during this period, however, was the result of a visit in 1924 to the laboratory of Sir Charles Sherrington where he studied the sensory symptoms which followed on local application of strychnine to the cerebral cortex of rhesus monkeys. The paper embodying his findings, now regarded as a classic, demonstrated for the first time the major functional subdivisions of the sensory cortex.[2]

By common consent, Dusser de Barenne had now become the foremost of the younger generation of Dutch physiologists. With the deaths of Einthoven and Magnus in 1927 and the retirement of Zwaardemaker, the three most eminent chairs of physiology and pharmacology in Holland became vacant almost simultaneously. Dusser de Barenne would have filled any one of them with distinction and he no doubt would have been called but for the religious restrictions in the Dutch universities; these were intolerable to a free-thinking man of Dusser de Barenne's outspoken tendencies, and thus the United States was able to claim one of the most distinguished physiologists ever to appear on the continent of Europe.

Dusser de Barenne arrived in New Haven, Connecticut, in September, 1930, to join the faculty of the Yale School of Medicine, and for the next ten years he engaged in a program of research which for sustained productivity has had few parallels. A succession of men, attracted by his presence in the States, became associated with him as pupils and assistants—Percival Bailey, Warren McCulloch, Leslie Nims, and Arthur Ward, to mention only a few. His primary contribution during this period lay in the introduction of the new technique of physiological neuronography which has made possible a vast research endeavor involving analysis of the interaction of various cortical and subcortical regions of the brain and it has also led to the discovery of many hitherto unsuspected fiber connections and projections (chiefly nonmyelinated).

Dusser de Barenne was a genial and friendly man, expansive in scientific discussion, but extremely reserved in everything that concerned his personal life. His stature as a man and as a physiologist continues to grow as time affords perspective against which to appraise his immediate contributions and his subsequent influence.

NEW HAVEN, CONNECTICUT   JOHN F. FULTON

References

[1]Fol. neurobiol., Lpz., 1910, *4:* 467–474 *et seq.*   [2]Proc. R. Soc., Lond., 1924, ser.B, *96:* 272–291.

References to Biography: 1) J. Neurophysiol., 1940, *3:* 283–292 (contains bibliography; Fulton and Garol).   2) Yale J. Biol. & Med., 1940, *12:* 743–746 (McCulloch).

SIR DAVID FERRIER (1843–1928)

*F*errier was born near Aberdeen, and was educated at the Universities of Aberdeen and Edinburgh. His most influential teachers were Alexander Bain, logician and psychologist at Aberdeen, and William Image, F.R.C.S. and general practitioner in Suffolk, whom Ferrier assisted while writing the thesis for his M.D. in 1870. That year Ferrier moved to London, where he lived the rest of his life.

He was connected chiefly with the National Hospital from 1880 and with the Medical School of King's College where he occupied the chair of neuropathology created for him in 1889. He was a charter member of the Physiological Society and in 1878 joined with Hughlings Jackson, Sir John Bucknill and Sir James Crichton-Browne in founding the journal, *Brain.* He was elected Fellow of the Royal Society in 1876, Fellow of the Royal College of Physicians (London), 1877, Laureate of the Institut de France, 1878, and received many other honors throughout his long, active life, including knighthood, 1911, the Hon. ScD. from Cambridge, 1914, and the Hon. LL.D. from Birmingham in 1927.

As Stanley Cobb has pointed out,[1] Ferrier was probably the link between Hughlings Jackson and Sherrington, for he worked with Jackson in the 1870's and Sherrington worked with him in the 1890's. Ferrier will be remembered primarily for his pioneer work in neurophysiology and especially the experiments by which he established the concept of localization of function in the cerebrum. In this connection, it may be mentioned that Friedrich Albert Lange (1828–75) in his *Geschichte des Materialismus und Kritik seiner Bedeutung in*

Sir David Ferrier

Portrait, courtesy of Dr. John F. Fulton, New Haven, Connecticut. (Photographer: Maull & Fox, London, England.)

der Gegenwart (1866), was the first to propose such a concept and to distinguish localization of function from localization of symptoms.[2]

Ferrier's studies were begun in 1873[3] and were published during that year and the three following years.[4-7] They were undertaken ". . . to put to experimental proof the views entertained by Dr. Hughlings Jackson . . ., and to follow up the path which the researches of Fritsch and Hitzig . . . indicated . . ." In this introduction to his first publication he gave warm credit to others, as was typical of him; the words, "to put to experimental proof," were an expression of his basic scientific philosophy.

He was one of the re-discoverers of the experimental method, and his work was marked by simple, direct practicality, careful control, and precise, full recording. By means of comparative studies he established general principles of the functions of the brain in mammalian species from rodents to apes. He continued his work in the clinic, applying these principles to his observations on man,[8] and on the basis of his experience with animals, strongly urged the surgeons to operate for intracranial disorders. Indeed, Rickman Godlee felt that Ferrier was one of the principal figures in opening the field which is now neurosurgery.

Ferrier was more than an experimenter; he was rather a philosopher who did not philosophize, but who experimented. He is to be credited with the discovery that removal of the percentral gyrus leads immediately to paralysis of the limbs of the opposite side, and that in the monkey the hemiplegic position is soon assumed.[6,7] Although his work established the "motor area" and certain "sensory areas," he was not himself misled by the concept of localization. For him the functions of the cerebrum were "sensorimotor" and he stated: "From the complexity of mental phenomena and the participation in them of both motor and sensory substrata, any system of localization of mental faculties which does not take both factors into account must be radically false." He thus presaged the present view which regards the brain as the organ *par excellence* of interaction.

Ferrier was a slight, erect man, quiet of manner, direct of speech, and of great energy. His life was that of a busy consultant, but he took time to continue some research in collaboration with others, effectively encouraging younger men. He attended scientific meetings assiduously, but avoided scientific polemics. His modest hope that he was "not in the way" while watching an experiment expressed by implication more forcibly than any protestation could have done, his feeling for the importance of the experimenter and the experiment. His vigorous defense of animal experimentation when he was taken to court by antivivisectionists at once won his case and made his name famous throughout England.

ROCKVILLE, MARYLAND   DAVID MCK. RIOCH

References

[1]Arch. Neur., Psychiat., Chic., 1948, 59: 63–98.   [2]J. Hist. M., N. Y., 1950, 1: 50–71 (Riese and Hoff).   [3]West Riding Lun. Asyl. Rep., Lond., 1873, 3: 1–50.   [4]Proc. R. Soc., Lond., 1874, 22: 229–232.   [5]Brit. M. J., 1874, 2: 766–767.   [6]Philos. Tr. R. Soc. London, 1875, 165: 433–488. [7]The functions of the brain. London, Smith, Elder, 1876.   [8]Brit. M. J., 1878, 1: 399–402 et seq. (Goulstonian Lectures).

References to Biography and Works: 1) Proc. R. Soc., Lond., 1928, ser.B, 103: viii–xvi (Sherrington).   2) Lancet, Lond., 1938, 1: 627–629 (not signed).   3) J. Ment. Sc., Lond., 1928, 74: 375–380 (Grainger Stewart).   4) Arch. Neur. Psychiat., Chic., 1948, 59: 63–98 (Cobb) 5) Bull. Inst. Hist. M., Balt., 1938, 6: 477–487 (Viets).

CHARLES ÉMILE FRANÇOIS-FRANCK (1849–1921)

*F*rançois-Franck was a Parisian by birth. His initial medical studies were carried out in Bordeaux and in 1870 he became assistant in the Hôpital Saint André. His work toward a medical degree was interrupted by the Prussian attack on France. He volunteered his services to the French army, and because of his excellent horsemanship he sometimes served as liaison officer. It was during one of his attempts to carry an official dispatch that he was wounded and taken prisoner by the Prussians. Being a physician, the carrying of dispatches constituted a violation of the Geneva Convention: he was tried, convicted, and sentenced to death, but after a miraculous escape he made his way back to Bordeaux.

With the war over, François-Franck returned to Paris to continue his medical education. He was recognized as a brilliant student, and was made chef de clinique and prosector in 1872. Upon receiving his doctorate in medicine in 1875, he was appointed assistant to

Charles Émile François-Franck

Marey in the laboratory of pathologic physiology of the Collège de France. Marey, because of frail health and a desire to devote all his energy to research, soon placed the responsibility of the lectures on François-Franck. This annual series of 40 lectures he conducted brilliantly for 30 years. Original experiments formed the foundation of these discourses, the principal subject of which was the physiology of the circulation. Marey[1] and François-Franck[2,3] were responsible for showing, for instance, that when variations of carotid-cephalic arterial pressure occur, cardiac and vasomotor compensatory reactions immediately set in. Thus these men may be considered forerunners of Heinrich Ewald Hering (1866–1948), whose

Portrait from *Nos grands médécins d'aujourdhui*, Paris, 1891, by H. Bianchon.

discovery of the carotid sinus mechanism in 1924 opened up the modern study in this field.[4,5]

During 1884–86 François-Franck's lectures were devoted almost entirely to a study of the cerebral circulation.[6] He played a large part in Marey's work on sphygmography, and he was especially skillful in adapting Marey's graphic method to experimental research.

A friendship had grown up between Pitres and François-Franck when both were studying for their doctorates. Pitres was later to become the professor of neurology at Bordeaux, but in the meantime he was working at the Salpêtrière under Charcot, who was then concentrating on cerebral localization of function. Pitres acquired the enthusiasm of his master and he, in turn, engaged the interest of François-Franck in this field of work.

These two young men initiated a series of experiments which François-Franck terminated alone, experiments noted for their originality and precision. Among their contributions was the observation that after removal of the motor region of the cerebral cortex—simian and canine—not only the crossed fasciculi of the pyramids, but also the homolateral, undergo degeneration.[7] The direct result of this collaboration was François-Franck's important book on motor functions of the brain,[8] in which he reported on the excitability of the cortex and the localization of cerebral function. In this book, to which Charcot wrote the preface, François-Franck included the following dedicatory note: "A mon cher ami le professeur Pitres—nous avons recueilli ensemble la plupart des documents utilisés dans ce volume: je te prie d'en accepter la dédicace, comme un juste hommage, et un souvenir de notre vieille amitié."

But François-Franck's life was not spent entirely in the laboratory. He was a beloved pupil of Potain and it was under this inspiration that François-Franck became also a clinician of the first rank. His opinions were much sought as a heart specialist, for which his physiological training and experiments under Marey had well prepared him.

As early as 1885—he was then 36—François-Franck became the director of the laboratory of pathologic physiology of the Collège de France. In 1887 he was elected to membership in the Académie de Médecine, Paris, and in 1905 he succeeded Marey to the chair of physiology. On this occasion, Hallion, speaking for François-Franck's pupils, collaborators, and friends, addressed these words to him: "Solicitude for the public good, generosity, unshakable faith in friendship, scrupulous observance of the pledged word, come what may—it was through such qualities as these that you conquered our hearts."

Following a long illness, François-Franck died in Paris.

NEW YORK CITY   DOROTHY GOODENOW
                                                 FRED A. METTLER

References

[1]*La circulation du sang à l'état physiologique et dans les maladies.* Paris, Masson, 1881.   [2]Trav. Lab. Marey, 1877, *3:* 273–292.   [3]*Ibid.,* 1878, *4:* 73–98.   [4]Arch. ges. Physiol., 1924, *206:* 721–723.   [5]*Die Karotissinusreflexe auf Herz und Gefässe vom normal-physiologischen, pathologisch-physiologischen und klinischen Standpunkt.* Dresden, Steinkopf, 1927.   [6]*Cours du Collège de France, de 1880 à 1904, et Travaux du laboratoire de 1875 à 1904.* Paris, Doin, 1904.   [7]Arch. physiol. norm. path., Par., 1885, 3.sér., *5:* 7–50 *et seq.*   [8]*Leçons sur les fonctions motrices du cerveau (réactions volontaires et organiques) et sur l'épilepsie cérébrale.* Paris, Doin, 1887.

Reference to Biography: Bull. Acad. méd., Par., 1921, 3.sér., *86:* 148–151 (Richelot).

WALTER HOLBROOK GASKELL (1847–1914)

*W*alter Gaskell, the son of a barrister, was born at Naples; his family home, however, was in the north of England. He entered Trinity College, Cambridge, in 1864, and took up the study of medicine at University College, London, in 1870. On the advice of his teacher, Sir Michael Foster (1836–1907), Gaskell interrupted his medical course in 1874 to undertake physiologic work in Carl Ludwig's laboratory. Called to the University of Cambridge in 1883, he continued there as lecturer on physiology, praelector on natural science, and fellow of Trinity Hall.

Gaskell's accomplishments in the field of autonomic nervous system from the time he became associated with Ludwig until 1889 have assured him a lasting position of prominence among physiologists. In 1874 he published a significant paper on the vasomotor nerves of striated muscle,[1] and in 1882 his great memoir on the muscular activity of the heart and its innervation appeared.[2] The latter,

Walter Holbrook Gaskell

in which the theory of the myogenic nature of cardiac contractions
was supported, constitutes a model of neatness and finality.

Gaskell's establishment of the histologic foundation of the autonomic nervous system, upon which Langley built so substantially, is
among the great achievements of English physiology. His innervation studies in different animals led to the mapping and interpretation of the nerve supply to the visceral organs, including the cardiovascular system. The results of this study, first announced in 1885,
were incorporated in an exhaustive treatise published in 1886[3]: this

Portrait, courtesy of the Army Medical Library, Washington, D. C.

was a landmark in the history of the investigation of the sympathetic nervous system.

One of the major contributions of this work was the delimitation of the preganglionic outflow to the thoracic and the first two lumbar segments. His work was based on the study of osmic acid-stained serial sections through the anterior and posterior spinal roots and the rami communicantes of the dog, and although in the light of subsequent findings based on silver impregnation methods many of his observations have been proven incorrect—for instance he asserted that no nonmyelinated fibers leave the spinal cord by way of spinal roots, but that all such fibers are branches of cells lying in the sympathetic ganglia—his fundamental conclusions have stood the test of time and have formed the basis of our present-day knowledge. In his 1886 paper, Gaskell referred to three separate outflows of fine myelinated fibers to peripherally-situated motor ganglion cells: bulbar, thoracolumbar and sacral, and some years later (1916) included all three in the "involuntary nervous system" (see below). Claude Bernard was the first to make a sharp distinction between visceral and vascular nerves, but it was Gaskell to whom we are indebted for first distinguishing among the visceral and vascular nerves two antagonistic groups (collateral and lateral), one excitatory, the other inhibitory; and thus he anticipated Langley's subdivision of the autonomic nervous system into sympathetic and parasympathetic divisions.

Another significant contribution was his pioneer work[3,4] in formulating the doctrine of functional nerve components, subsequently established on a firm basis by Herrick (1889, 1931),[5,6] Strong (1895),[7] Johnston (1901),[8] and Coghill (1902).[9] There was, in fact, hardly any phase of the existing knowledge of the physiology of the nervous system to which he did not add materially. The results of his long years of study are embodied in *The involuntary nervous system* (London, Longmans, Green & Co., 1916), the last pages of which were revised the night before he was fatally stricken with cerebral hemorrhage. In recognition of his scholarship, the University of Edinburgh and McGill University conferred upon him the honorary LL.D. He was also a Marshall Hall prizeman and was awarded the Baly medal and a medal by the Royal Society.

During his later years, Gaskell developed a theory of the origin of vertebrates from invertebrate ancestors, one of the chief tenets being that the central canal of the nervous system was originally the lumen of the primitive gut.[10] Although this theory has not met with approval, Gaskell, in its elaboration, accumulated a wealth of data which merits serious consideration.

As a tribute to his kindly, unassuming, sympathetic character, it has been said of Gaskell that every physiologist who worked in the Cambridge laboratories during his time was his personal friend, and that all recognized his home as their favorite meeting place.

ST. LOUIS, MISSOURI

ALBERT KUNTZ

References

[1]Proc. R. Soc., Lond., 1876, 25: 439–445.   [2]Philos. Tr. R. Soc. London, 1882, part 3, 173: 933–1033 (The Croonian Lecture).   [3]J. Physiol., Lond., 1886, 7: 1–80.   [4]Ibid., 1889, 10: 153–211. [5]J. Comp. Neur., 1899, 9: 153–455.   [6]An introduction to neurology. ed. 5. Philadelphia, Saunders, 1931; p. 417.   [7]J. Morph., 1895, 10: 101–230.   [8]Zool. Jahrb., 1901, 25: 1–204.   [9]J. Comp. Neur., 1902, 12: 205–289.   [10]The origin of vertebrates. London, Longmans, Green & Co., 1908.

References to Biography and Works: 1) Proc. R. Soc., Lond., 1915, ser.B, 88: xxvii–xxxvi (Langley).   2) Science, n.s., 1914, 40: 802–807 (Garrison and Pike).   3) Arch. Neur. Psychiat., Chic., 1936, 35: 1081–1115 (Sheehan).

FRIEDRICH LEOPOLD GOLTZ (1834–1902)

Goltz stands at the forefront of the physiologists of the past who were concerned with the effects of decerebration and of spinal ablation on behavior. He and his contemporary Sechenov (of Russia) were among those who initiated the modern study of reflexology, carrying on where Marshall Hall (1790–1857) and Johannes Müller (1801–58) had left off. Sherrington is said to have attempted on one occasion to induce Goltz to test Ferrier's work on cerebral localization of function, but Goltz would not be sidetracked from his central theme, which occupied him for some 30 years (1869–1900).

Goltz was born in Posen, the son of a police inspector. A few years later the family moved to Danzig, where Friedrich had his first schooling. When his father died in 1846, Friedrich left Danzig

Friedrich Goltz

for Thorn to live with his uncle, Bogumil Goltz, who was widely recognized as a naturalist, philosopher and poet.

In 1853 Goltz entered the University of Königsberg. In time he became Assistant in the surgical clinic, then Prosector. His heart, however, was in physiology and when he could find the time he would steal to his modestly furnished room to conduct experiments on frogs which he himself caught, his laboratory armamentarium consisting only of scissors, tweezers, and thread. No wonder then that in describing his experiments before learned societies, he often began by saying, "Man nehme zwei Frösche . . ."

Portrait, courtesy of Dr. W. Krücke, Frankfurt-am-Main, Germany.

At the age of 36, aided by a recommendation from Helmholtz, he was made Ausserordentlicher Professor of physiology at Halle (1870). After two years there he was appointed Ordentlicher Professor of physiology of the newly-founded University of Strassburg, a position which he occupied until 1900 when he was forced to retire because of a severe chronic illness.

Early in his career, while a Prosector at Königsberg, Goltz demonstrated that when rapidly repeated blows were struck on the belly of a frog its heart stopped beating ("Klopfversuch"), and he concluded that this shock-like state was the result of reflex inhibition mediated through the vagus nerve.[1,2] In 1869 he turned to decerebration and ablation of the spinal cord in the frog, with telling effect.[3,4] He found that decerebrated (or "spinal") frogs could still croak "like the frogs in Aristophanes," and that they could be made to do so reflexly ("Quakversuch"). At the Hannover Meeting of Physiologists in 1865 he was asked by a fellow-physiologist to make each of the frogs he had brought along croak five times, and he did so, much to the astonishment of his audience. His frogs could respond in an intelligent way to certain stimuli; they could hop, swim, crouch, and slither from the hand that grasped them. However, when left alone they would sit motionless, and although surrounded by food would die of starvation. When the thalami were left intact, the frogs retained sexual instinct and were able to eat.

His work on mammals began in 1874. At first his cerebral ablations were small, but later he removed more and more of the brain until eventually he was successful in accomplishing subtotal decerebration, producing "Hunde ohne Grosshirn." He observed that a direct relation existed between the amount of cerebral cortex removed and the degree of resulting dementia, and thus he anticipated the holistic concepts formulated by S. I. Franz (1874–1933) and K. S. Lashley (1890–   ), namely, that except for the visual area there are no well defined functional centers. Goltz's view that the total functional loss in the brainless dog is due to "irritative inhibition" was effectively countered by von Monakow (1914), who attributed the loss to diaschisis. In the course of his experimentation, Goltz had human physiology always in mind, and he would say, "Auch meine Gehirnuntersuchungen werden einmal der leidenden Menschheit zu Gute Kommen."

Goltz's "spinal" dogs, which he succeeded in keeping alive for as long as eight months, were incapable of purposive movements or actions,[5,6] and to use Bernard Shaw's phrase, they "blundered into death" (Garrison). His decorticated dogs were able, on the other hand, to walk with adequate coordination, indicating that the pallium was not a requisite to the walking reflexes. However, the animals with frontal decortications were extremely restless, pacing the floor most of the time, and at the slightest annoyance growling and snapping viciously (sham rage).[7] From these experiments he drew the conclusion that the site of integration of pseudoaffective mechanisms is subcortical. In this realm Goltz was the forerunner of Cannon and Bard.

Equally illuminating were Goltz's observations on the effects of transection of the spinal cord in dogs. Reduction in coordination and in adaptation were among the results.[8,9] His demonstration that a female dog with the uppermost lumbar cord sectioned could still become pregnant and bear young normally [10] is still widely quoted by the skeptics who say that fibers coursing down the cord have no gonadotrophic influence; had the cord been sectioned at a higher level the result may have been different.

Goltz's observations were landmarks, and his penetrating mind led him to conclusions which are for the most part accepted today. At Strassburg, where among his colleagues were Waldeyer, von Recklinghausen, Hoppe and Kussmaul, he exerted a profound influence. Sherrington was so impressed by Goltz's demonstration of a decorticate preparation at the International Medical Congress in London in 1881—Sherrington was then 24—that he decided to enter the field of neurophysiology. Sherrington's first publication (with Langley) was on the anatomic aspects of spinal degeneration observed in Goltz's dogs.[11,12] He received training in Goltz's laboratory in 1885 and frequently returned during the ensuing ten years. To be counted among Goltz's other pupils were J. von Mering, Freusberg, Loeb, Jensen, A. Bethe, and his worthy biographer, J. R. Ewald.

Goltz's private life was one of even tenor. At 34 he entered into a happy marriage. To his colleagues he was brusque and blustering, but among his rather narrow circle of friends he was noted for his ability as a raconteur and for his refreshing informality. The cut of his jaw and the intentness of his expression revealed a man of determination and persistence: it was these qualities of his character which helped to elevate him into the company of the great physiologists of the past century.

BETHESDA, MARYLAND   EVELYN ANDERSON
WASHINGTON, D.C.   WEBB HAYMAKER

References

[1]Königsb. med. Jahrb., 1862, 3: 271–274.   [2]Virchows Arch., 1863, 26: 1–33.   [3]Beiträge zur Lehre von den Functionen der Nervenzentren des Frosches. Berlin, Hirschwald, 1869.   [4]Pflügers Arch., 1872, 5: 53–76. [5]Ibid., 1874, 8: 460–468.   [6]Ibid., 1896, 63: 362–400 (with Ewald). [7]Ibid., 1892, 51: 570–614.   [8]Ibid., 1874, 8: 460–498.   [9]Ibid., 1896, 63: 362–400 (with Ewald).   [10]Ibid., 1874, 9: 552–565 (with Freusberg). [11]J. Physiol., 1884, 5: vi.   [12]Ibid., p. 49–65.

References to Biography and Works: 1) Pflügers Arch., 1903, 94: 1–64 (contains annotated bibliography; Ewald).   2) An introduction to the history of medicine. Philadelphia, Saunders, 1929 (Garrison); p. 540–541. 3) Reflex action. A study in the history of physiological psychiatry. Baltimore, Williams & Wilkins, 1930 (Fearing).

HERMANN LUDWIG FERDINAND VON HELMHOLTZ
(1821–1894)

*H*elmholtz was born at Potsdam of a respected academic father and a mother who was descended from William Penn. He was a weakling as a boy. Early interested in physics, he undertook the study of medicine rather than pure science because it was his only opportunity to get an education in at least a related field without forcing pecuniary sacrifices on his parents, who had to take care of five boys. He entered the army medical school in Berlin and served for some years after graduation as an army surgeon. In Berlin he became one of the twelve disciples of Johannes Müller (1801–58), who, in 1826, had developed the theory of specific nerve energies. Helmholtz's thesis, written in Berlin in 1842, *De fabrica systematis nervosi evertebratorum,* demonstrated the integral connection between nerve cell and nerve fiber. With du Bois-Reymond (1818–96) and Brücke (1819–92), neurophysiologists with a background in physics, Helmholtz began a new era of medical investigation based on the application of physical principles.

From 1842 to his death from cerebral hemorrhage, Helmholtz published 217 contributions of prime significance. His early studies on the generation of heat in muscles led to his great generalization, *Ueber die Erhaltung der Kraft,* in Berlin, 1847, in which he demonstrated his mathematical skill and established a physical principle of fundamental importance, the indestructibility of energy. This

Hermann Ludwig Ferdinand von Helmholtz

resulted in his appointment as professor of physiology at Königsberg, where he remained until 1856. He then obtained the chair in the same field at Heidelberg. In 1871 he became professor of physics

Portrait, courtesy of the Army Medical Library, Washington, D. C.

at Berlin and from 1888 to 1894 was president of the Physikalisch-technische Reichsanstalt, the prototype apparently of the Bureau of Standards in Washington, D. C.

Helmholtz's most influential practical work in neurology was done at Königsberg. Here he first successfully measured the velocity of nerve conduction,[1] a feat Müller had thought impossible. Helmholtz accomplished this with a special pendulum-myograph which he invented. Medicine is also indebted to him for his invention of the ophthalmoscope, designed first to demonstrate to his pupils how light is reflected from the retina of the eye. The little volume describing the invention appeared in 1851.[2] The instrument was devised as a result of the careful mathematical and physical considerations involved, and was a thrilling example of the practical significance of a theoretical and academic proposal.

Helmholtz's work on accommodation, color vision, and the sensation of tone is profoundly important not only in neurology but also in psychology. His contributions to the nervous reflexes of equilibrium are also significant in neurology. It is not pertinent to indicate here Helmholtz's great contributions to physics. It was his suggestive influence, however, which led his pupil, Heinrich Hertz, to demonstrate the existence of electromagnetic waves as predicted by Clerk Maxwell, and thus to make possible the development of modern radiation theory.

Helmholtz's one weakness was lecturing. Max Planck[3] relates: "It is obvious that Helmholtz never prepared his lectures properly. He spoke haltingly, and would interrupt his discourse to look for the necessary data in his small notebook; moreover, he repeatedly made mistakes in his calculations at the blackboard, and we had the unmistakable impression that the class bored him at least as much as it did us. Eventually his classes became more and more deserted, and finally they were attended by only three students . . ."

In other ways the influence of the Jovian Helmholtz was profound. He was remarkable as a scientist, as a philosopher, and as a personality. It is clear that his scientific studies aroused in him a great philosophic interest, which was majestically reflected in his splendid personal character and appearance. He was fond of mountaineering and travel, but most of all enjoyed his scientific friendships. Max Planck, one of the three students who listened to Helmholtz's lectures down to the bitter end, says: "This was the first time (1889) that I came in closer contact with the world leaders in scientific research in those days—Helmholtz, above all others . . . With his well-rounded personality, integrity of convictions and modesty of character, he was the very incarnation of the dignity and probity of science. These traits of character were supplemented by a true human kindness, which touched my heart deeply. When during a conversation he would look at me with those calm, searching, penetrating, and yet so benign eyes, I would be overwhelmed by a feeling of boundless filial trust and devotion, and I would feel that I could confide in him, without reservation, everything I had on my mind, knowing that I would find him a fair and tolerant judge; and a single word of approval, let alone praise, from his lips would make me as happy as any worldly triumph." It is not surprising that another biographer, J. G. M'Kendrick, called him one of the greatest geniuses of the 19th century.

GALVESTON, TEXAS   CHAUNCEY D. LEAKE

References

[1]Arch. Anat. Physiol., Lpz., 1850; p. 71–73; 1852; p. 199–216.   [2]*Beschreibung eines Augen-Spiegels zur Untersuchung der Netzhaut im lebenden Auge.* Berlin, Förstner, 1851.   [3]*Scientific autobiography and other papers.* New York, Philosophical Library, 1949 (trans. by Gaynor); p. 15, 24.

References to Biography: 1) *Hermann von Helmholtz.* 3 vol. Braunschweig, Vieweg, 1902–03 (Königsberger). (Engl. trans. by Welby: *Hermann von Helmholtz.* Oxford, Clarendon Press, 1906.)   2) *Hermann Ludwig Ferdinand von Helmholtz.* London, Unwin, 1899 (M'Kendrick).   3) Proc. Mayo Clin. 1951, *26:* 209–231 (Keys, Rucker, N. M. Keith, Woltman).

EDUARD HITZIG (1838–1907)

*H*itzig, a native of Berlin, came of a distinguished family. His grandfather was a criminologist, writer and poet, and his father was one of Europe's most renowned architects. Hitzig at first embarked on the study of law, then turned to medicine. After some semesters at Würzburg, he completed his studies at Berlin, where, in 1862, he received his doctorate. He then engaged in the practice

Eduard Hitzig

of medicine in Berlin. Called to Zürich in 1875, he became professor
of psychiatry and director of the Burghölzli Asylum. Here, a year
later, von Monakow became one of his pupils. Hitzig held this position until 1879, when he was made a member of the faculty of the
University of Halle and director of the psychiatric clinic of the
Irrenanstalt Nietleben. Later, in 1885, he was appointed director of
the newly founded neuropsychiatric clinic of the University of Halle.
He remained in this position until 1903 when he retired because of

Portrait, courtesy of Dr. Maurice Genty, Académie de Médecine, Paris, France.

failing vision, correctly diagnosed by himself as atrophy of the optic nerves complicating diabetes.

Among his fellow students in medicine were Cohnheim and Karl Schröder. Exerting an important influence on Hitzig's scientific career were Romberg in neurology, Traube and Virchow in pathology, du Bois-Reymond in physiology, and Griesinger and Carl Westphal in psychiatry.

Hitzig's epochal studies of the electrical excitability of the cerebral cortex were initiated during the 1860's with experienced Gustav Theodor Fritsch (1838–1927) as his collaborator. At that time there were no laboratories available at the Physiological Institute in Berlin for work on warm-blooded animals, and as a consequence Hitzig and Fritsch did their first studies on dogs in Hitzig's home, operating on Frau Hitzig's dressing table. Their joint paper in 1870,[1] of which Fritsch was the senior author, marked the beginning of a new era in the study of brain physiology. According to Percival Bailey, the legend goes that Fritsch discovered in dressing a wound of the brain during the Prussian-Danish war in 1864 that irritation of the brain causes twitching of the opposite side of the body. Earnest[2] states that Weir Mitchell was aware as early as 1860 that one side of the brain innervates the opposite side of the body; this was just before the time that Mitchell took up his study of the war-wounded in Philadelphia. (In this connection it should be mentioned that Roberts Bartholow, of Cincinnati, Ohio, was the first to apply electrodes to the human cortex [1874], using as his subject a servant of his household who had cancer of the scalp. Weak faradization of the cortex produced muscular contractions of the limbs of the opposite side of the body and turning of the head to that side.[3] On publication of this observation, Bartholow was forced to leave Cincinnati.) Fritsch's work with Hitzig was his only important contribution. Fritsch was a man of wealth, a globe-trotter, who spent about ten years in South Africa. Some time after 1870 he was made Ausserordentlicher Professor of physiology at the University of Berlin. He never became Ordinarius.

Working subsequently without the aid of Fritsch, Hitzig defined the limits of the motor area in the cerebral cortex of dog and monkey, and using this discovery as a starting point, he[4] disproved the holistic theory of the equivalence of all parts of the cerebrum proposed in 1842 by Marie Jean Pierre Flourens (1794–1867)[5] and adopted by Goltz. He also struck a blow at Munk's view[6] that the property of intelligence is discretely distributed through the cortex in aggregates (rather than uniformly as contended in the holistic theory of intelligence), a view supported by Monakow[7,8] and Kleist[9-11] on the basis of brain injuries in man. "I believe," wrote Hitzig[3] (p. 261), "that Munk is correct in his view that intelligence— or better, the store of ideas—is a property of all parts of the cortex, or rather of all parts of the brain, but I contend that abstract thought must require particular organs, and these I find in the frontal lobe" (translation by Halstead, 1947).

As a pioneer in experimental investigation, much of Hitzig's work was carried out under conditions which would have discouraged less ardent investigators. He had even to battle with the Ministry of Finance for oil paint to brighten the walls of his laboratory. In all of his investigative work and his teaching he constantly emphasized the importance of exact data obtained under controlled conditions; he held no brief for philosophic speculations. His comprehensive grasp of the problems involved in the physiology of the brain and his capacity to evaluate the data at hand are particularly evident in his Hughlings Jackson Lecture on the motor cortex[21] and in his *Welt und Gehirn* (Berlin, Hirschwald, 1905).

His contributions to medical education, particularly in the fields of neurology and psychiatry, were also noteworthy. Through his influence, psychiatrists became increasingly aware that the brain is the instrument of the mind and that the treatment of mental patients must be placed on a more scientific basis. He also brought to public attention the need for more adequate provisions for the care of mental patients.

Hitzig was a stern man—sharp, abrupt, disagreeable. It was hard to win from him either affection or dislike, but toward those whom he disliked he could be most caustic. He was a lover of polemics, and took great relish in his long controversy with Munk on localization of function in the brain of the dog. To him, controversy was necessary if science was to progress. When Forel arrived at Burghölzli in March, 1879, to succeed Hitzig, he found the institution in a topsy-turvy state, with an atmosphere of confusion and agitation reigning. Hitzig, with the soul of a jurist, actually reveled in his lawsuit against the economist Schnurrenberger, but nonetheless was burning to be off. He left Zürich with the air of a martyr, thanks to his "incorrigible conceit and vanity complicated by Prussianism."

Near the end of his life, Hitzig became almost blind, and thus was forced to put his sword in its scabbard. He often said that he did so with the greatest reluctance.

ST. LOUIS, MISSOURI   ALBERT KUNTZ

References

[1]Arch. Anat. Physiol., Lpz., 1870; p. 300–332.   [2]S. *Weir Mitchell, novelist and physician*. Philadelphia, Univ. Pennsylvania Press, 1950. [3]Am. J. M. Sc., 1874, 67: 305–313.   [4]*Untersuchungen über das Gehirn. Abhandlungen physiologischen und pathologischen Inhalts*. Berlin, Hirschwald, 1874.   [5]*Recherches expérimentales sur les propriétés et les fonctions du système nerveux*. Paris, Baillière, 1842.   [6]*Ueber die Funktionen der Grosshirnrinde: gesammelte Mittheilungen mit Anmerkungen*. Berlin, Hirschwald, 1890.   [7]*Gehirnpathologie*. Wien, Hölder, 1905.   [8]*Die Lokalisation im Grosshirn und der Abbau der Funktion durch kortikale Herde*. Wiesbaden, Bergmann, 1914.   [9]Mschr. Psychiat., 1931, 79: 338–350.   [10]Jahrb. Psychiat., Neur., Wien, 1933, 50: 23–34.   [11]*Gehirnpathologie*. Leipzig, Barth, 1934.   [12]*Hughlings Jackson und die motorischen Rindencentren im Lichte physiologischer Forschung*. Berlin, Hirschwald, 1901.

References to Biography and Works: 1) Kirchhoff (ed.), *Deutsche Irren-ärzte*. Berlin, Springer, 1924, 2: 148–156 (Wollenberg).   2) *Brain and intelligence. A quantitative study of the frontal lobes*. Chicago, Univ. Chicago Press, 1947 (Halstead).   3) *Auguste Forel mémoires*. Neuchatel, Baconnière, 1941.

Biographies of Fritsch: 1) J. Comp. Neur., 1892, 2: 84–88 (C. L. Herrick). 2) Deut. med. Wschr., 1908, 34: 605–606 (Benda).

JOHN NEWPORT LANGLEY (1852–1925)

*L*angley, English physiologist, was born at Newbury. He was educated partly at home by his father, who was headmaster at a private school. In 1871 he matriculated at St. John's College, Cambridge, and in 1874 graduated with honors. During his second year at the College he abandoned his program leading to a civil service career and began the study of natural science, a change of purpose largely due to the influence of Sir Michael Foster, whose

classes in physiology Langley attended.   For nine years, beginning
in 1875, Langley was demonstrator for Foster and during this time
collaborated with him in writing *A course of elementary practical
physiology and histology* (ed. 7, London, Macmillan, 1899).   While

Portrait, courtesy of the Army Medical Library, Washington, D. C.

still a student, he had already begun to observe, under Foster's keen tutelage, the action of pilocarpine on the heart, giving the results in his first published paper in 1875. This led to a study of its effects on secretion, thus opening the first phase of the work which occupied him for almost fifteen years. These studies, histological and chemical, were correlated with the effects on vasomotor and secretory activity.

Beginning in 1877, Langley held a series of posts at Trinity College, including a lectureship along with Gaskell and Sheridan Lea, and ultimately succeeded Foster in the chair of physiology in 1903. In 1889 Langley showed with Dickinson that on painting a sympathetic ganglion with nicotine, the passage of impulses across it is blocked[1]; thus, when nicotine was applied to the superior cervical ganglion (of the rabbit), stimulation of sympathetic fibers distal to the ganglion still caused pupillary dilatation and constriction of vessels of the ear, whereas stimulation proximal to the ganglion produced no such effects. This observation refuted the view of Hirschmann (1863) and Heidenhain (1872) that the site of action of nicotine as far as the pupil was concerned was in the nerve endings of the pupillodilator fibers.

Through this classic discovery Langley entered in 1890 the most notable phase of his work on the autonomic nervous system. With H. K. Anderson he demonstrated the unity of postganglionic neurons.[2-4] It was shown that visceral efferent neurons are not present in the dorsal root ganglia. Langley's "axon reflexes" explained what others thought were true reflex actions obtained from peripheral ganglia. His observations led him to introduce the terms "preganglionic" and "postganglionic" nerves in 1893[5] and "autonomic nervous system" in 1898.[6] The cells of the plexus of Meissner[7] and Auerbach[8] he referred to as the "enteric nervous system" since he could find no proof that they were part of the autonomic nervous system. Langley worked on segmental distribution of the sympathetic fibers and eventually elaborated a general plan of distribution of fibers of the white rami. It was in 1905 that he coined the term "parasympathetic system" to signify the cranial and sacral outflows of the autonomic system; he separated them from the sympathetic outflow by their differing responses to adrenalin, pilocarpine, and other drugs.[9] He never gave consideration to the problem of integration of central and peripheral autonomic pathways.

From 1905 on, Langley was concerned with functional relations between nerve fiber and muscle, and again made effective use of drugs, such as nicotine, curare and adrenalin. His observations led him to conclude that the region just under a nerve ending is especially excitable, due probably to the presence of "receptive substances," with which most poisons react specifically.[9]

During World War I, he studied regeneration of nerves and the effect of stimulation and massage on degenerated muscle. After the war he returned to the study of the autonomic nervous system, concentrating on vasomotor reflexes and the control of the capillaries. During this period he was also preparing his book, *The autonomic nervous system*, Part I of which was published in 1921 (Cambridge; Heffer & Sons). Of his works, Fletcher has stated: "They stand permanently in their place not merely as additions here and there to knowledge, but as indispensable stepping stones along which, at this point or that, the progress of knowledge has actually made its way." He edited the *Journal of Physiology* with great distinction for more than 30 years. As editor he had an uncanny skill in condensing the papers of verbose authors, detecting their fallacies, and clarifying their arguments; it is to him that credit goes for making this journal a model of scientific achievement for all other physiological journals to follow.

Langley was elected Fellow of the Royal Society in 1883 and became its vice president in 1904. He received many honors, among them the Retzius Medal of the Swedish Society of Physicians. His pupils included Elliot Smith, A. V. Hill, Barcroft, and Adrian.

Langley had very wide interests outside the field of science. He was one of a close-knit circle concerned with the humanities. He participated actively in outdoor sports, and for 20 years was manager of the Trinity Lawn Tennis Club. Following a brief illness, during which he contracted pneumonia, Langley died at his home in Cambridge.

PHILADELPHIA, PENNSYLVANIA   WILLIAM F. WINDLE

References

[1]Proc. R. Soc., Lond., 1889, *46*: 423–431.   [2]J. Physiol., Lond., 1895, *19*: 71–84 *et seq.*   [3]*Ibid.*, 1896, *20*: 372–406.   [4]Schäffer, E. A. (ed.), *Textbook of physiology*. Vol. 2. Edinburgh & London, Pentland, 1900;

p. 616–696.   [5]Proc. R. Soc. Lond., 1893, 52: 547–556.   [6]J. Physiol., 1898, 23: 240–270.   [7]Zschr. rat. Med., 1857, ser.2, 8: 364–366.   [8]Virchows Arch., 1864, 30: 457–460.   [9]J. Physiol., Lond., 1905, 33: 374–413.

References to Biography and Works: 1) J. Physiol., Lond., 1926, 61: 1–27 (contains bibliography; Fletcher).   2) Arch. Neur. Psychiat., Chic., 1936, 35: 1081–1115 (Sheehan).

LUIGI LUCIANI (1840–1919)

*L*uciani, a pioneer in cerebellar physiology, was born in Ascoli Piceno, Italy. At the age of 20 he graduated from the Gymnasium where his intelligence and industry had greatly impressed his Jesuit teachers. Italy was then undergoing political upheaval, and the young man—a nephew of the great patriot Candido Augusto Vecchi—became deeply engrossed in its causes; instead of continuing his studies at the University, he lingered at home absorbing what he could of politics and statesmanship and their basis, philosophy. Only in 1862, his "mind filled with the critique of pure reason" (as he says in his unpublished autobiography), he began his medical studies at the University of Bologna. After an interlude at the University of Naples and a year or so as assistant at the Eye Clinic of Magni, he received the M.D. at Bologna (1868). Soon thereafter he became Vella's assistant at the Physiological Institute, a position which he held until 1874. In this period falls what he considered a crucial event: his year and a half period of study at the Physiological Institute of the University of Leipzig (1872–73). "This stay in Germany is the most important period of my life as a scientist; it has left in me deep and lasting impressions. In a feeling of gratitude and justice which I shall harbor forever, I recognize Ludwig as my real teacher."

It was quite natural that Luciani's mind greatly profited by the sceptical and practical attitude of this German physiologist. His increased stature soon gained him recognition: successively he became Privatdozent in general pathology in Bologna (1873), Extraordinarius in the same field in Parma (1875), and Ordinarius of physiology at Siena (1880), Florence (1883) and finally Rome (1893-1917). There he dier from a chronic disease of the genitourinary tract.

High honors had been bestowed upon him both at home and

Luigi Luciani

abroad. In 1895 the Accademia dei Lincei received him as Socio-nazionale, he was elected Rector of the University of Rome, and from 1905 until his death he was Senatore del Regno. From academies and societies in Leipzig, London and Göttingen came honorary memberships.

As early as 1864, while a second-year medical student, Luciani presented his first paper, *Vom vergleichenden organischen Plastizismus,* to his teacher, Giovanni Franceschi, who found so much of merit in it that he had it printed without consulting Luciani. His first important discovery was made in the laboratory of Ludwig. Observations based on the earlier experiments of Stannius had en-

Portrait, courtesy of the Army Medical Library, Washington, D. C.

abled him to distinguish three phases of cardiac activity preceding
heart failure: the phenomena of the attack, the periodic rhythm,
and the crisis (collectively "Luciani's phenomenon"). These experiments led him to important theoretical conclusions on the nature of
the automatic activity of the heart; later he succeeded in applying
them to the activity of the respiratory centers, the periodic rhythm
of which he studied (Cheyne-Stokes phenomenon).

On returning to Italy he centered his interests on physiology of
the nervous system. In Parma, his friend Tamburini provided the
opportunity for him to work at the insane asylum at near-by Reggio.
The fruits of this period were the classical studies on cerebral
localization of function,[1] undertaken together with Tamburini and
Seppilli. In 1878, he established the theory of the cortical pathogenesis of epilepsy.[2] But it was during his Florentine period that he
wrote the two monographs on which his fame securely rests: the
physiology of starvation in man (in which he distinguished three
stages—hunger, physiological inanition, pathological inanition),[3] and
the physiology and pathology of the cerebellum.[4] In the latter monograph he described his observations on decerebellated dogs and
apes. While Ferrier had thought it impossible to keep mammals
alive after destruction of the cerebellum, he now conceded his error
and asserted that Luciani "was the first to examine the consequences
of partial or total extirpation of the cerebellum in higher mammals
by skilfully planned and executed experiments." Thanks to his extraordinary skill, Luciani was able to keep decerebellated dogs and
monkeys alive for as long as one year. This work initiated the
modern study of cerebellar function; it led him to the classic theory
that the cerebellum serves as a center for tonic, sthenic and static
functions, a theory now accepted as fact.

His last years were devoted to the completion of his 5-volume
treatise on human physiology,[5] which was brilliantly conceived and
written with great clarity and fluency. The text reached five editions in Italian, and was translated into several foreign languages,
including English.

His keen and paternal interest in the guidance of young workers
and his contagious enthusiasm and excellence as a speaker gained
him such pupils as Marchi, De Sanctis and Baglioni. His fundamental belief, often expressed in his teaching and writing, was that

the physician should think physiologically and that physiology and pathology are inseparable.

NEW YORK CITY   ARMANDO FERRARO

References

[1]Riv. sper. freniat., 1879, 5: 1–76 (with Tamburini).   [2]Ibid., 1878, 4: 617–646.   [3]Fisiologia del digiuno: studi sull'uomo. Firenze, Successori Le Monnier, 1881.   [4]Il cervelletto. Nuovi studi di fisiologia normale e patologica. Firenze, Le Monnier, 1891.   [5]Fisiologia dell'uomo. Milano, Societa edit. libraria, 1901–11 (ed. 5, 1919–21) (Engl. trans. by Welby; London, Macmillan, 1911–21).

References to Biography: 1) Arch. ital. biol., 1920–21, 70: 228–244 (contains bibliography; Baglioni).   2) Personal communication from Prof. Gozzano, Bologna.

RUDOLF MAGNUS (1873–1927)

Magnus was born in Braunschweig, Germany, into a family rich in medical tradition. At first he was attracted by literature and philosophy, but acting on the advice of a friend of the family, the chemist Richard Meyer, he undertook the study of medicine. At Heidelberg, where he pursued most of his medical studies, he was influenced particularly by the physiologist W. Kühne, and the chemist Victor Meyer. It was here that his enduring friendship with Jakob von Uexküll and Otto Cohnheim (later Kestner) began.

While still a medical student he presented a paper at the meeting of the International Congress of Physiology at Bern in 1895, on a method of measuring the blood pressure of an exposed artery. In his doctoral thesis in 1898 the technique of measuring blood pressure was further expounded. During the time he was associated with Gottlieb in Heidelberg—first as Assistant (1898) and later as Privat-dozent (1900)—his interests were in water balance in tissues and renal function. A sojourn in Schäfer's laboratory in Edinburg resulted in their joint discovery of the diuretic action of pituitary extracts. In 1904, at Heidelberg, he devised a new technique for studying the surviving small intestinal loop, now used in almost all pharmacologic laboratories, and from its use came a host of important observations on automatic rhythm, local reflexes, and the re-

Rudolf Magnus

sponses to certain alkaloids. His demonstration that the degree of
stretching of the intestinal muscle determines the direction of conduction of the stimulus was a fundamental discovery.

Magnus gained much from his association with Langley in 1905;
and in 1908, attracted by Sherrington's epochal research on the
neural regulation of movement, he went to Liverpool, where, in collaboration with Sherrington, he undertook the study of reflex mechanisms of the central nervous system. In the same year he accepted
the chair of pharmacology at Utrecht. His inaugural address on
Ziele und Aufgaben des pharmakologischen Unterrichts remains a
masterpiece.

Portrait, courtesy of the Army Medical Library, Washington, D. C.

A chance observation, made independently by Magnus and by Sherrington—that rotation of the head in a decerebrated animal alters muscle tonus in the limbs—led to innumerable experiments and to 82 publications by Magnus and his small and happy group of gifted workers.[1-5] Among the notable works which came from his laboratory was one by de Kleijn in which it was shown that proprioceptive impulses arising in the neck influence the position of the eyes.[6] These many joint studies culminated in 1924 in his greatest work, *Körperstellung* (Berlin; Springer). As Cameron Prize Lecturer (1926) he related the now classical experiment performed in an effort to determine the function of the otolithic mechanism as compared to that of the semicircular canals: anesthetized guinea pigs were centrifugalized at high speeds, thereby detaching the otolithic membranes but leaving the canals, the ampullae, and the cristae intact, with the result that all labyrinthine reactions evoked in the animals by angular and rectilinear acceleration were retained, but reflexes resulting from static posture were abolished.[7] What is now known of the function of the otoliths, postural reflexes, tonic neck reflexes, tonic labyrinthine reflexes, righting and supporting reflexes, the centers and pathways for regaining and maintaining body position—in short, the complicated system by which the brain stem and cervical cord control the body musculature—is the fruit of Magnus' genius. No one knew better than Magnus that though his data were final and conclusive, his work on body position was just the beginning of much further research on the problems of body movements as a whole.

Three hundred publications by Magnus and his Utrecht colleagues, de Kleijn, Le Heux, Rademaker and others, testify to the abounding energy of this man of small physical stature but gigantic intellect. In supervising virtually every detail of the many research projects under way in his laboratory, he was able to grasp immediately the significance of any of his associates' observations.

A series of ten lectures which he delivered in 1906 on *Goethe als Naturforscher* (Leipzig; Barth), now available in English,[8] indicates the many aspects of his mind. He was an historian, philosopher, botanist and anatomist in addition to being a physiologist of the first rank. Also he was a gifted speaker and teacher.

In need of a vacation before undertaking the Lane Lectures at Stanford University, San Francisco, he journeyed to the high Alps.

He wrote to a friend of the great vistas from Pontresina and of the beauty of the flowers. Soon afterward he suddenly died. Had he lived two months longer he would have witnessed the inauguration of a magnificent laboratory built for him in Utrecht by the Rockefeller Foundation.

NEW YORK CITY   IGN. NIC. W. OLNINCK

References

[1]Pflügers Arch., 1912, 145: 455–548 (with de Kleijn).   [2]Ibid., 1912, 147: 403–416 (with de Kleijn).   [3]Ibid., 1913, 154: 163–177 (with de Kleijn).   [4]Münch. med. Wschr., 1913, 60: 2566–2568 (with de Kleijn). [5]Pflügers Arch., 1916, 163: 405–490.   [6]Ibid., 1921, 186: 82–97.   [7]Lancet, Lond., 1926, 2: 531–536 et seq.   [8]Goethe as a scientist. New York, Schuman, 1949 (trans. by Norden).

Reference to Biography: Stanford Univ. Pub., Med. Sc., 1930, 2: 241–277 (contains bibliography; Dale).

IVAN PETROVICH PAVLOV (1849–1936)
Pavlov is a star which lights the world, shining down on a vista hitherto unexplored . . . Wells

Born 100 years ago, the son of a peasant priest in the village of Riazan in central Russia, Pavlov was educated first for the priesthood, but in 1870 undertook the study of medicine at the University of St. Petersburg under such men as Mendeleyev, Buttlerov, and Tsyon. Abroad he studied further with Carl Ludwig at Leipzig and Heidenhain at Breslau, investigating the circulation with the former and pancreatic and gastric secretions with the latter. He returned to St. Petersburg to work with the clinician Botkin in experimental pharmacology.

Pavlov's contributions fall into four fields: cardiac physiology, digestion, central nervous system, and psychophysiology. He discovered independently of Gaskell the special trophic nerves of the heart. In his investigation of the digestive glands,[1] for which he was awarded the Nobel prize in 1904, he succeeded, where others had failed, through the method of the chronic fistula, in bringing to the surface of the skin the salivary, pancreatic and choledochus ducts. For the study of the gastric secretion he devised a miniature stomach

(the "Pavlov pouch") differing from that of Heidenhain in that the vagal nerve branches were preserved. His substitution of the chronic experiment for the acute was an important advance in physiology, enabling him to observe an animal over its life span. He was probably the first to apply modern surgical techniques and asepsis in physiology—techniques which were equal even at that time (1890) to the best in use in hospitals today.

The use of salivary and gastric fistulae in long term study of secretion in a healthy animal led to the discovery of the conditioned reflex.[2] After he had become 55 the main line of his research con-

Portrait courtesy of Dr. J. R. M. Innes, Washington, D. C.

cerned the higher nervous activity as determined by the conditioned reflex. At the age of 80 he began the study of psychiatry, making application of his physiologic studies to that field. His book on conditioned reflexes, translated into English in 1941,[3] has been called the greatest book ever written on psychiatry (G. Sutherland).

His professional career in Russia was frequently halted owing to his vehement altercations on matters of principle with institutional as well as national politicians. Nevertheless his laboratory was endowed by members of the Russian nobility. He suffered the vicissitudes of war and revolution, stoutly refusing personal aid and privileges from a government whose actions he opposed in spite of Lenin's sponsorship of his work and laboratory. He was fearless in his denunciation of principles of which he disapproved. The Soviet Government recognized his worth and under the aegis of Lenin and his posthumous influence, Pavlov's laboratory fared better than others. For himself Pavlov refused to accept special favors until he had passed 80. With the gathering clouds of war his patriotism became dominant and he reversed himself in his attitude toward the Soviet Government, and acknowledged his gratitude for its aid to his laboratories and its sponsorship of science. Today Pavlov continues to be the hero of Russian science, and those of the outside world who deviate from his views are considered forces of evil.[4]

Pavlov was one of the most dynamic, brilliant, and zealous scientific figures of all time. His genius rested on his ability to design an experiment so as to eliminate extraneous factors, to his keen powers of observation, and to his use of imagination in developing concepts. His extreme skill at the operating table and in devising new procedures placed him in the front rank of the most eminent surgeons. By nature he was simple in his tastes and home loving, but vehement in his likes and dislikes, fearlessly honest, ferocious in defending his principles.

His son died of a tumor, and after that Pavlov had trouble in sleeping. Mme. Pavlov viewed his insomnia with alarm, for his habits had always been as regular as clockwork: he would sit down to lunch exactly at twelve o'clock; he would play the same records on his phonograph on the same night of each week, month after month; he would retire at precisely the same time each night; and he would always leave St. Petersburg for Estonia on an extended summer vacation on the same day each year, settling down on his estate, there to play strenous games and read French novels. Pavlov's scientific zeal persisted to the end: despite his sleeplessness he worked on full schedule in his laboratory until a week before his death at the age of 86, and in the last hour of his life discussed with a neurologist the meaning of the symptoms of his obscure illness and of the complicating pneumonia.

BALTIMORE, MARYLAND   W. HORSLEY GANTT

References

[1]*The work of the digestive glands.* Philadelphia, Lippincott, 1902; trans. by Thompson. (ed. 1, in Russian, 1897).   [2]*Lectures on conditioned reflexes.* London, Lawrence, 1928 (trans. by Gantt).   [3]*Conditioned reflexes and psychiatry.* New York, International Publ. Co., 1941 (trans. by Gantt),   [4]Science, 1951, *114:* 227–233 (London).

References to Biography: 1) *Lectures on conditioned reflexes.* London, Lawrence, 1928 (Pavlov) (trans. by Gantt); p. 11–31.   2) Ganad. M. Ass. J., 1929, *21:* 582–583 (Babkin).   3) *Pavlov.* Chicago, Univ. Chicago Press, 1950 (Babkin).

IVAN MIKHAILOVICH SECHENOV (1829–1905)

Sechenov (also Ssetchenoff, Sechenow or Setchenow), the "father of Russian physiology," was born in the province of Simbirsk, on the Volga River. At the age of 14 he entered the St. Petersburg School for Military Engineers, but soon after graduation he gave up military ambitions to study medicine at the University of Moscow (1851). After graduation (1856) he left at once for Germany. There he worked with Helmholtz, du Bois-Reymond, Hoppe-Seyler, and his lifelong friend, Carl Ludwig.

After his return to Russia, he successfully defended, in 1860, his dissertation[1] and was appointed assistant professor of physiology at the Imperial Medico-Chirurgical Academy of St. Petersburg. For a time he worked with the famous Russian chemist, Mendeleyev, but soon had to leave St. Petersburg because of the upsurge of reactionary forces. He took this occasion to go to Paris, where he studied under Claude Bernard. Quiet restored, he returned to St. Petersburg. From 1870–76 he transferred his activities to the University of Odessa, but came back six years later to St. Petersburg as

Ivan Mikhailovich Sechenov

professor of physiology at its University. In 1888 he resigned for
personal reasons and moved to Moscow, where he was active first
as lecturer, and three years later became professor (until 1901). He
died there of pneumonia.

The early contributions of Sechenov were to general physiology
and physiological chemistry, but his life work was centered on
neurophysiology. His most noteworthy contribution, the result of
studies carried out in Claude Bernard's laboratory, was that on cerebral reflex activity.[2-6] His major work, *The reflexes of the brain,* appeared in 1863. In this field he stands with Goltz as a pioneer.
Sechenov considered cerebral reflex activity the source of voluntary

Portrait from *Avtobiograficheskie zapiski.* Moskva & Leningrad, Academy of Sciences, U.S.S.R., 1945.

actions. Stimulations, according to him, arise in the peripheral sense organs and are mediated to the psychic realm, which determines the nature of muscular response. Absence of all senses would thus make psychic life impossible. However, the reflex activity itself is regulated by other cerebral centers (especially that in the mid-brain), which serve in an inhibitory capacity.[7] His assertion that "the initial cause of any human action lies outside of the person" ran counter to the point of view of the Czarist government, which regarded the concept as materialistic, anti-religious and immoral, and therefore dangerous to society. For a time the Government considered destroying Sechenov's monograph and indicting him under the penal code. In spite of this he went even further and claimed that "physiology possesses a number of data that establish the affinity of psychic phenomena to those purely somatic acts which are called the nervous processes of the body."[7]

Sechenov's independence as a thinker was also demonstrated by his opposition to Virchow's dominant teaching that only the cell is responsible for disease. He maintained, as did Lasègue, that physicochemical factors in the environment of the cell are of equal if not greater importance, a view which brought him in conflict with numerous contemporary worshippers of Virchow. This and the government's hostility toward him were the causes of his frequent changes in academic residence. Wherever he went, the ablest physiologists (Voroschilov, Tarkhanov, Spiro, Pashutin, Kravkov, Vvedensky, to mention only a few) flocked to his laboratory. His work was also a great inspiration to Pavlov.

Sechenov was admired not only for his intellect and scientific achievements, but even more for his idealism, exceptional honesty, and fearlessness in fighting injustice and stupidity. In 1861, when only 32 years old, he declined the invitation to become a member of the Imperial Academy of Sciences, though assured of election. The reason given was that his contributions to science were, in his opinion, not of sufficient importance to entitle him to so great an honor. When 25 years later he was elected—this time not against his objections—his appointment was vetoed by the government.

The scientific world, and especially the intellectuals in Russia, held him in high esteem and revered his memory. Each of the members of the 15th International Physiological Congress held in Russia (1936) was presented with a special edition of selected works of

Sechenov and a Sechenov medal. In 1943 the Academy of Science of the U.S.S.R. republished a volume by him on *Elements of thought*. The *Russian Journal of Physiology* was named the "Sechenov Journal," which is only proper, for Sechenov is justly considered the founder of the Russian school of physiology, which achieved a fame equivalent to that of any of the great schools of Western Europe.

CHICAGO, ILLINOIS   GEORGE B. HASSIN

References

[1]*Materialy dlia budschei fiziologii alkogolnago opianieniia.* St. Petersburg, Treja, 1860.   [2]C. rend. Soc. biol., 1863, *66:* 50–53 *et seq.*   [3]Ann. Sc. Nat., 1863, *19* (Zool.): 109–134.   [4]Ztsch. rat. Med., 1865, *23:* 6–15. [5]*Ibid.*, 1866, *26:* 292–294.   [6]*Selected works of Sechenov.* Moscow, State Publ. House of Biol. Med. Literature, 1935 (articles in English and German).   [7]*Physiologische Studien über die Hemmungsmechanismen für die Reflexthätigkeit des Rückenmarkes im Gehirne des Frosches.* Berlin, Hirschwald, 1863.

References to Biography: 1) *Selected works.* p. vii–xxxvi (Shaternikov). 2) *Avtobiograficheskie zapiski.* Moskva & Leningrad, Izd. Akad. U.S.S.R., 1945. 3) *Sechenov.* Moskva, Izd. Akad. Nauk., 1945 (Kozhtioants). 4) *Soviet Psychiatry.* Baltimore, Williams & Wilkins, 1950 (Wortis).

EDMÉ FÉLIX ALFRED VULPIAN (1826–1887)

*V*ulpian was born at Paris, and came up in poverty as a consequence of the early death of his father, a lawyer. He was a contemporary of Charcot, and like him studied diligently at the Salpêtrière in Paris, and in the department of pathologic anatomy at the University of Paris. Together they worked out many of the details of multiple sclerosis, tabes dorsalis, poliomyelitis, and senile osteomalacia. While Charcot turned more to the clinical side of neurology, Vulpian devoted himself to exacting studies in the laboratory in connection with his patients, and to the physiological and pharmacological studies that were at that time being developed so largely in France.

It was by a fortunate accident that Vulpian became one of the first clinical neurophysiologists. Being defeated for a fellowship in the fine arts, he became preparator for Flourens and worked as com-

Edmé Félix Alfred Vulpian

parative physiologist in the museum while he completed his education. He received his doctorate in 1853, became agrégé in 1860, and
continued to teach the physiology of the nervous system until 1866
when he was named to the chair of pathologic anatomy vacated by
Cruveilhier. Vulpian was seated, however, only over violent opposition, because he had written a memoir on the higher functions of the

Portrait courtesy of Dr. Maurice Genty, Académie de Médecine, Paris, France.

brain that had aroused the wrath of the clericals and the conservatives. Vulpian stood his ground, but thereafter interested himself in less controversial aspects of the nervous system.

Vulpian was an experimenter. He worked out the principles of degeneration and regeneration of nerves; he established principles concerning the vasomotor[1] and sudomotor apparatus, which are now common knowledge; he discovered the chromaffin system by the application of chromium salts to the suprarenals; he showed that curare had its effects at the point between the nerve and the muscle; he wrote about the action of various drugs upon the nervous system—strychnine, pilocarpine, anaesthetics, and nicotine.[2] He went over and over his experiments, checking and controlling them until he was certain of the results. His effect upon his students was profound. Mme. Dejerine spoke of his kindly visage, his Hippocratic head, and of the fairness but disapproval with which he met her pleas to be allowed to study medicine.

Entering upon his duties in the teaching of pathologic anatomy after the retirement of Cruveilhier, Vulpian found that microscopy had been neglected in France, and that the Germans following Virchow were making vast strides. He undertook to overcome this handicap, settling for his colleagues the acrid dispute concerning the various lesions of tuberculosis. With the crude sectioning and staining methods then in use he was nevertheless able to describe the lesions of poliomyelitis and spinal muscular atrophy, the retrograde changes that take place in the spinal cord after amputation or nerve section, and he was the first (1879) to repudiate the then prevalent view that tabes dorsalis is primarily a dorsal column disease, by arguing that the posterior column degeneration could not lead to atrophy of the posterior roots.[3]

Those who knew Vulpian spoke of his prodigious labors, of his memory for detail, of his encyclopedic knowledge, of his artistry in presenting his subject. When the centenary of his birth was celebrated in Paris an international gathering contributed to a review of his life and work.

Through his 225 published papers, Vulpian had a more profound effect upon neurological thought in France than he did abroad. In this respect he was overshadowed by Charcot, and also by his own followers, the Dejerines. His efforts were directed in so many channels that he failed to reach the top. Yet his influence upon his many followers in several fields of knowledge made him the intellectual leader of his day.

Dominating the short rue Antoine Dubois next to the École de Médecine in Paris is a great statue of Vulpian, hewn from stone. Among the other inscriptions on the pedestal is a list of what the French of that day regarded as Vulpian's greatest contributions:

Physiologie et pathologie des nerfs craniens vaso-moteurs et sécréteurs.

Déscription symptomatique de la sclérose en plaques.

Nosographie de la paralysie agitante.

Analyse et synthèse des affections de la moelle épinière.

Essai sur l'origine de plusieurs paires de nerfs craniens.

Leçons sur la physiologie générale et comparée du système nerveux.

Leçons sur l'appareil vaso-moteur.

Leçons sur des substances toxiques et médicamenteuses.

Clinique médicale de la Charité.

Traité des maladies du système nerveux.

WASHINGTON, D. C.   WALTER FREEMAN

References

[1]*Lecons sur l'appareil vaso-moteur (physiologie et pathologie) faites à la Faculté de Médecine de Paris.* 2 vol. Paris, Germer-Baillière, 1874–75.
[2]*Leçons sur la physiologie générale et comparée du système nerveux faites au Muséum d'histoire naturelle.* Paris, Germer-Baillière, 1866.
[3]*Maladies du système nerveux; leçons professées à la Faculté de Médecine.* 2 vol. Paris, Doin, 1879–86.

References to Biography: 1) Arch. physiol. norm. path., Par., 1887, 3.sér., 9: 345–352 (Charcot).   2) *Ibid.*, p. 353–355 (Brown-Séquard). 3) Paris méd., 1913, 12 (suppl.): 733–747 (Camus).   4) Bull. Acad. méd., Paris, 1927, 97: 724–738 (Hayem and Gley).   5) Rev. neur., Par., 1927, 1: 1087–1187 (Centenaire de Vulpian) (Roger, Lacroix, Rathery, Mme. Dejerine, *et al.*).

III

NEUROPATHOLOGISTS

ALOIS ALZHEIMER (1864–1915)

*A*lzheimer will always be remembered for having demonstrated in an unequivocal manner the changes in the brain in certain organic mental diseases. The leading psychiatrists of the late 19th century seriously doubted the value of anatomic research in mental disease and favored the psychologic investigation of the "centers of thinking." But Emil Kraepelin (1856–1926), "the Linnaeus of psychiatry," was an exception, for in planning the institutes of psychiatry of which he was to be the director, he provided unparalleled facilities for the study of morphologic pathology and appointed the most promising men of the day to pursue the study of pathology and related fields, among them Alzheimer.

Kraepelin's faith in patho-anatomic research was kindled at about the middle of his career. Oskar Vogt relates that he visited Kraepelin at Heidelberg in 1894, bringing him greetings from Forel, and that Kraepelin asked him what he planned to do in the future. "Brain anatomy of the psychoses," replied Vogt. "Then," said Kraepelin, "I must give you a bad prognosis, for anatomy can contribute nothing to psychiatry." He had in mind the experiments of his teacher, von Gudden, on rabbits, and the studies of Forel on the subthalamic region of man, neither of which contributed to the understanding of psychic behavior. In 1905 Kraepelin visited Oskar Vogt in Berlin. He had read his and Brodmann's papers on cortical cytoarchitectonics and now carefully studied the preparations. As a consequence, he was becoming convinced of the importance of brain anatomy. Finally, in 1916, in Munich, he said to Vogt: "Die Zukunft unseres Instituts liegt bei Nissl und Brodmann."

The characteristic of Alzheimer's work was that it combined the clinical and pathological approach to brain disease. He saw with clarity the determining factors of a clinical picture. He observed patiently the most characteristic cases of each disease group, waiting sometimes for years until he was able to describe the pathologic features found at necropsy. In this tedious way, he succeeded eventually in outlining sharply the clinical and pathologic pictures in general paresis, arteriosclerosis, senility, and delirium acutum. Having established once and for all the basic peculiarities of every disease group, he was then able to identify their variants.

Alois Alzheimer

Alzheimer established his reputation with a standard work on the histopathology of general paresis, both typical and atypical.[1] He stressed the frequency of the inconspicuous intracortical changes in arteriosclerosis and emphasized the fact that arteriosclerotic and senile processes are unrelated. Finally, he described the pathologic changes underlying senile dementia and its variants, among which he classified that form which Kraepelin called "Alzheimer's disease."[2]

Portrait, courtesy of Dr. F. H. Lewey, Philadelphia, Pennsylvania.

The twenty seats in his laboratory in Munich were always filled with students from all over the world. None of them will ever forget the many hours which Alzheimer spent with each of them, his large head bent over the microscope, his pince-nez dangling on a long string. There was always the indispensable cigar which he forgot as soon as he sat down, only to light another when he moved to the next student; by the end of the day some twenty of his stumps were to be found around the laboratory.

Alzheimer was born in Marktbreit, a small town in Bavaria. He went to school in Aschaffenburg, and attended the medical schools of the Universities of Würzburg, Tübingen and Berlin from 1882 to 1887. He considered himself a pupil of von Kölliker, under whom he worked as a young student in Würzburg. Following his internship, he took a position at the Städtische Irrenanstalt in Frankfurt-am-Main (1888), where Nissl joined him one year later. Here began the close co-operation which lasted a lifetime. It was so perfect a companionship that it is impossible to decide which of the two owed more to the other. Having known both of them, one might guess that the flood of startling ideas was Nissl's, but that it was Alzheimer who demonstrated histologically the correctness of the premises. Alzheimer had such a gift for describing vividly and clearly what Nissl and he had seen under the microscope, that the importance of their findings became immediately evident. His independent means permitted him to supplement his text profusely with instructive illustrations which enabled students to identify any detail of the histologic picture in their own slides.

When Alzheimer's application for the position of director of a state institution had been turned down. Kraepelin, who had called Nissl to Heidelberg in 1895, added Alzheimer to his staff in 1902. In 1903 Alzheimer followed Kraepelin to Munich, where he worked in the Anatomisches Laboratorium der Psychiatrischen und Nervenklinik. Alzheimer habilitated himself as Privatdozent in 1904 and became Extraordinarius in 1908.

Alzheimer was a good friend of Wilhelm Erb. The story goes that Erb, internationally known as an authority on syphilis, was consulted by a banker who had contracted the disease. At the termination of the treatment, the banker, to demonstrate his gratitude, offered to finance a scientific expedition to North Africa, provided that he and his wife could go along. Erb consented. The expedition had hardly

gotten underway in Algeria when Erb received a frantic telegram
that the banker had had a mental breakdown. Erb contacted Alzheimer, who complied with Erb's request that he go to Algeria to
bring the banker and his party home. Subsequently, after the
banker died, Alzheimer married the widow.

In 1912 Alzheimer was appointed to the chair of psychiatry at the
University of Breslau. Unfortunately, years of strenuous night work
in the laboratory had sapped so much of his strength that little re-
sistance was left when, at the age of 51, he contracted rheumatic
endocarditis to which he succumbed.

PHILADELPHIA, PENNSYLVANIA   F. H. LEWEY

References

[1]*Histologische und histopathologische Arbeiten über die Grosshirnrinde*
(Nissl-Alzheimer), Jena, 1904, *1:* 315–494.   [2]Zschr. ges. Neur. Psychiat.,
1911, *4:* 356–385.

References to Biography and Works: 1) Kirchhoff (ed.), *Deutsche Irren-
ärzte.*   Vol. 2. Berlin 1924; p. 299–307 (Kraepelin).   2) Münch.
med. Wschr., 1920, *67:* 75–78 (Kraepelin).   3) Allg. Zschr. Psychiat.,
1949, *125:* 63–76 (Scholz).   4) *A short history of psychiatric achievement. With a forecast for the future.* New York, Norton, 1941 (Lewis).

MAX BIELSCHOWSKY (1869–1940)

*B*ielschowsky was born in Breslau, the son of a merchant. He received his medical education at the universities of Breslau, Berlin and Munich, and the M.D. was conferred on him at Munich in
1893. Three years later, at the invitation of Ludwig Edinger, he
joined the staff of the Senckenberg Pathologisches Institut at Frankfurt-am-Main. Here Weigert influenced him the most. It was not
until after he had gone to Berlin in 1896 to head Kurt Mendel's laboratory that he began to contribute to neurological literature. In
that year his first work with Paul Schuster on the histopathology of
disseminated sclerosis appeared (additional publications in 1903,
1927 and 1932), and it was at about this time that he commenced his
fundamental studies on the silver impregnation of nerve fibers, published in 1902[1] and 1903,[2] modified in 1908, and applied in intravital
staining with Stanley Cobb in 1924. His monograph on myelitis

and inflammation of the optic nerves was published in 1901,[3] and in the same year appeared his initial study on brain tumors, which he continued in collaboration with Ernst Unger, Henneberg, Simons, and Bruno Valentin.

A new period in his scientific work began when in 1904 he joined the Neurobiologisches Universitäts-Laboratorium in Berlin under the direction of Oskar Vogt, which 20 years later became the Institut für Hirnforschung der Kaiser-Wilhelm Gesellschaft, with Bielschowsky as Abteilungsleiter. Many publications in the *Journal für Psychologie und Neurologie* resulted from the stimulating partnership with both the director and Cécile Vogt. After the Institute had been moved to new quarters at Berlin-Buch (1931), Bielschow-

Portrait, courtesy of Dr. Robert Wartenberg, San Francisco, California.

sky's work continued unabated, but unfortunately his friendship with Vogt became strained.

In the old laboratory originated the studies on the cytoarchitecture of the cerebral cortex and the striate body, in which he participated with K. Brodmann (1901–10) and M. Rose (1921–25). Here, too, he worked on amaurotic family idiocy, describing a late infantile type,[4] and on tuberous sclerosis and its relation to von Recklinghausen's disease and gliosis. In his study on regeneration of fibers within the central nervous system (1909), he supported the idea then prevalent that such regeneration is possible. His important paper in 1918[5] on the occurrence of hemiplegia in two cases of encephalitis in which the pyramidal tracts were preserved, foreshadowed the discovery by Fulton and his associates[6] and Tower[7] that damage of transcortical association fibers and extrapyramidal cortical projections may cause many of the phenomena of spasticity. Following World War I, Bielschowsky studied the problem of trauma and surgery of peripheral nerves in association with Unger and Valentin.

During the years 1926–33 he published only four major papers: on von Recklinghausen's disease (1927, with M. Rose), on myotonia congenita (1929), on cerebellar progressive paralysis (1933, with R. Hirschfeld),[8] and on dystrophia myotonica (1933, with Maas and Ostertag). This period was the harvest time when from his wide knowledge he prepared contributions to standard textbooks on neurology. Major chapters to handbooks also appeared: general histology and histopathology of the central nervous system, in Lewandowsky's *Handbuch* in 1910 and herpes zoster in 1941; the status of the neuron theory, in von Möllendorff's *Handbuch* in 1928;[9] the histopathology of nerve cells and neuroblastic tumors of the sympathetic nervous system, in Penfield's three volumes;[10] and the general histology and histopathology of the nervous system, in Bumke and Foerster's *Handbuch* in 1935.[11] In these contributions his true nature as a scientist, astute observer, diligent worker, and excellent teacher was revealed, though he never was an aggressive fighter for new ideas. There is, strangely enough, little evidence in the literature that Bielschowsky was a clinician, though he conducted his own clinic in Berlin and was known to his colleagues as an excellent diagnostician. His brother, A. Bielschowsky, became internationally famous for his work on extraocular movements.

Bielschowsky's most creative years (1900–25) were coincident with the zenith of European neurology and scientific life in general and its early decline after World War I. During the last decade of his life he was drawn into the whirlpool which destroyed all. In 1933 he lost his position at the Kaiser-Wilhelm Institut in Berlin-Buch. An opening was soon created for him, however, in the Laboratorium of the Wilhelmina Gasthuis in Amsterdam. Here he found life a little grim. He moved in 1934 to Utrecht where, supported by a grant from the Rockefeller Foundation, he worked in the laboratory of the psychiatric clinic of the University. Here, Leendert Bouman was his staunch supporter.

In June, 1936, he suffered a stroke which put him to bed for three months, after which he returned to Berlin, under the threat that otherwise his old age pension would be withdrawn. At the outbreak of World War II he and his family went to London, where one of his three sons—Hans—joined the Royal Air Force as gunner. For a time he worked in the Laboratory of Prof. Green of Sheffield. In August, 1940, Bielschowsky was the victim of another stroke, from which he succumbed three days later. The urn containing his ashes was placed next to that of his friend Paul Schuster, in the chapel at Golders Green, as had been his wish.

NEW YORK CITY   ARTHUR WEIL

References

[1]Neur. Cbl., 1902, 21: 579–584.   [2]Ibid., 1903, 22: 997–1006.   [3]Myelitis und Sehnerventzündung. Berlin, Karger, 1901.   [4]J. Psychol. Neur., Lpz., 1920, 26: 123–199.   [5]Ibid., 1918, 22: 225–266.   [6]Brain, Lond., 1932, 55: 524–536 (with Jacobsen and Kennard).   [7]Ibid., 1940, 63: 36–90.   [8]J. Psychol. Neur., Lpz., 1933, 45: 185–213.   [9]von Möllendorff, W., Handbuch der mikroskopischen Anatomie des Menschen. Berlin, 1928, 4: 1–201.   [10]Penfield (ed.), Cytology and cellular pathology of the nervous system. 3 vol. New York, Hoeber, 1932, 1: 146–188; 3: 1085–1094.   [11]Bumke, O., and Foerster, O., Handbuch der Neurologie. Berlin, 1935, 1: 35–226.

Reference to Biography: 1) Tr. Am. Neur. Ass., 1941, 67: 243–244 (Lewy).

JEAN CRUVEILHIER (1791–1874)

*I*n the ancient Roman city of Limoges, France, anno Domini 1791, there was born into the family of an army surgeon, a son who was destined to rise to fame, not only in his native country but also in the entire medical world. Inheriting a serious turn of mind from his mother, he decided while a student at the College of Limoges to enter the priesthood. But his mother's devotion was as practical as it was sincere, and she sent him off to Paris to study medicine, armed with letters to the famous Dupuytren. By the time Cruveilhier had passed the competitive examinations for interne in the hospitals of Paris (1811), Napoleon had already launched France on its imperial program. So the youthful surgeon had the opportunity to serve his master Dupuytren in both the civil and military hospitals of Paris and its environs.

Meanwhile the interest of Cruveilhier had become directed to morbid anatomy, a new medical discipline, which gave promise of providing a solid foundation for medicine as a science. In 1816, when but a young man, he published his *Essai sur l'anatomie pathologique* (Paris; privately printed), a treatise based on his work as an interne under Dupuytren. But in spite of this introduction he purposed in his heart to practice medicine. He returned to Limoges, married, and settled down to the prosaic life of a small town doctor. Stung by his failure to secure an appointment as surgeon to the city hospital and stimulated by his father's overwhelming ambition for him, he returned to Paris, where he won a competitive examination for a professorship on the Faculté de Médecine. In the meantime, Dupuytren had secured for him an appointment to the chair of operative surgery at Montpellier, which he accepted; but the yearning for the haunts of his native city were stronger than the inducements of a scholastic career, so he returned again to Limoges and tried to establish himself in practice. Then the chair of anatomy at the University of Paris was suddenly vacated by the resignation of Béclard, and once again he returned to Paris to accept this appointment. His growing popularity enabled him to re-establish the Anatomical Society of Paris, a society organized in 1803 by Dupuytren and discontinued in 1808 while under the leadership of Laennec. Cruveilhier was to remain its president for over forty years.

His great opportunity came when he was made first appointee (at

Dupuytren's request) to the professorship of pathology of the
Faculté de Médecine, provision for which had been made in the will
of Dupuytren, only recently deceased. The vast amount of material
from the deadhouse of the Salpêtrière, the establishment of the
Musée Dupuytren, and the lectureship in morbid anatomy, furnished both necessary material and incentive, and Cruveilhier continued to publish his folios of colored lithographs of his *Anatomie
pathologique du corps humain* (Paris, Baillière, 1829–42), which
was dedicated to the memory of Dupuytren. He escaped the siege

Portrait, courtesy of the Army Medical Library, Washington, D. C.

of Paris by moving to his country estate at Succac, near his native city of Limoges, where he died at the age of 83.

Cruveilhier's achievements were the result of inherent artistic and intellectual talents, his indefatigable industry, the inspiration of a deep and sincere humanitarianism, the friendship of noble minds, and the opportunities of a new science, coupled with a flood of pathologic material. His contributions to the science of neurology lay chiefly in the realm of the neoplasia. He is credited with the first description of an intracranial epidermoid (which he designated in 1829 as a *tumeur perlée*), and the portrayal of several anatomic types of meningioma (1856). His famed atlas also included many notable examples of infectious, vascular and degenerative lesions of the nervous system; here also can be found his classical description of disseminated sclerosis—the first on record (1835). Cruveilhier may, therefore, be considered as one in the long ancestry of the modern science of neuropathology.

LOS ANGELES, CALIFORNIA   CYRIL B. COURVILLE

References to Biography: 1) Biogr. méd., Par., 1934, 8: 293–308 (Genty). 2) Presse méd., 1926, 34: 1643–1644 (Roussy). 3) Med. Rec., N. Y., 1929, 130: 42–45 (not signed). 4) Arch gén. méd., 1874, 23: 594–599 (Lasègue). 5) Prog. méd., Par., 1927, 42: 357–364 (Ménétrier).

JAMES WALKER DAWSON (1870–1927)

*D*awson was born in India, the son of a missionary. His early school days in Edinburgh were interrupted by a tuberculous infection, an illness which marked the beginning of his perpetual struggle against ill health and which terminated his life years later.

He became a medical student in Edinburgh in 1887, but suffered a setback which forced him to abandon his medical studies for thirteen years. During this interval he visited Canada and the United States, then spent two years in India, and three in New Zealand as a hand in a lumber camp and a shepherd on a ranch. He returned to Edinburgh in 1897. During the subsequent four years he acted as nurse to one of his brothers who was afflicted with myelitis and, as though his cup were not yet full, he himself contracted double pneumonia. He had gained a reputation for courage, and against such adversities this quality was needed to recommence as a medical

James Walker Dawson

student. He graduated in 1904 M.B., Ch.B. with first-class honors.

Under J. G. Greenfield he took up research in pathology and first studied inflammation and repair. In 1907 he was awarded the Syme Surgical Fellowship for a thesis on wound healing, and in the following year he received the M.D., with gold medal, for work extended along these lines. He then became associated with Alexander Bruce in neurology at the Royal College of Physicians Laboratory, Edinburgh, with which institution he was connected for the rest of his life. This collaboration resulted in the production of papers on the pathology of disseminated sclerosis[1] and multiple neuromata of the central nervous system,[2,3] and the distribution of lymphatics in the

Portrait, courtesy of the Armed Forces Institute of Pathology, Washington, D. C. (From portrait in *J. Path. Bact., Lond., 31:* 117–121, 1928.)

spinal cord.[4]　For his work on disseminated sclerosis he was awarded the D.Sc. and the Freeland Barbour Fellowship by the Royal College of Physicians, Edinburgh.　The *Lancet*'s review of his work in this field stated that "The research which the late Dr. Bruce had initiated and which Dr. Dawson has so ably carried out is a monument of tireless industry and patient analysis; it is a splendid contribution to the subject and supplies fresh proof of the very high standard of British neurology."　An Italian journal described it as "the most important contribution to British neurology of this generation."　Fundamentally little has been added to his contribution since that time, and no modern treatise on the pathological aspects of disseminated sclerosis should fail to refer to it.

During World War I, Dawson was unable to serve actively.　He undertook teaching and during this period he published an address on *The spirit of leisure and the spirit of work*,[5] which he called a "Religio medici"; here "the full spirit of the man was laid bare for the benefit of those whom he was guiding."　For many years it was the custom of the University of Edinburgh to present a copy of this address to every first-year medical student.　In 1923 his memoir (with J. W. Struthers) on generalized osteitis fibrosa appeared.[6]　In 1925 he published his most important work, which remains today the same classical contribution to medical literature it was then— *The melanomata*.[7]

Dawson was a student in the real sense of the word.　All his studies were based on a wide knowledge of the literature, especially the German.　He worked untiringly, for he felt that "there is nothing so dangerous as knowledge easily acquired."　Consequently, whether reference is made to osteitis fibrosa, pigmented tumors, or disseminated sclerosis, there have been few works of equal merit; they are unsurpassed for their completeness, clarity of expression, and style.　His writings were obviously never completed in haste and repented in leisure.　He was a man with an extremely kind and generous heart, deeply religious, and a friend to all who came to him in time of need.

EDGEWOOD, MARYLAND　　　　　　　　　　　　　　　J. R. M. INNES

References

[1]Tr. R. Soc. Edinburgh, 1915, 50: 517–740.　[2]J. Path. Bact., Lond., 1910, 15: 127.　[3]Tr. R. Soc. Edinburgh, 1913, 48: 697–798.　[4]J. Path. Bact.,

Lond., 1910, *15:* 169–178.   [5]Edinburgh M. J., 1924, *31:* 1–21.   [6]*Ibid.,* 1923, *30:* 421–564.   [7]*Ibid.,* 1925, *32:* 501–732.

References to Biography: 1) J. Path. Bact., Lond., 1928, *31:* 117–121 (contains bibliography; M'Kendrick).   2) Edinburgh M. J., 1927, *34:* 476–481 (M'Neil).

CONSTANTIN VON ECONOMO (1876–1931)

Constantin Baron Economo von San Serff was born of wealthy aristocratic Greek parentage in Braila (Romania) and was brought up in Austrian Triest, where his family became established the year after his birth. At the age of 14 he happened to read Lombroso's famous work, *Genius and insanity* (1864), which impressed him so deeply that he decided to study medicine. However, in 1893, after obtaining from the Trieste Gymnasium the certificate of maturity with highest honors, he had no other recourse than to follow the wish of his father that he study engineering. After two years in Vienna, which he later considered by no means wasted, he finally obtained his father's consent to study medicine. He became a student demonstrator at the Histological Institute of von Ebner in Vienna and during this time completed a paper on the avian hypophysis. Before obtaining his doctor's degree in 1901, he also worked as assistant in the Physiological Institute of Exner.

After graduation, Economo spent one year in medicine at the University of Vienna under Nothnagel. He then went to Paris for a year, where he worked in psychiatry under Magnan and in neurology under Pierre Marie. Following this he visited Bethe in Strassburg, and Kraepelin in Munich, and published a paper on the normal anatomy of nerve cells. In 1906 he returned to Vienna as assistant at the psychiatric clinic of Wagner von Jauregg. Here he was an enthusiastic aeronaut, becoming a balloon pilot and, in 1908, one of the first Austrian airplane pilots. He organized international air meetings, promoted the building of the Vienna airports, and became president of the Austrian Aeroclub. During World War I he served for a time as a pilot on the South Tyrol front.

His early neurological investigations, partly in collaboration with Karplus and Redlich, were concerned with physiology and anatomy of the midbrain.[1] He then worked on pons tumors and trigeminal pathways.[2] In 1916, during World War I and after being ordered

Constantin von Economo

back from his aviation activities to medical duties, he studied and treated brain injuries in the clinic of Wagner von Jauregg. In 1917 he began his outstanding studies on encephalitis lethargica,[3,4] for which he is best known. He did impressive work also on Wilson's disease[5] and on the nature of sleep.[6]

In 1920 he married a daughter of the Austrian general, Prince Alois von Schönburg-Hartenstein. About this time, assisted by Koskinas (who now lives near Athens, Greece), he turned his attention to studies on cortical architecture which he had begun in 1912, and in 1925 published his great text and atlas on the cytoarchitecture of the adult human cerebral cortex.[7] In 1928, on the retirement of Wagner von Jauregg, he was urged both by his chief and the Austrian government to assume the directorship of the psychiatric clinic and to take over the chair of psychiatry. He declined

Portrait, courtesy of Prof. Hugo Spatz, Giessen, Germany.

because he preferred to pursue his research work unhampered by administrative duties. In 1931 he became director of the newly organized brain research institute in connection with the psychiatric clinic. During his last years, he continued his cytoarchitectural studies and, in addition, published a monograph on encephalitis lethargica and its sequelae.[8]

Economo was a gentleman of independent means and a wide range of interests. He travelled extensively, and was very active in international scientific organizations. Shortly after his attendance at the First International Neurological Congress in Bern in 1931, he died suddenly of cardiac disease. He was one of the most brilliant and colorful of the Austrian neurologists.

PHILADELPHIA, PENNSYLVANIA HARTWIG KUHLENBECK

References

[1]Arch. Psychiat., Berl., 1909, 46: 377–429 (with Karplus). [2]Jahrb. Pshchiat. Neur., Wien, 1911, 32: 107–138. [3]Wien. klin. Wschr., 1917, 30: 581–585. [4]Neur. Cbl., 1917, 36: 866–868. [5]Zschr. ges. Neur. Psychiat., 1918, 43: 173–209. [6]J. Nerv. Ment. Dis., 1930, 71: 249–259. [7]*Die Cytoarchitektonik der Hirnrinde des erwachsenen Menschen.* Wein u. Berlin, Springer, 1925 (with Koskinas). [8]*Die Encephalitis lethargica, ihre Nachkrankheiten und ihre Behandlung.* Wien u. Berlin, Urban & Schwarzenberg, 1929.

References to Biography: 1) *Constantin Freiherr von Economo. Sein Leben und Wirken.* Wien, Mayer & Co., 1934 (contains bibliography; Freifrau von Economo and J. von Wagner-Jauregg). (Engl. trans. by Spillman: *Baron Constantin von Economo. His life and work.* Burlington, Vermont, Free Press, 1937.) 2) Deut. Zschr. Nervenk., 1932, 123: 219–229 (Marburg).

SALOMON EBERHARD HENSCHEN (1847–1930)

*H*enschen was born in Upsala, Sweden, of a family well known there for 300 years. As a student he took trips to northern Norway, Lapland, and South America. His medical studies were pursued mostly in Stockholm, and among his teachers were Malmsten, Key and Retzius. He received the M.D. in Upsala in 1880. At intervals during the years that followed he had the advantage of working with Carl Ludwig and Cohnheim in Leipzig and with Ziemssen in Munich.

He was called to Upsala in 1881 and one year later became professor of medicine and chief of the clinic for internal diseases. For
some years he gave his attention to internal medicine, publishing
papers on such varied subjects as cholera, typhus, neuritis, and pulmonary and intestinal diseases; but his greatest interest was in
cardiovascular diseases. He was attracted to neurology by two of

Portrait, courtesy of Prof. Folke Henschen, Stockholm, Sweden.

his patients, one of whom had hemianopia, and the other aphasia; and soon he abandoned many of his other interests in an effort to track down the anatomical bases of these disorders. His work dealt with the gross features of the brains concerned; he did no fine microscopic studies and performed no experiments.

In 1888 appeared the first of a series of studies on the visual pathways[1] which was to bring him renown. Articles in 1893 and 1894[2,3] and volumes I and II of his *Klinische und anatomische Beiträge zur Pathologie des Gehirns* (Upsala, Almquist & Wiksell, 1890–1911) carried his basic observations concerning the projections of the retina on the calcarine cortex: it was he who first proved that hemianopia is due to a lesion involving the region of the calcarine fissure. When he had finished corralling the pertinent data on visual pathways as well as those on auditory[4] and gustatory and olfactory pathways[5] and on aphasia, amusia, agraphia, acalculia,[6-8] and color perception, there were eight large volumes of the *Beiträge* to show for his efforts.

In 1900 he was appointed professor of medicine in the Caroline Institute in Stockholm, and around him gathered a coterie of promising young men, such as Forsaner, Holmgren, Jacobaeus, Josefson and Tillgren. He served as a great stimulus to his pupil Carl Hammarberg (1865–93) in the latter's study of histology of the cerebral cortex and the pathology of idiocy.[9] At 65 he was made professor emeritus.

When Henschen first presented his discovery of the cortical visual center in London in 1892, its reception by Horsley, Beevor, Hitzig, and E. A. Schäfer was either circumspect or one of outright incredulity. To Paris and Rome he went on his crusade (1894, 1895), and later again to Paris (1900),[10] where in spirited discussions, von Monakow and Bernheimer opposed his theory of the significance of the parastriate areas 18 and 19. His travels took him to Madrid in 1903, where he found in Cajal a proponent of his views. Skepticism of his observations concerning the parastriate areas prevailed at a meeting in Budapest in 1909.[11] Oppenheim attended that meeting and when he returned to Berlin he related to Oskar Vogt that Henschen was on the rostrum holding forth at a blackboard with a pointer, one end in each hand, demonstrating some lantern slides, and, referring to a statement of von Monakow, he exclaimed: "Eine neue Dummheit von Monakow," and at that point he became angered and so tense that the pointer broke in the middle. Oppenheim remarked, "Henschen hat tatsächlich den Stab über Monakow gebrochen."

Work done during the Russo-Japanese War and World War I completely confirmed his views on retinal projection. When, in his later years, his battle won, Henschen spoke at Congresses, it was no longer as a warrior but as a renowned scientist. Even so, he was still embroiled in controversy over priorities during the closing years of his career, writing an article on his "40-jähriger Kampf."[12] The pioneers in the field of the cortical representation of macular vision were Inouye[13] and Holmes and Lister,[14] and the first to demonstrate that the lateral geniculate body is concerned with vision was Minkowski.[15]

Throughout his life, Henschen's interests were broad. He carried on a lively campaign against alcohol, crusaded against prostitution, and waged a war of his own on tuberculosis. He was a hard worker and was often heard to say: "The most attractive are the men who serve others." In his youth he had the voice of a professional singer, but in later years he had difficulty in keeping time. He was fond of music and would say, "My! I never have time to go to the opera," but when he did go he invariably fell asleep. In his prime he was a lively, outspoken person, often excitable and argumentative, with the result that he became enstranged from some of his friends, among them, Retzius.

Having failed to receive the Nobel Prize, Henschen registered his protest in a letter to the Nobel Committee, as follows: "As the highest recognition of my life work I regard the fact that for several years my work on the brain was repeatedly proposed for the Nobel Prize by the most eminent neurologists in Scandinavia as well as some foreign authorities, one of whom was Paul Flechsig, the leading expert in our times in cerebral anatomy and physiology. All these recommendations by experts made no impression whatever on the committee members, who were not specialists themselves in this field. Because of the secrecy maintained by the Nobel jury, all arguments and proposals are unfortunately withheld from the public, and before this jury the candidate for a Prize stands completely helpless."[16]

His international reputation was such that in 1923 he was called to Moscow as consultant to see Lenin, then aged 52, who had been stricken with aphasia and other signs of cerebral disease. Foerster,

Nonne and Bumke were also at his bedside and there was no disagreement in the diagnosis of arterial disease, but Henschen alone was correct in the prognosis, namely that the disorder would be rapidly progressive. Henschen, the internist, based his opinion on the family history: Lenin's father and two sisters had died at about 50 of cerebral apoplexy and one brother had had his leg amputated because of arterial disease. According to most accounts Lenin died of "overwork."

In Norway for a vacation when 81, Henschen fell on the ice and broke his leg. After that he began to fail. Progressive cataracts plagued him. Gastric symptoms developed and cancer was suspected, but operation failed to reveal cancer. He continued to have pain in his abdomen and leg and received morphine until he needed it habitually. His physician decided to break the habit and abruptly stopped giving the morphine. Henschen died soon afterward. As an act of piety and devotion, Henschen's son, Prof. Folke Henschen, of Stockholm, presented his father's brain to Oskar Vogt, at that time in Berlin-Buch, so that it might be put to use for scientific purposes.

PHILADELPHIA, PENNSYLVANIA   N. W. WINKELMAN

References

[1]Upsala läk. fören. förh., 1888, 27: 507–601.   [2]Brain, Lond., 1893, 16: 170–180.   [3]Upsala läk. fören. förh., 1893–94, 29: 83–126.   [4]J. Psychol. Neur., Lpz., 1918, 22: 319–474.   [5]Mschr. Psychiat., 1919, 45: 121–165.   [6]Hygiea, Stockh., 1919, 81: 721–747.   [7]Arch. Neur. Psychiat., Chic., 1925, 13: 226–249.   [8]Klinische und anatomische Beiträge zur Pathologie des Gehirns. Upsala, Almquist & Wiksell, 1920; pt. 5. [9]Studien über Klinik und Pathologie der Idiotie nebst . . . Akad. Buchdruckerei, Upsala, 1895 (trans. from the Swedish original, publ. 1893). [10]XIIIe Congr. Internat. Med., Paris, Sect. d'ophtal. Paris, Masson, 1900; p. 232–249.   [11]Med. Klin., Berl., 1909, 5: 1321–1323.   [12]Zschr. ges. Neur. Psychiat., 1923, 87: 505–535.   [13]Die Sehstörungen bei Schussverletzungen der korticalen Sehsphäre. Leipzig, Engelmann, 1909. [14]Brain, Lond., 1916, 39: 34–73.   [15]Arb. hirnanat. Inst. Zürich, 1913, 1: 255–362.   [16]Nobel; the man and his prizes. Norman, Univ. of Oklahoma Press, 1951; p. 159 (Schück et al).

References to Biography: 1) Acta med. scand., 1931, 74: 325–333 (Ingvar).   2) Deut. Zschr. Nervenh., 1931, 120: 111–116 (Friedrich

Schultze).   3) Grote (ed.), *Die Medizin der Gegenwart in Selbstdar-*
stellungen. Vol. 5. Leipzig, Meiner, 1925 (contains autobiography and
bibliography by Henschen).   4) Zschr. ges. Neur. Psychiat., 1924, *90:*
628–637 (Lenz).

ALFONS MARIA JAKOB (1884–1931)

Jakob was born in the Bavarian city of Aschaffenburg and received
his medical training in Munich, Berlin and Strassburg.   On
graduating in 1909 from the University of Strassburg, he joined
Kraepelin and Alzheimer at Munich.   Two years later he moved to
Hamburg where subsequently he became head of the anatomical laboratory of the Staatskrankenanstalt Hamburg-Friedrichsberg.   In
1915 he enlisted in the German army and after the end of the war
returned to Hamburg, where in 1919 he became Privatdozent at the
University, and in 1924, Extraordinarius.

In the short period of his life, Jakob published five monumental
books and made seventy-five contributions to various fields of neuropathology.   His most outstanding works were those on experimentally induced trauma and secondary degeneration of the central
nervous system, both from Alzheimer's laboratory (1909–12).   In his
paper on secondary degeneration,[1] Jakob followed the changes in
nerve fibers (pyramidal, for instance) during the course of the degenerative process.   This did much to clarify the underlying pathological changes in such diseases as multiple sclerosis, amyotrophic
lateral sclerosis, and Friedreich's ataxia.   His experimental studies
were fully substantiated by research in human neuropathology.[2]

The enormous material pertaining to neurosyphilis at Jakob's
disposal in Friedrichsberg enabled him and his pupils to amplify our
knowledge of the pathology of virtually all forms of the disease.[3]
His interest in extrapyramidal diseases resulted not only in an excellent monograph,[4] but also in the description of a peculiar morbid
entity now known as Creutzfeldt[5]-Jakob's[6] disease (a clinical picture
of multiple sclerosis combined with abnormal mental state and
marked spasticity).   Jakob wrote two volumes on normal and pathologic anatomy of the brain for Aschaffenburg's *Handbuch der*
Psychiatrie (1930) and a volume on the normal histology of the
cerebellum for von Möllendorff's *Handbuch der mikroskopischen*

Alfons Maria Jakob

Anatomie des Menschen (1928). His review of dystonia musculorum deformans[7] was also a significant contribution.

His laboratory attracted pupils and scholars from almost every country. From Japan came Onari, Kashida and Hayashi; from Moscow, Robustov; from Turkey, Schükri; from the United States, Alpers, Leo Davidoff, Globus, Grinker, Rabiner, Winkelman, to name only a few. Mingazzini of Rome made frequent trips to study the rich material in Jakob's laboratory. In my opinion, no other individual was so instrumental as Jakob in arousing interest in neuropathology, and no other pupil of Nissl and Alzheimer better repre-

Portrait, courtesy of Dr. K. Scharenberg, Ann Arbor, Michigan.

sented the traditions of the school founded by these two great men. In 1923, Jakob delivered a series of lectures in South America and studied the changes in the central nervous system caused by yellow fever,[8] and in 1928 he was a guest-lecturer in the United States.

When in 1914 World War I broke out, like other "guests" in Europe, I became stranded and could not obtain money because of the blockade of Germany. Jakob showed sincere eagerness in coming to my assistance, even to the point of offering to pay for the return trip to America. When, after the end of the war, the economic situation in Germany became precarious, I endeavored to show my gratitude by sending him some money. Refusing to use the money for his personal needs, he invested it in a microscope and other laboratory necessities.

It is remarkable that Jakob could so successfully meet the immense responsibilities of his laboratory and his large private consultative practice, if one considers that for seven years he had been ill with a streptococcic osteomyelitis in the right thigh. This flared up shortly after his return from the Second International Neurological Congress in Bern in 1931, and became complicated by an abdominal abscess and paralytic ileus. Death came when he was 47.

CHICAGO, ILLINOIS   GEORGE B. HASSIN

References

[1]*Histologische und histopathologische Arbeiten über die Grosshirnrinde* (Nissl-Alzheimer), Jena, 1912, 5: 1–181.   [2]*Normale und pathologische Anatomie und Histologie des Grosshirns.* 2 vol. Leipzig, Deuticke, 1927–29.   [3]Bumke, O., *Handbuch der Geisteskrankheiten.* Berlin, 1930, 11: 349–416.   [4]*Die extrapyramidalen Erkrankungen.* Berlin, Springer. 1923.   [5]Zschr. ges. Neur. Psychiat., 1920, 57: 1–18.   [6]*Ibid.*, 1921, 64: 147–228.   [7]Deut. Zschr. Nervenh., 1932, 124: 148–153.   [8]*Ibid.*, 1929, 111: 111–116.

Reference to Biography: Deut. Zschr. Nervenh., 1931, 123: 1-IV (Weygandt).

ETTORE MARCHIAFAVA (1847–1935)

M archiafava was born in Rome and throughout his long and distinguished career remained in that city. His ability was early
recognized by the award of a gold medal at the completion of his
medical course and by promotion to the rank of professor of pathological anatomy at the Royal University of Rome when he was only
36. He held this position until he was appointed professor of clinical
medicine in 1917.

Marchiafava, like Golgi, divided his research activities between
malaria and the nervous system. Soon after assuming his professorship, Marchiafava began work on malaria, which culminated in the
establishment of the life cycle of Plasmodium falciparum. His book,
La infezione malarica (Milano, Vallardi, 1902), based on his investigations, still remains an important source for malariologists. In
fact, the reputation of Marchiafava today rests at least as much on
these investigations as it does on his studies of the nervous system.

Throughout his career, however, Marchiafava maintained an intense interest in diseases of the nervous system, both infectious and
degenerative. Among his early contributions to this field was the
first description of syphilitic cerebral arteritis.[1] In 1897 he first observed primary degeneration of the corpus callosum in the brain
of an alcoholic patient, and in 1903[2] published (with Bignami) a
definitive account of the disorder. The recognition of this disease
throughout the world and the eponym, "Marchiafava's disease," have
given prominence to this discovery. He and his associates did important research also on other pathologic changes in the brain in
alcoholism.[3,4]

At the same time that these investigations were going on, Marchiafava was a busy and highly successful practitioner of internal medicine. Publications on such subjects as angina pectoris and myxedema found their way into his bibliography. He was the personal
physician of three popes and of the House of Savoy. Of the many
honors which Marchiafava received, he valued most his appointment
as Senator of the Realm in 1913 and the award of the Manson Medal.

In spite of these great distinctions, Marchiafava remained a modest, kindly and cultured Roman, interested in the classics as well as
in his contemporaries. One of his later publications dealt with a

Ettore Marchiafava

detailed study of Horace's references to wine. He remained aloof from the clamorings for credit which marred so much of the work of some of his contemporaries in malaria research.

It is with amazement that the specialist of the present day looks at the career of a man like Marchiafava—a career characterized by almost equal distinction in malariology, neurology and internal medicine.

INDIANAPOLIS, INDIANA   ORVILLE T. BAILEY

Portrait, courtesy of Prof. Dott. Paolo Colombo, Verona, Italy.

References

[1]Atti Accad. med. Roma, 1877, 3: 101–140.   [2]Riv. pat. nerv., 1903, 8: 544–549.   [3]Mschr. Psychiat., 1911, 29: 181–215 et seq.   [4]Proc. R. Soc. M., Lond., 1933, 26: 1151–1158.

References to Biography: 1) Policlinico (Sez. Pratica), 1935, 42: 2348–2349 (Mem. 47),   2) Arch. ital. anat. pat., 1936, 7: 207–225 (Sotti). 3) Bol. Accad. med. Roma, 1936, 62: 119–127 (Bastianelli).

GEORGES MARINESCO (1864–1938)

M arinesco (or Marinescu) was born in Bucharest. On completing his medical schooling he was sent by Victor Babès (1854–1926), his preceptor, to Paris to study with Charcot at the Salpêtrière. While there he was also associated with Pierre Marie, Babinski, and Raymond. Later he worked with Weigert at Frankfurt-am-Main and with du Bois-Reymond at Berlin.

With nine years' training behind him, most of it in Paris, Marinesco returned to his native city where he received his doctorate and an appointment to the staff of the Pantélimon Hospital. Shortly thereafter, in 1897, a chair of clinical neurology was created for him in the University of Bucharest. This was the beginning of Rumanian neurology, which, under his guiding genius was to reach great heights during his 41 years' tenure.

Marinesco's contribution to science was immense. Altogether about 250 articles and a few books put on record the richness of his experiences in the laboratory and on the wards of the Pantélimon and later the Colentina, where he came in daily contact with scores of the infirm. He had the astuteness to put to use new methods as they became available: the roentgen ray, with which, as a pupil of Pierre Marie in the early days, he investigated the bone changes in acromegaly; the moving picture, for the study of body movements in health and disease; the method of Nissl, by which he studied normal nerve cells and reparative processes in neurofibrils in degenerated cells following nerve section,[1] publishing a book on the subject[2] (he coined the term "chromatolysis"); the ultramicroscope, with which he proved that Nissl bodies in nerve cells are not artefacts. Priority in the field of hypophysectomy goes to Marinesco, for in 1892[3] he was successful in keeping dogs alive for as long as 18 days after destruction of the pituitary by cautery. His conclusion

Portrait, courtesy of Prof. Ludo van Bogaert, Antwerp, Belgium. (Photographer: Fayer.)

was that removal of the pituitary was compatible with life for some weeks.

Early in his career he published with Babès and Blocq a much needed atlas on the pathologic histology of the nervous system.[4] His description with Blocq of a case of parkinsonian tremor due to tumor of the substantia nigra, in 1893,[5] was the basis of Brissaud's theory, announced the next year, that parkinsonism occurs as a consequence of damage to the substantia nigra. With Blocq he was the first to describe senile plaques (1892), and with Minea he first confirmed Noguchi and Moore's discovery of treponema in the brain in general paresis. For many years he was interested in hereditary and familial diseases: with Trétiakoff he published important work on Friedreich's ataxia[6] and with Draganesco and Stoicisco he described a new form of familial spasmodic paraplegia with extrapyramidal motor symptoms.[7] In 1928 his important paper with Nicolesco on clinico-anatomic aspects of the thalamic syndrome[8] anticipated by several years many of the data on thalamo-cortical projections which experimentalists elsewhere were to uncover. Marinesco also contributed much to our knowledge of the juvenile form of family amaurotic idiocy.[9] He was a leader in the study of degenerative changes in the spinal cord following amputations.[10]

There was hardly a more distinguished exponent of the great French school than Marinesco. His pupils, many of whom have made their mark, included Goldstein, Minea, Radovici, Draganesco, Sager, Parhon, Kreindler, Grigoresco, Ionesco-Sisesti, and the Nicolescos. As a teacher, Marinesco was among the most eminent; in his lectures he emphasized ideas and gave perspective for further investigations. Recognition in the form of honors came to him from many countries. It was he above all others who was chosen to represent the students of Charcot when the centenary of the birth of that great master was celebrated.

ROCHESTER, MINNESOTA   JAMES W. KERNOHAN

References

[1]Rev. neur., Par., 1905, *13*: 5–16.   [2]*La cellule nerveuse.* 2 vol. Paris, Doin, 1909.   [3]C. rend. Soc. biol., 1892, *4*: 509–510.   [4]*Atlas der pathologischen Histologie des Nervensystems.* Berlin, Hirschwald, 1892. [5]C. rend. Soc. biol., 1893, *5*: 105–111.   [6]Rev. neur., Par., 1920, *27*: 113–

131.   [7]Encéphale, 1925, 20: 645–654.   [8]Bull. Acad. roumain., 1928, 11: 1–12.   [9]J. Psychol. Neur., Lpz., 1930, 41: 1–75.   [10]Neur. Cbl., 1892, 11: 463–467 et seq.

References to Biography: 1) Bull. Acad. méd. Roumanie, 1937, 3: 373–385 (Parhon).   2) J. Nerv. Ment. Dis., 1938, 88: 730–731 (not signed). 3) Presse méd., 1938, 46: 1547–1548 (Guillain).

GIOVANNI MINGAZZINI (1859–1929)

M ingazzini was born in Ancona, Italy. He received the M.D. in Rome in 1883. After studying under Moleschott at the Instituto di Fisiologia in Rome, he spent several years with the anatomist Todaro and then a short period with von Gudden in Munich. During all this time he had acquired an immense clinical experience, especially in the hospitals in Rome. In 1895 he was appointed to the coveted position of professor of neurology and psychiatry to the University of Rome, a post keenly sought after by De Sanctis as well. For many years he was also director of the Ospedale Psichiatrico of Rome, and it was here that he founded the laboratory of pathologic anatomy.

Mingazzini had an especial interest in the lenticular nucleus. He observed that connections exist between the third frontal convolution and the lenticular nucleus,[1] and on the basis mainly of a fronto-lenticulo-bulbar pathway he framed an hypothesis as to the neural mechanism concerned in motor aphasia.[2] (The region just in front of the left lenticular nucleus where the fibers from Broca's area of the two sides come together was later called "Mingazzini's field" by Henschen.) Another contribution was his establishment of the "acute syndrome of the putamen" (Mingazzini's lenticular hemiplegia), in which it was shown that the hemiplegia resulting from lesions of this nucleus may be due to the destruction of supplementary motor fibers in the lenticular nucleus.[3] He is known also for his work on the components of the cerebellar peduncles[4,5] and the origin, course and destination of the nervus hypoglossus,[6] and for his treatise on applied anatomy of the nervous system.[7]

Although his study of aphasia was highly important, most neurologists would agree that his greatest contribution was his monograph on the corpus callosum. In this volume he collected a great fund of data, including bibliographic, which has made of it the standard

Giovanni Mingazzini

work on the subject.   It appeared in rather poor German,[8] the
translation of the manuscript being entrusted to a Roman monk un-
acquainted with medical terminology.

Mingazzini, by the extraordinary color of his personality, fitted
well into his surroundings.   He was high-strung, easily upset, vola-
tile.   He was usually liberal with his money and yet parsimonious
in little things: at the café his assistants knew that they could accept the cup of coffee he graciously offered, but not the pastry.   He
was given to a hearty round of oaths when the occasion demanded.
Decided in his dislikes, he was not on speaking terms with De

Portrait, courtesy of the Army Medical Library, Washington, D. C.

Sanctis or Rossi in the later years of his life. In his private life he was a man of the world. Possessing the proverbial professor's absent-mindedness he would go to the opera with his wife and return home alone, having forgotten that he had escorted her there.

The walls of Mingazzini's office were covered with certificates of honorary memberships and degrees, and when his attention was drawn to them by an associate he would say, "Oh, but you should see the many more I have in my study at home!" His was an open vanity. In this respect he differed from Cajal who on one page of his *Recuerdos* would picture himself as the epitome of humility, stating that he never really amounted to much, and on the next few pages describe and illustrate his medals and decorations.

In contrast to one of the other Italian neurologists dealt with in this volume, Mingazzini, being a liberal of the Garibaldi type, refused to sign the oath of allegiance to Fascism, and plans were on foot to have him transferred to Sardinia. Mussolini is said to have interceded by remarking: "Let the professor study his brains; leave him alone." Mingazzini's wife was German, and he was a Germano-phile so far as science went; he had great respect especially for Wallenberg. Stories about Mingazzini filtered down to the man in the street in Rome and his name became part of the vernacular. Altschul relates that he often heard the exclamation, "Go to Mingaz-zini!" which meant, "Go to the asylum; you are a fool."

He knew well the art of teaching, and at his 7:00 A.M. lectures, which were always impromptu, very few students were tardy. He was beloved by his associates, which included Ayala, Altschul, Pisani and Fumarola: he called them "the best figs in my basket." He had a simple formula for expressing dissatisfaction with a paper sub-mitted to him by any member of his staff for publication: he would simply keep the paper in his desk for years.

While on a visit to Prague, after being honored in Germany, he was observed to stop in the streets, bent over with pain from what seemed to be abdominal angina. A few puffs from a cigarette, which otherwise he never used, would bring him relief. Some time after-ward he died. A pupil wrote a fitting epitaph: *Labor et gloria vita fuit, mors requies.*

NEW YORK CITY   ARMANDO FERRARO

References

[1]*Lezioni di anatomia clinica dei centri nervosi.* Torino, Unione Tipo-grafico-editrice, 1908. (ed. 2, 1913). [2]Deut. Zschr. Nervenh., 1922, *74:* 189–193. [3]Zschr. ges. Neur. Psychiat., 1911, *8:* 85–106. [4]Riv. pat. nerv., 1908, *13:* 433–452. [5]von Möllendorff, W., *Handbuch der mikroskopischen Anatomie des Menschen.* Berlin, 1928, *4:* 579–643. [6]J. Psychol. Neur., Lpz., 1923, *29:* 273–402. [7]*Trattato di anatomia clinica dei centri nervosi.* Torino, Unione tipografico-editrice, 1913. [8]*Der Balken. Ein anatomische, physiopathologische und klinische Studie.* Berlin, Springer, 1922.

References to Biography: 1) Policlinico (Sez. Pratica), 1929, *36:* 1900–1902 (Fumarola). 2) Arch. Psychiat., Berl., 1930, *92:* 1–7 (C. Frank). 3) *In memoria di Giovanni Mingazzini.* Roma, Sormani, 1931 (contains bibliography; articles by several authors).

FRANZ NISSL (1860–1919)

*B*orn at Frankenthal in the Bavarian Palatinate, Nissl's illustrious career began early. As a student at Munich, under von Gudden's paternalistic guidance, but at the suggestion of von Gudden's assistant, Ganser, he wrote a prize essay, *Die pathologischen Veränderungen der Nervenzellen der Grosshirnrinde* (1885; not published). By using alcohol as a fixative and staining with magenta red (soon replaced by methylene blue, then by toluidine blue) he demonstrated previously unknown constituents of nerve cells, and thus opened up a new era in neurocytology and neuropathology.

On receiving the M.D. in 1885, Nissl became assistant at the Münchener Kreisirrenanstalt. In 1889 he was called to the Städtische Irrenanstalt at Frankfurt-am-Main as second physician under Sioli; here he found Alzheimer, who was to become his chief disciple, collaborator, and friend.

In 1895, at Kraepelin's invitation, Nissl went to Heidelberg, where he became Privatdozent (1896), then Extraordinarius (1901). When, in 1904, Kraepelin was called to Munich, Nissl succeeded him to the chair of psychiatry and the directorship of the clinic. Again in 1918 he accepted the invitation of Kraepelin to take a research position in the newly founded Deutsche Forschungsanstalt für Psychiatrie at Munich. Here he worked for a year with Spielmeyer and Brodmann, and then died from an old kidney ailment.

Franz Nissl

Nissl's writings embraced 62 titles. While he made much of the stainable substances brought out by basic aniline dyes (Nissl granules) in an elaborate classification of normal cells (1891–94),[1] and in reporting the selective action of poisons (1896), he stressed the importance of the substance between the nerve cells (Nissl's "Grau"). In the neuron controversy he sided with the nerve-net theory.[2] His demonstration in 1894 of the reaction in nerve cell bodies following interruption of the axon ("primäre Reizung") has been of inestimable value. Thanks to his numerous contacts with Weigert, who was then developing a neuroglial stain, he made important contributions in neuropathology through his studies of the reactions of the parenchyma, glia, blood elements and blood vessels to various disease conditions.[3] He early utilized spinal

Portrait, courtesy of Prof. W. Scholz, Munich, Germany.

puncture (1902) and devised a method for quantitative determination of the albumen in spinal fluid. To clinicians he is best known for his epic work with Alzheimer on the cortical pathology of general paresis.[4]

During the last ten years of his life he was intensively engaged in establishing connections between the cortex and certain thalamic nuclei in the rabbit. In the developing cortex of newborn rabbits he observed that the superficial strata undergo greater differentiation than the deeper strata. Death prevented completion of the task, but there were two important papers to show for his work—one published in 1911[5] and the other in 1913.[6] Thus he had a hand in initiating the study of cytoarchitectonics not only by providing the most useful technical tool—his stain—but also by working out some of the corticothalamic projection systems.

Outwardly Nissl was a gnome of a man, with bad posture and a tilting of the head due perhaps to an effort to conceal the large birthmark on the left side of his face. He remained a bachelor. He was a genius, spilling over with ideas. Some seemed abstruse, for instance those on the neuron theory. He was critical of his own *Die Neuronenlehre* . . ., and when it first appeared he joked about the many mistakes he found in Part I—written a considerable time before the manuscript went to the printer. To his friends he pointed out his bizarre statement that Betz cells were among the few which needed to be examined histologically for they mirrored the pathologic changes in the brain as a whole. When pitted against Forel in 1911 as an expert alienist he fared none too well in Forel's opinion, but he won the case.

Work was almost an obsession with Nissl. At Heidelberg the days belonged to his patients and the nights to his research, but time was always found for his music. Hugo Spatz relates his first meeting with Nissl at Heidelberg when he approached the professor to ask for a place in his laboratory. Nissl was busy that morning and asked Spatz—then a student—to come to his home at twelve. The appointment was duly kept on the stroke of noon, but Nissl was not there. His housekeeper said that Nissl must have meant midnight. Spatz returned at midnight, but had to wait in the anteroom for a half hour until Nissl had finished the sonata he was playing on the piano.

Many Nissl expressions have become legend. For instance, to emphasize his observation that chromophil bodies in nerve cells stain best when the brain has been allowed to stand a half hour before plunging it in alcohol, he would say: "Take the brain out, put it on the desk, spit on the floor and when the spit is dry, then put the brain in alcohol."

Nissl was full of good humored mockery, particularly of his chief, Kraepelin, who seemed to be constantly worried or distraught. Nissl contrived every means to tease him. For instance, he would place a row of empty beer bottles outside the door of his laboratory early in the morning and circulate the rumor that he had been found intoxicated under his desk, so that the news would reach the ears of Kraepelin, who was a crusader against alcoholism.

Withal, a kindlier man than Nissl never lived.

MINNEAPOLIS, MINNESOTA   A. T. RASMUSSEN

References

[1]Neur. Cbl., 1894, 13: 676–685 et seq.   [2]Die Neuronenlehre und ihre Anhänger. Jena, Fischer, 1903.   [3]Beiträge zur Frage nach der Beziehung zwischen klinischem Verlauf und anatomischen Befund bei Nerven- und Geisteskrankheiten. Berlin, Springer, 1913–23.   [4]Histolog. histopath. Arb. (Nissl-Alzheimer), 1904, 1: 315–494.   [5]Sitzber. Heidelbg. Akad. Wissensch., Math.-naturw. Kl., 38. Abh., 1911.   [6]Arch. Psychiat., Berl., 1913, 52: 1–87.

References to Biography: 1) Arch. Psychiat., Berl., 1929, 87: 96–170 (contains bibliography; Schröder, Spatz, Steiner).   2) Münch. med. Wschr., 1919, 66: 1058–1060 (Kraepelin).   3) Ibid., 1920, 67: 75–78 (Kraepelin).   4) Ibid., 1929, 76: 1339–1340 (Spatz).   5) Berl. klin. Wschr., 1919, 56: 1006–1007 (Spatz).

HEINRICH OBERSTEINER (1847–1922)

Obersteiner was born at Vienna, the son and grandson of physicians. At the University of Vienna he studied medicine at the time (1865–70) that its medical school had reached its peak under Hyrtl, Brücke, Rokitansky, Skoda, Oppolzer and Billroth. While still an undergraduate, he started research in Brücke's laboratory. He became Privatdozent in anatomy and pathology of the nervous system in 1873, Extraordinarius in 1880, Ordinarius in 1898, and Hofrat in 1906.

In 1882 he founded the Neurologisches Institut at the University of Vienna, the first of its kind, and for years he supported it, and ultimately gave it his unique library of about 40,000 volumes. Graduate students came to him from every corner of the earth. Well over 400 of them were listed by Marburg in his historical account of the Institute on the occasion of the twenty-fifth anniversary of its founding.[1] During Obersteiner's directorship, 22 volumes of the *Arbeiten* of the Institute and about 500 papers and monographs were published.

His versatile mind encompassed nearly every aspect of neurology and psychiatry. In his clinical studies he gave a classical description of the symptomatology of concussion of the spinal cord.[2] He was the first German neurologist to describe status epilepticus;[3] he discovered the peculiar symptom of allochiria;[4] he wrote an important monograph on general paresis;[5] he recognized not only that organic diseases often display a psychogenic component, but also that constitutional factors in nervous and mental disorders are important, as exemplified by his dictum: *Paralyticus nascitur atque fit.* Long before the "discovery" of psychosomatic medicine, he studied in psychotics the fluctuations of body weight and their prognostic significance, and observed that paralytic attacks were frequently preceded by a fall of body temperature. His interest in experimental and psychological research is illustrated by his studies in experimental epilepsy, by the construction (with S. Exner) of a "psychodometer" for measurement of the reaction time in psychic disorders, and by studies of the comparative psychology of the various senses.

Obersteiner's chief interest, however, centered on the morphol-

Heinrich Obersteiner

ogy of the nervous system. His textbook on the anatomy of the central nervous system[6] was the bible for generations of budding neurologists; twice it was translated into English, twice into Russian, and into French and Italian. Virtually all of the text was based on his personal observations. His special studies dealt with the peripheral granular zone in the cerebellum of the newborn where he distinguished two zones, glial and neuroblastic; the significance of the spatial arrangement and interrelationship of Purkinje and granular cells in the cerebellum; the structure of the cerebral vessels, on which he was able to demonstrate nerve fibers; the variations in the course of neural pathways such as the pyramidal tract; Hell-

Portrait, courtesy of Mrs. Malvine Marburg, New York City.

weg's bundle; an analysis of cerebral association systems (with Redlich); and the various types of pigment (lipoid and melanotic) in nerve cells.

One striking result of his studies (with Redlich) on pathology was the proposal that tabetic degeneration of the posterior columns begins in the posterior roots.[7,8] Their postulate that the initial site of involvement is at the place where the root becomes a central tract (the Obersteiner-Redlich zone) set off a controversy which is still not settled. As early as 1905 Obersteiner found that radium irradiation may produce hemorrhages and inflammatory reactions in the brain.[9] He also demonstrated the importance of vascular factors in the genesis of porencephaly, and the existence of internal microgyria.[10]

Until shortly before his last illness, which proved to be due to myocardial degeneration, he came every day to the laboratory, spending some time with each pupil, treating everyone with the same personal interest and unequaled charm, whether a famous foreign scientist or an undergraduate. He was exceedingly fond of classical music. A confirmed collector, he acquired not only antique clocks and rare books, but also such oddities as microtome sections of various sausages. Virtually every Viennese neurologist of importance spent some time in his laboratory—for instance, von Economo, von Frankl-Hochwart, Karplus, Redlich, Schlesinger and Spitzer. His outstanding and most devoted student and successor was Otto Marburg, who was director of the institute until 1938. Then followed Otto Gagel (1938–45), and after him Hans Hoff who was appointed in 1949.

PHILADELPHA, PENNSYLVANIA   ERNEST A. SPIEGEL

References

[1]Arb. Neur. Inst. Wien, 1907, 15: VII–XXIII.   [2]Med. Jahrb., Wien, 1879, 3: 531–562.   [3]Wien. med. Wschr., 1873, 23: 544–547.   [4]Brain, Lond., 1884, 7: 289–309.   [5]Die progressive allgemeine Paralyse. ed. 2. Wien u. Leipzig, Hölder, 1908.   [6]Anleitung beim Studium des Baues der nervösen Centralorgane im gesunden und kranken Zustände. Leipzig u. Wien, Toeplitz u. Deuticke, 1888 (ed. 5, 1912).   [7]Arb. Neur. Inst. Wien, 1894, 2: 158–172.   [8]Die Pathologie der tabischen Hinterstrangserkrankungen. Jena, Fischer, 1897.   [9]Arb. Neur. Inst. Wien, 1905, 12: 87–104.   [10]Ibid., 1902, 8: 1–66.

Reference to Biography: Arb. Neur. Inst. Wien, 1923, *24:* 5–32 (contains bibliography; Marburg).

ARNOLD PICK (1851–1924)

*P*ick was born of Austrian parents in the small town of Gross-Meseritsch (now Velbe Mezitici), in Moravia. During his course in medicine at Vienna, he was student assistant to Meynert. After graduation in 1875, he became assistant to Westphal in Berlin. Wernicke, at the time, was also with Westphal. All three—Meynert, Westphal and Wernicke—exerted an important influence on Pick's subsequent work on aphasia.

Pick became physician to the Irrenanstalt at Prag in 1877, director of a newly opened hospital for mental diseases at Dobrzan in 1880, and professor of psychiatry at the University of Prag in 1886. The hospital in Prag, previously a medieval monastery, much overcrowded and ill adapted to the maintenance of even the most primitive hygiene, also contained the Landesirrenanstalt; the hospital belonged to the province of Bohemia, while the University was the property of the state (Austria-Hungary). The province and the state were constantly at odds; the Czechs, who made up the majority of the population of Bohemia, were engaged in a struggle against the old monarchy, from which they were resolved to break loose. Coupled with the political stresses was the necessity of teaching in the German language and caring for psychiatric patients, the majority of whom spoke only Czech. Finding competent assistants who could speak Czech was one of Pick's problems; he used to say: "The surgeon is well off. All he needs to say is 'boli-to?' (does it hurt?), but since we have to search the patients' minds, we need far more."

Pick's contributions to medical literature numbered approximately 350. He is best known for his work on presenile dementia due to lobar atrophy, since called "Pick's disease." The first of a series of publications on this disorder appeared in 1892.[1] No small part of his prodigious effort was devoted to pathology of the central nervous system, on which he wrote a textbook.[2] He was the first to put Wernicke's ideas of asphasia on a sound pathoanatomic basis, and his studies on this subject[3-5] and on apraxia[6] and agrammatism[7]

Arnold Pick

brought him recognition as one of the greatest contributors to the knowledge of the localization of cerebral function.

From his daughter, Dora Pick Fuchs, we learned that he had colleagues in many lands with whom he kept up a lively correspondence: Dejerine, Marie, Head, Raymond, von Strümpell, Jolly, and above all, Hughlings Jackson. The portrait of his best friend and frequent collaborator, Otto von Kahler, a handsome bearded man, who died early, was always on his desk. The physicist, Mach; the philosopher, Friedrich Jodl; the musicologist, Guido Adler; the philologist, Sauer; the biologist and physiologist, Steinach; the phi-

Portrait, courtesy of Prof. F. Jahnel and Lt. Col. H. Sprinz, M.C., Munich, Germany.

losopher, von Ehrenfels; and the jurist, Count Gleispach, were counted also among his friends. Pick was a great collector of books, books in German, French and English, which at his home reached to the ceiling and were piled on the floor. Whenever he went on vacation one or two volumes of Goethe or Carlyle went into the large case of medical books. He had a great love of music, having a special preference for Beethoven and chamber music.

Pick was a noble-minded and modest man—perhaps too modest. He was the essence of calm serenity. He was active to the end. His death resulted from sepsis following operation for a bladder calculus.

BOSTON, MASSACHUSETTS   MADELAINE R. BROWN

References

[1]Prag. med. Wschr., 1892, *17:* 165–167.   [2]*Beiträge zur Pathologie und pathologischen Anatomie des Centralnervensystems, mit Bemerkungen zur normalen Anatomie desselben.* Berlin, Karger, 1898.   [3]Arch. Psychiat., Berl., 1892, *23:* 896–918.   [4]*Über das Sprachverständnis.* Leipzig, Barth, 1909.   [5]Zschr. ges. Neur. Psychiat., 1925, *95:* 231–247.   [6]*Studien über motorische Apraxie und ihr nahestehende Erscheinungen; ihre Bedeutung in der Symptomatologie psychopathischer Symptomenkomplexe.* Leipzig, Deuticke, 1905.   [7]*Die agrammatischen Sprachstörungen; Studien zur psychologischen Grundlegung der Aphasielehre.* Berlin, Springer, 1913.

References to Biography: 1) Arch. Psychiat., Berl., 1925, *72:* 1–20 (contains bibliography; Sittig).   2) Jahrb. Psychiat. Neur., Wien, 1925, *44:* I–X (Sittig).

EMIL REDLICH (1866–1930)

*I*n the classical period of neurology in Vienna, when it was still possible for one individual to master an entire field, to possess a complete knowledge of the literature, and to make many original contributions, Redlich stands out as one of the most worthy representatives. His Viennese fellow neurologists called him "the living conscience of neurology" because of his implacable scientific mind and deeply rooted intellectual and personal honesty, which made him a strict censor of vague theories and unsubstantiated statements.

Emil Redlich

Redlich was born at Brünn, Moravia. He came of poor parents and had to overcome great financial obstacles before he received his degree in medicine at the University of Vienna (1889). His first paper, on degeneration of the posterior columns of the spinal cord due to vascular disease (1891), prepared while he worked at Obersteiner's Institut für Anatomie und Physiologie des Centralnervensystems (1889–92), already demonstrated the future trend of his investigations, his method of analyzing clinical and histological findings, his lucid style, and his critical penetration of problems.

Portrait from *Zschr. ges. Neur. Psychiat.*, *133:* 325, 1931.

An appointment as Sekundärarzt at the Wiener Versorgungsanstalt (1892) improved Redlich's still precarious financial situation, and the Oppolzer scholarship, which he received in 1894 almost simultaneously with the *venia legendi*, made it possible for him to spend several months at Paris with Marie and Dejerine. Upon his return in 1895, Wagner von Jauregg selected him as an assistant.

When Redlich took charge of the Privat-Irrenanstalt Inzersdorf in 1898, he also became chief of the section for nervous diseases at the Mariahilfer Franz-Josef-Ambulatorium (until 1908). Here he continued his research activities with unabated vigor. His publications (140 altogether) were on greatly diversified neurological topics, the more outstanding of which include encephalitis pontis et cerebelli,[1] acute disseminated encephalomyelitis including transverse myelitis,[2] mental disturbances in the meningitides,[3] alexia, agnosia, brain tumor, spinal concussion, and most particularly tetany,[4] epilepsy,[5] and narcolepsy.[6] His important *Epilegomena zur Narkolepsiefrage* appeared posthumously.[7] For a considerable period he sought spirochetes in the plaques of disseminated sclerosis following Steiner's alleged discovery of them in 1928, but his results were equivocal. He felt that the polysclerotic form of congenital syphilis was difficult to distinguish clinically from disseminated sclerosis.[8] Redlich is often said to have been the first to describe senile plaques, but actually an account of them, under the designation "sclerotic plaques of neuroglia," was first given by Blocq and Marinesco in 1892; Redlich, in 1898, referred to the disorder as "miliary sclerosis,"[9] and Simchowicz, in his classical study of senile dementia in 1911, applied the term "senile plaques"[10] to them. Today some agree with Béla Hechst[11] that the amyloid formed in the plaques represents a degeneration product of diseased nerve cells, and others with Divry[12] that they are precipitates of blood plasma, the precipitation being induced through altered properties of the colloidal ground substance.

The climax of Redlich's career came in 1914 when he was appointed director of the Nervenheilanstalt Maria-Theresienschlössel, a model hospital for mental disorders, constructed and equipped in accordance with his suggestions, and supported by a Rothschild Foundation. There he enjoyed many years of productive activity, engaging in intensive research and training his pupils, among them Hans Zweig, Paul Loewy, and Erwin Wexberg. Students from many countries visited his clinic. All through the years he was connected with the University of Vienna, becoming Extraordinarius in 1906 and Ordinarius in 1922.

Redlich in his prime was a small-framed wiry individual with a leathery deep-wrinkled face, set off by piercing black eyes. He was of serious demeanor, always intense and never casual in his neurological interests. He lacked the urbanity and capacity for sarcasm of his associate, Poetzl, and did not have the spectacular presence of his chief, Wagner von Jauregg, but in his quiet way he shone nevertheless. Those of us who were with him were impressed also by his modesty; he refused, for instance, to accept the offer that the Hofrat title be conferred on him. A man of varied interests, he was also an ardent naturalist and art collector. From his students he exacted their best. But one could sense that inwardly he was never satisfied with his own accomplishments, possibly because the goal he had set for himself exceeded his reach.

NEW YORK CITY   JOSEPH WILDER

References

[1]Zschr. ges. Neur. Psychiat., 1917, *37:* 1–35.   [2]Mschr. Psychiat., 1927, *64:* 152–184.   [3]Wien. med. Wschr., 1908, *58:* 2315–2319.   [4]Mschr. Psychiat., 1911, *30:* 439–475.   [5]Lewandowsky, M. H., *Handbuch der Neurologie,* Berlin, 1923, Ergänzungsband, 1.Teil; p. 407–492.   [6]Zschr. ges. Neur. Psychiat., 1925, *95:* 256–270.   [7]*Ibid.,* 1931, *136:* 128–173. [8]Wien. med., Wschr., 1928, 78: 932–935.   [9]Jahrb. Psychiat. Neur., Wien, 1898, *17:* 208–216.   [10]*Histologische und histopathologische Arbeiten über die Grosshirnrinde* (Nissl-Alzheimer), Jena, 1911, *4:* 263–444. [11]Arch. Psychiat., Berl., 1929, 88: 126–148.   [12]J. belge neur. psychiat., 1939, *39:* 444–461.

Reference to Biography: Zschr. ges. Neur. Psychiat., 1931, *133:* 325–328 (von Economo).

KÁROLY SCHAFFER (1864–1939)

*K*ároly (or Karl) Schaffer, the founder of Hungarian neuropathology, was born in Vienna, the son of a sculptor. While he was still a medical student at Budapest he published his first paper, on the mode of transmission of the rabies virus (1887)—an outgrowth of his work as clinical assistant at the laboratory of Károly

Au Professeur L. van Bogaert
en souvenir
Charles Mayet
Budapest le 14 mai 1926.

Laufenauer. In 1891 he went to Frankfurt-am-Main to study under Weigert, and there he met Edinger, who became one of his closest friends.

Portrait, courtesy of Prof. Ludo van Bogaert, Antwerp, Belgium.

Returning to Budapest, he was appointed Privatdozent, then chief of neurology and psychiatry at a municipal hospital and at the Gróf Apponyi-Polyclinic. In 1895 he established a small laboratory of neuropathology, where for 17 years he worked with such distinction that he received (in 1901) the appointment as Ausserordentlicher Professor in both neurology and neuropathology. An Institute of Neurohistology (Agyszövettani Intézet) was built for him in 1912 by the University of Budapest, at which time he was elevated to ausserordentlicher öffenlicher Professor. Later he became full professor of neuropathology, and in 1925 succeeded Ernö Moravcsik to the directorship of the neurological clinic of the University. The reputation which Schaffer and his pupils achieved during this time (their work eventually filled 18 volumes of the *Hirnpathologische Beiträge*) brought Schaffer, in 1925, the Achúcarro prize, for which Cajal had recommended him, and in 1927, the Balassa medal, one of the highest honors in medicine which Hungary could bestow.

Schaffer published approximately 200 original articles. First and foremost he was a pioneer in the study of hereditary diseases of the nervous system. His most significant work on the subject, embracing cerebellar, striatal and pyramidal system disorders, appeared in monograph form in 1926.[1] In it were laid down the three criteria of hereditary disease of the nervous system (the "triad of Schaffer"): defect in germ-plasm (ectoderm); localization to a level determined by the neuraxial defect; and system selectivity. For many years he was a stout defender of the neuron theory, agreeing with Cajal and his Hungarian compatriot Michael von Lenhossék (1863–1937) that the theory must serve as the basis for neuropathologic investigation. Schaffer's masterpiece, prepared in collaboration with Dezsö Miskolczy (now professor of neurology at the University of Marosvasarhely, Hungary), was his *Histopathologie des Neuron* (Jena, Fischer, 1938). On the neuron theory he opposed the view of his fellow-countryman István Apáthy (1863–1922), but he respected Apáthy's opinion, and when, in 1934, he received an honorary doctorate from the University of Szeged, he was careful to point out in his acceptance speech that he was proud to receive a degree from the faculty of which Apáthy had been a member. Other works for which he was well known included those on the pathogenesis of a variety of neurological disorders,[2] the significance of constitution in neurological and psychiatric diseases,[3] tabes and general paresis[4] and

Suggestion und Reflex (Jena, Fischer, 1895). His gifted pupil, Privatdozent Hugo Richter (who, in 1945, was killed in Budapest when struck by an automobile), proved that tabes dorsalis is not a metasyphilitic disorder but a neurological disease in its own right. On his retirement from the University of Budapest at the age of 70, Schaffer turned his attention to an old interest, stimulated originally by Ernst Kretschmer's *Körperbau und Charakter*, namely, a psychosomatic analysis of the outstanding Hungarian poets, statesmen and physicians—among the latter, Ignác Fülöp Semmelweis (1818–65). One of his last writings was a biographical sketch of von Lenhossék.[14]

In 1939, Schaffer, then 75 years of age, was invited to participate in a symposium at the Third International Neurological Congress in Copenhagen. His paper on amaurotic family idiocy, a subject on which he had labored for years,[5-11] was presented by his pupil Professor Miskolczy.[12] In this valedictory discourse he contended that in amaurotic family idiocy the lipoid changes are present only in the ganglion cells of the nervous system, and that the disorder therefore differs from Niemann-Pick's disease. Bernard Sachs, then 82, was also invited to participate, and likewise was unable to attend. In his paper on amaurotic family idiocy, read by Henry Riley, it was maintained politely but firmly that the diseases are the same. More recently, chemical analysis of the brains and internal organs of infants succumbing to amaurotic family idiocy and to Niemann-Pick's disease has shown that they differ, there being in the former a neuronal phosphatide lipoidosis in the brain alone and in the latter a lipoidosis of the reticuloendothelial system of the body as well. To date Schaffer has won the encounter.

Schaffer was brilliant both as clinician and teacher, and had the artist's touch when it came to drawing. He was fond of quoting Goethe, particularly his "nach ewigen eh'rnen grossen Gesetzen müssen wir alle unseres Daseins Kreise vollenden." But his heart was in the laboratory, where he had nurtured several of his pupils to full stature, among them Miskolczy, Richter, Béla Horányi (now professor of neurology at the University of Budapest), Tibor Lehoczky (now chief of neurology at one of Budapest's hospitals), József Baló (neurologist to Budapest's "Istvian"-Hospital/kórház), and Kálmán von Sántha (now professor of neurology at Debrecen). In an obituary on Cajal[13] he referred to himself as a "neuropathologist."

When offered the coveted directorship of the University Clinic in 1925 he turned it down, preferring the quiet of his laboratory, but later yielded when he was assured that the laboratory could be made an integral part of the clinic. He worked hard to the very end of his 75 years; he had just put a dot at the end of the last sentence of his article on Semmelweis, when he fell dead, the victim of a heart attack. His successor was László Benedek, pupil of Apáthy in neurohistology.

Boston, Massachusetts   Madelaine R. Brown
Washington, D. C.   László N. Tauber

References

[1]*Über das morphologische Wesen und die Histopathologie der hereditär-systematischen Nervenkrankheiten.* Berlin, Springer, 1926.   [2]Jahrb. Psychiat., Neur., Wien, 1934, *51:* 237–255.   [3]Psychiat. neur. Wschr., 1930, *32:* 463–467.   [4]*Anatomisch-klinische Vorträge aus dem Gebiete der Neuropathologie. Ueber Tabes und Paralyse.* Jena, Fischer, 1901. [5]Neur. Zbl., 1905, *24:* 386–392 *et seq.*   [6]J. Psychol. Neur., Lpz., 1907, *10:* 121–144.   [7]*Ibid.,* 1908, *11:* 96–104.   [8]Zschr. jugend. Schwachsinn., 1909, *3:* 19–73 *et seq.*   [9]Arch. Psychiat., Berl., 1922, *64:* 570–616. [10]Arch. Neur. Psychiat., Chic., 1925, *14:* 731–741.   [11]Arch. Psychiat., Berl., 1930, *89:* 814–817.   [12]Proc. 3d Intern. Neur. Congr., Copenhagen. Copenhagen, Monksgaard, 1939; p. 248–266.   [13]Orvosképzés, 1935, *25:* 852–857.   [14]Arch. Psychiat., Berl., 1937, *106:* 407–409.

References to Biography: 1) Schweiz. Arch. Neur. Psychiat., 1940, *45:* 477–479 (Richter).   2) Zschr. ges. Neur. Psychiat., 1940, *168:* 36 (Scholz).   3) Orvosképzés, 1940, *30:* 21–28 (Miskolczy).   4) *Ibid.,* 1939, *29:* 657 (Grósz).   5) Orvosihetilap, 1925, *59:* 13 (not signed). 6) *Ibid.,* 1939, *83:* 941 (Miskolczy).   7) *Ibid.,* 1934, *83:* 1025 (not signed).   8) *Révai kétkötetes lexikona,* 1947, *1:* 86, 173.

PAUL FERDINAND SCHILDER (1886–1940)

*S*childer was born in Vienna and attended the University there, graduating in medicine in 1909. He was influenced chiefly by the philosopher Laurenz Müller and the physiologist Exner. Although of strong philosophic bent, his first paper, published as a student, was in neuropathology, and while assistant to Gabriel Anton at Halle (1909–12) he carefully analyzed choreic and athetoid move-

Paul Ferdinand Schilder

ments.[1,2] He noted, for instance, that athetosis complicating hemiplegia was caused probably by a lesion in the dentate nucleus of
the cerebellum.[1] During this period he also made his first observations on encephalitis periaxialis diffusa,[3,4] since known as "Schilder's
disease." His philosophic and psychologic interests found expression in the study of language, aphasia, and states of consciousness,
and while at Leipzig (1912–14) he published a paper on symbolism
in schizophrenia[5] and a book, *Selbstbewusstsein und Persönlichkeits-
bewusstsein* (Berlin, Springer, 1914).

At the outbreak of war he volunteered and saw active duty. However, he continued his studies and received the Ph.D. from Vienna

Portrait, courtesy of Dr. Lauretta Bender, New York City.

in absentia in 1917. He was called to Vienna in 1918 by Wagner
von Jauregg, and was made Privatdozent in 1921 and Professor Extraordinarius in 1925. Having heard Freud's lectures as a student
he now developed a greater personal intimacy with him and became
an active member of the Psychoanalytic Society. He never became
a disciple; in fact he disagreed strongly with a number of the doctrines—particularly that of the death instinct—and elaborated his
own theories of personality and techniques of therapy. He used
not only his brilliant psychologic insight but also his broad knowledge of the mental symptoms of organic disease, particularly chronic
epidemic encephalitis[6,7] general paresis,[8] and Wernicke's polioence-
phalitis hemorrhagica superior.[9] His combined neurological and
psychiatric thinking was presented in *Das Körperschema* (Berlin,
Springer, 1923) (Schilder borrowed the term "body scheme" from
Henry Head) and in the much enlarged English edition, *The image
and the appearance of the human body; studies in constructive energies of the psyche* (London, Paul, Trench, Trubner, 1935), which
he considered his most important contribution. Other significant
neurological works were *Die Lagereflexe des Menschen* (with H.
Hoff) (Wien, Springer, 1927) and an article, *Zur Lehre von den
Sprachantrieben* (with E. Pollak).[10] He was an indefatigable
writer. The story goes that when Schilder heard that Wagner von
Jauregg was to receive the Nobel Prize in Medicine he was one of
the first to congratulate him. Wagner von Jauregg remarked:
"Don't worry; you will receive the Nobel Prize, too—but in literature."

In 1930 he came to New York as clinical director of the psychiatric division of Bellevue Hospital and research and associate professor of psychiatry of New York University Medical School. At
the medical school he continued his diverse studies on consciousness,
basing his conclusions not only on psychiatric observations but also
on clinical and experimental neurological data dealing with vestibular functions, extrapyramidal motility, and postural reflexes. The
psychiatric observations were carried out in large measure
in work on children in conjunction with Lauretta Bender, his wife.
This material was presented from the philosophical viewpoint of
constructive action of the individual toward the outer world of
reality. In a biography[11] written in 1940 he concluded, "The behavior of the child can only be understood as a continuous process
of trial and error, which leads to construction and configuration as

a basis for action . . . . Human beings drive into the future by trial and error and thereby find their happiness . . ."

Paul Schilder had a brilliant mind and a dynamic and colorful personality. He was a noted figure on the Vienna faculty, medium-sized, swarthy and handsome, his scholarly appearance accentuated by a dense, close-cropped beard. Intense and driving in his work, he still could relax and be composed and exhibit cheerfulness and humor. But in lectures and discussions, he gesticulated in the grand manner, and his already high-pitched voice ascended out of range at climactic points.

His death, in 1940, came as a consequence of having been struck by an automobile: he had always been disdainful of traffic signals and was known to cross Times Square in the rush hour in spite of the red light, with books piled to eye level on one arm and the other held aloft motioning the speeding cars to come to a halt.

Schilder's research and teaching left an enduring impression not only on clinical neurology, but also on that more abstruse field of brain, mind and motivation.

ROCKVILLE, MARYLAND   DAVID MCK. RIOCH

References

[1]Zschr. ges. Neur. Psychiat., 1911, 7: 219–261.   [2]Ibid., 1912, 9: 35–42. [3]Ibid., 1912, 10: 1–60.   [4]Ibid., 1913, 15: 359–376.   [5]Ibid., 1914, 26: 201–244.   [6]Ibid., 1921, 68: 299–340.   [7]Ibid., 1929, 118: 327–345. [8]Studien zur Psychologie und Symptomatologie der progressiven Paralyse. Berlin, Karger, 1930.   [9]Arch. Neur. Psychiat., Chic., 1933, 29: 990–1053 (with Bender).   [10]Zschr. ges. Neur. Psychiat., 1926, 104: 480–502. [11]J. Crim. Psychopath., 1940, 2: 221–234.

Reference to Biography: Psychoanal. Q., 1941, 9: 131–134 (Wittels).

WALTHER SPIELMEYER (1879–1935)

Spielmeyer was born in Dessau, the youngest of a large family. In danger of "flunking out" in grade school, he was forced to give up piano lessons so that he could direct greater energy to his studies. His daughter, Dr. Ruth Spielmeyer, relates that for a time he thought of going into the ministry but finally decided in favor of medicine, spending most of his student years in Halle, where he worked espe-

Walther Spielmeyer

cially under the physiologists Hitzig and Heilbronner and the pathologist Eberth. After becoming Privatdozent at Freiburg in 1906, he embarked on the study of psychiatry under Hoche, and at the same time established a laboratory of histopathology. Soon he contributed basic facts in support of the concept that amaurotic family idiocy is the result of disturbed lipoid metabolism,[1] and in a brilliant monograph on experimental trypanosomiasis[2] demonstrated cerebral changes and primary degeneration of the posterior columns, which contributed much to the understanding of the pathogenesis of general paresis and tabes dorsalis. In 1911 appeared the first edition of his *Technik der mikroskopischen Untersuchung des Nervensystems*

Portrait, courtesy of Dr. Konrad Dobriner, New York City. (Photographer: Friedrichs, Munich.)

(Berlin; Springer), which became a familiar manual to his many students.

In 1912 Kraepelin called him to Munich to head the Anatomisches Laboratorium der Psychiatrischen- und Nervenklinik as successor to Alzheimer, and here he became Extraordinarius in 1913, Director of the histopathology section of the newly-founded Deutsche Forschungsanstalt für Psychiatrie in 1917, and Honorarprofessor in 1918. During World War I he paid special attention to injuries and regeneration of peripheral nerves. These studies culminated in monographs[3,4] rivaling those of Tinel,[5] Foerster,[6] Athanassio-Benisty,[7,8] and Purves Stewart and Evans.[9]

In 1918 Nissl came to Munich to be chief of a second histopathology section of the Forschungsanstalt, and Spielmeyer had a period of close and happy collaboration with him, cut short by Nissl's death in 1919.

In 1922 appeared his superbly illustrated *Histopathologie des Nervensystems* (Berlin; Springer). This, the first textbook of its kind, was on general histopathology. The closest counterpart in the field of special histopathology was his carefully documented monograph on the histopathology of the psychoses[10] which embraced the work of his whole school.

Chief among Spielmeyer's later investigations was his introduction into neuropathology of the concept of disordered cerebral function resulting from temporary circulatory disturbances. Gustav Ricker (of Magdeburg), in many experiments, had demonstrated the influence of reduced blood circulation in producing a variety of tissue changes, including necrosis and malacia, in the thoracic and abdominal viscera. Spielmeyer went further to demonstrate that incomplete necrosis could occur under the influence of anoxia, as for instance in the sclerosis of Ammon's horn.[11] His support of the vascular (i.e., circulatory) factor in incomplete necrosis brought him into conflict with Oskar Vogt who favored the topistic factor. Both were correct but they could never harmonize their views. Later Scholz was to build on Spielmeyer's framework the concept of elective neuronal necrosis occurring as the result of transient anoxia accompanying convulsive seizures, the end stages of which were such disorders as status marmoratus, ulegyria, lobar sclerosis, and even hemispheric atrophy.

Spielmeyer also did much original work on the histology of encephalitis, correlating different types of lesions with clinical syndromes.[10,12] He was largely responsible for demonstrating that Westphal-Strümpell's pseudosclerosis and Wilson's disease belong to the same general category.[13] His outline of the historic events in neuropathology from 1875 to 1925 was also an important contribution.[14]

Great hopes for the advancement of psychiatry on a broad front were raised when the new building of the Deutsche Forschungsanstalt für Psychiatrie (Kaiser Wilhelm Institut), financed by the Rockefeller Foundation, was opened in 1928, with Spielmeyer as Director of its Hirnpathologisches Institut. Many of these hopes had indeed been realized when, seven years later, Spielmeyer's career was brought to an end by pulmonary tuberculosis. His able assistant and friend, Willibald Scholz, was appointed his successor.

Spielmeyer was unassuming, polished, and rather formal. He had a fine sense of humor. Also he was highly musical, and often would join his daughter in singing selections from Schubert, Brahms or Wolff, to the piano accompaniment of his wife. On many occasions celebrated musicians and singers from the National Theater in Munich would gather at his home after they had completed their concerts. Possessing an intense dislike of superficiality and affectation, he could castigate openly although he preferred quiet innuendo. He would not let go unchallenged those ideas obviously elaborated in the armchair without recourse to the microscope: he spoke out against the view of Alzheimer's pupil, A. Jakob, that antiluetic therapy could transform general paresis into some other form of cerebral syphilis; he was highly critical of Raecke who considered all problems solved when the spirochete was found in the brain; and he all but exploded when Pette proposed (at a meeting in Würzburg) that in encephalitis due to visible microorganisms only mesenchymal reactions occurred while in that due to viruses only the glia reacted.

He was proud of the performances of his disciples and never failed to give them due credit in his publications. He had perhaps not the genius that Nissl and Alzheimer possessed, but was a perfectionist, like Jakob. His intimate knowledge of minute details in the realm of neuropathology was amazing. Karl T. Neubuerger relates that one could turn to him with his slides and have his doubts removed as far as was humanly possible—with one exception: for some freakish reason he declined to examine neoplasms, claiming "Davon verstehe ich nichts." He had positive opinions in regard to the value of the metallic impregnation methods. Harry M. Zimmerman relates that he once suggested to Spielmeyer that gold chloride impregnation be used in a certain case, to which Spielmeyer a confirmed pupil of Nissl and Alzheimer, replied that it would reveal nothing that an aniline dye would not show. Later he spoke to Spielmeyer's chief technician, Frau Grombach, asking for some gold chloride. "Oh, no," she said, "we don't dare keep it in stock; the Professor is dead set against it." So when Spielmeyer went away on Easter holiday, Zimmerman purchased a supply of gold chloride in a downtown Apotheke, impregnated some sections, and showed them to Frau Grombach, who urged him not to tell the Professor what he had done. But the next day Zimmerman slipped his sections into a set of slides to review with Spielmeyer, and when Spielmeyer found them he became agitated. Only after a long discussion did he reluctantly admit that gold chloride might have a little value.

Spielmeyer's accustomed optimism suffered a great setback at the seizure of power by the Nazis. The openness of his denunciation of the Nazi system frequently brought him into great personal danger. Little is known in the outside world of his untiring efforts in helping many a scholar uprooted by the Third Reich. Indeed it has been said that an unselfish readiness to help was his outstanding trait.

BOSTON, MASSACHUSETTS   STANLEY COBB
WASHINGTON, D. C.   WEBB HAYMAKER

References

[1]Histologische und histopathologische Arbeiten über die Grosshirnrinde (Nissl-Alzheimer), Jena, 1908, 2: 193–251.   [2]Die Trypanosomenkrankheiten und ihre Beziehungen zu den syphilogenen Nervenkrankheiten. Jena, Fischer, 1908.   [3]Zur Klinik und Anatomie der Nervenschussverletzungen. Berlin, Springer, 1915.   [4]Bethe, A., Bergman, G., et al., Handbuch der normalen und pathologischen Physiologie. Berlin, 1929, 9: 285–333.   [5]Les blessures des nerfs. Paris, Masson, 1916.   [6]Lewandowsky, M. H., Handbuch der Neurologie. Ergänzungsband, 2.Teil. Berlin, 1929.   [7]Formes cliniques des lésions des nerfs. Paris, Masson, 1916. [8]Traitement et réstauration des lésions des nerfs. Paris, Masson, 1917. [9]Nerve injuries and their treatment. ed. 2. London, Oxford Univ. Press, 1919.   [10]Bumke, O., Handbuch der Geisteskrankheiten. Berlin, 1930,

11: 1–41.   [11]Mschr. Psychiat., 1928, *68:* 605–620.   [12]Virchows Arch.,
1928, *242:* 479–499.   [13]Zschr. ges. Neur. Psychiat., 1920, *57:* 312–351.
[14]Arch. Psychiat., Berl., 1925, *76:* 47–57.

References to Biography: 1) Zschr. ges. Neur. Psychiat., 1935, *153:* 1–36
(contains bibliography; Scholz).   2) Schweiz. Arch. Neur. Psychiat.,
1935, *36:* 191–196 (Walthard).   3) Arch. Psychiat., Berl., 1935, *103:*
455–470 (contains bibliography; Spatz).

RUDOLF LUDWIG CARL VIRCHOW (1821–1902)

*I*t is the privilege of few men to share so greatly in the scientific,
cultural, and political events of their time as did Rudolf Virchow.
Born in the small Pomeranian town of Schievelbein, Virchow came
to Berlin in 1839 to study at the University.   Johannes Müller was
then professor of physiology and among his students were the
histologists Henle and Schwann and the physiologists du Bois-Reymond and Helmholtz.   Certainly Virchow is indebted to these men,
master and pupils alike, for his recognition that changes in the structure and function of the cell must play a prominent role in disease.

After writing his doctoral dissertation in 1843, Virchow became
assistant to Froriep at the Charité and was delegated to perform
all chemical and microscopic examinations for the hospital.   The
good use to which he put these studies is shown by the series of
articles he published in the early numbers of his *Archiv für pathologische Anatomie und Physiologie.*   When only 26 years old, he
founded this journal jointly with Benno Reinhardt.

During the revolution of 1848 Virchow was at the barricades.
The following year he was severely reprimanded by the Ministry of
Education for political agitation among the employees of the Charité.
Despite such activities the reputation of this young man had become
so great that in the same year he was offered the professorship of
pathology at the University of Würzburg.

While at Würzburg, Virchow laid the foundations for his concept
of cellular pathology and made many contributions to normal as
well as pathological histology.   He was recalled to the University
of Berlin in 1856 and in the spring of 1858 gave a series of twenty
lectures which were published that same year in book form as *Die
Cellularpathologie* (Berlin; Hirschwald).[1]   The almost equally well

Rudolf Ludwig Carl Virchow

known survey of neoplasms, *Die krankhaften Geschwülste,* appeared in 1863–67 (Berlin; Hirschwald).

Virchow's contributions to neuropathology are many and varied. Among the 35 or more papers he published in this field were studies on pachymeningitis hemorrhagica interna; encephalomalacia; cerebral hemorrhage; meningitis; melanosis of the arachnoid; tumors of the central nervous system and peripheral nerves; and congenital anomalies of the skull, vertebrae, brain and spinal cord. Better known than any of these, however, were two discoveries he made in the field of histology of the brain.

The first, in 1851, was the description of the perivascular spaces now associated with the names of Virchow and Robin. (The latter's contribution to the subject was made in 1859.)[2] These spaces were

Portrait, courtesy of Dr. Hans Schlumberger, Columbus, Ohio.

called to Virchow's attention by von Kölliker, who found them filled with blood in cases of subarachnoid hemorrhage and thought they represented dissecting aneurysms. Virchow corrected this view, pointing out that no rupture existed in these vessels and that the blood had passed into the space from a hemorrhage in the arachnoid.[3]

In an appendix to a paper on corpora amylacea, which appeared in 1854, Virchow first described the cellular nature of the cerebral interstitial substance.[4] Two years later he identified and named this tissue as follows: "Diese Bindesubstanz bildet in dem Rückenmark und den höheren Sinnesnerven eine Art von Kitt (Neuroglia), in welche die nervösen Elemente eingesenkt sind."[5] On the basis of the word "Kitt," or glue, used in this sentence, Virchow is frequently accused of having failed to recognize any function in the neuroglia other than that of a supporting structure. However, in an article published that same year he clearly described the phagocytic action of certain of these cells in an area of encephalomalacia.[6]

After 1870, Virchow's productivity in the field of pathology declined while he devoted increasing attention to politics, public health, and anthropology. In the latter he is regarded by some as having achieved an eminence almost equal to that assured him in pathology.

COLUMBUS, OHIO   HANS G. SCHLUMBERGER

References

[1]Engl. trans. by Chance: *Cellular pathology.* London, Churchill, 1860. [2]J. Physiol., Par., 1859, *2:* 536–548.   [3]Virchows Arch., 1851, *3:* 428–462. [4]*Ibid.,* 1854, *6:* 138.   [5]*Gesammelte Abhandlungen zur wissenschaftlichen Medizin.* Frankfurt a.M., Meidlinger, 1856; p. 890.   [6]Virchows Arch., 1856, *10:* 407–408.

References to Biography: 1) Virchows Arch., 1921, *235:* 1–452 (Memorial Volume) (Lubarsch).   2) Arch. Path., Chic., 1944, *37:* 396–407 (Schlumberger).   3) Abh. k. preuss. Akad. Wissensch., Berl., 1903, 1–52 (Waldeyer).   4) Arch. path. Anat., Berl., 1903, *121:* 2–7 (von Recklinghausen).   5) Johns Hopkins Univ. Circ., Balt., 1891, *11:* 17–19 (Osler).   6) Science, 1902, n.s., *15:* 441–445 (Boas). *Rudolf Virchow und die deutschen Naturforscherversammlungen.* Leipzig, Akad. Verlagsgesellschaft, 1922 (Sudhoff).

CARL WEIGERT (1845–1904)

Carl Weigert was born at Muensterberg, Silesia, Germany. He studied medicine in the Universities of Breslau, Berlin, and Vienna, and was influenced chiefly by the physiologist, Heidenhain and the anatomist, Waldeyer. After graduation in 1868, he was assistant to Waldeyer in Breslau. He saw active service during the Franco-Prussian War in 1870–71 and thereafter became assistant to the clinician Lebert in Breslau (1871–73). In 1874, Cohnheim, attracted by Weigert's authoritative paper on the pathology of smallpox, made him first assistant at the Breslau Institute of Pathology, where his habilitation took place (1875). With Cohnheim, Weigert went to Leipzig in 1878 and was promoted to Extraordinarius of pathology in 1879. In 1885—after Cohnheim's death—he moved to Frankfurt-am-Main to accept a post as chief of the pathology section at the Senckenbergisches Pathologisch-Anatomisches Institut. This "Institut" was an ill-equipped old private cottage, where, in the early 1900's, Ehrlich and Edinger were chiefs of the two other sections. Here the three of them—Weigert, the quiet introspective unremitting worker, Ehrlich, the fighter and the most ebullient, Edinger, the solid purveyor of constantly new ideas, with the genius to find rapidly the answers he was seeking—brought to Frankfurt a position equalling if not surpassing that of the universities of other German cities.

Weigert published about 100 papers over a period of almost four decades.[1] Significantly, his first and his last papers dealt with the nervous system. The former was his doctor's thesis: *De nervorum lesionibus telorum ictu effectis;* the latter was on cerebellar changes in tabes. He was among the first to stain bacteria (1871). His research on inflammation, coagulation necrosis, pathogenesis of tuberculosis, Bright's disease, morphology of neuroglia,[2] and biology of the cell, resulted in signal contributions to our knowledge and clearly show that his interests encompassed the whole realm of pathology. It would be entirely wrong to call him only an inventor of technical methods, though it is said that he displayed a greater fondness for staining cells than for pursuing a study of their nature and functions. It is his methods, however, which have founded his reputation in neurology. Weigert introduced aniline dyes, and it

Carl Weigert

may be more than coincidence in this connection that he was a cousin of Ehrlich. He also perfected the technique of celloidin embedding, which was introduced in 1882 by Schiefferdecker. His methods for the staining of fibrin, elastic fibers, myelin sheaths, and glia, and his modification of the hematoxylin-van Gieson stain still are in use in laboratories of general and neural pathology everywhere. The technic for the staining of myelin sheaths, based on his observation that when brain tissue is mordanted in chromic salts the myelin sheaths stain selectively with acid fuchsin or hematoxylin,[3-5] opened new avenues to the understanding of many dis-

Portrait, courtesy of Dr. W. Krücke, Frankfurt-am-Main, Germany.

eases of the spinal cord and brain. The glia method was Weigert's "child of sorrow"; he had experimented seven years before he published it in 1895.[2] And for another nine years he tried to improve it. Weigert would say to his student Raubitschek from time to time: "That staining technic of mine just published took me ten years to work out, and I'd be surprised if someone didn't publish a modification within three weeks." From all this, it is not surprising that Alzheimer once remarked that Weigert "war der Meister der uns unser Werkzeug schuf."

Weigert was a delightful individual, the soul of an evening's gathering. Seated in a great chair, generally with a red-tasseled turban on his head and with legs crossed, he would recount one story after another. But these were rather rare occasions, for his circle was small. He discouraged visitors from coming to his laboratory, and those who were taken in had to do their work in quiet. At lunch time he seemed to disappear, but in the evening it was his custom to invite an assistant or two out for dinner at a Gasthaus where he assumed the role of attentive host. His associates were aware that Weigert was a disappointed man, for his hope to become an Ordinarius at a German university was never fulfilled, ostensibly because he was of Jewish extraction. He performed many autopsies for my father and grandfather, both general practitioners in Frankfurt. They praised his ability in the elucidation of complicated cases, his modest, amiable, balanced, and sincere personality, his critical philosophical mind, and his keen, nonsatiric sense of humor.

One can never forget the array of dye-containing little Liebig meat extract bottles on his desk (he preferred these to standard glassware), over which he hovered, nor cease to wonder at his unending patience in probing the mysteries of the affinities of different tissues for dyestuffs. Solutions were still filtering in his laboratory at the time of his death, which came suddenly and unexpectedly from coronary thrombosis.

DENVER, COLORADO   KARL T. NEUBUERGER

References

[1]*Gesammelte Abhandlungen von Carl Weigert.* 2 vol. Berlin, Springer, 1906. [2]*Beiträge zur Kenntnis der normalen menschlichen Neuroglia.* Festschr. zum 50-jährigen Jubil. d. ärztl. Vereins zu Frankfurt a.M., 1895.

[3]Cbl. med. Wissensch., 1882, *20:* 753–757 *et seq.* [4]Deut. med. Wschr., 1891, *17:* 1184–1186. [5]Ciba Zschr., 1943, *8:* 3074–3109 (history of histological staining techniques; Hintzsche).

References to Biography: 1) *Carl Weigert und seine Bedeutung für die medizinische Wissenschaft unserer Zeit. Eine biographische Skizze.* Berlin, Springer, 1906 (Rieder). 2) J. Am. M. Ass., 1907, *48:* 412–415 (contains bibliography; Dunham, Herter). 3) Ann. Med. Hist., N. York, 1924, *6:* 163–177 (Morrison).

OTTO IVAR WICKMAN (1872–1914)

*W*ickman's studies on poliomyelitis, coming midway between the pioneering work of Heine and the present, served to usher in the modern era of investigation of this disease. Jacob von Heine (1800–79), of Cannstatt, Germany, had indicated in 1840 that the essential lesion was in the spinal cord and that the disorder was an entity,[1] but his description did not surmount the then current belief that the muscle atrophy was due to inactivity. Credit for the recognition that the "primary" lesion is in the anterior horns goes to Duchenne (*see* p. 278), to Prévost, Charcot and Joffroy (*see* p. 268) and to Cornil[2] and Clarke.[3] The epidemic in Sweden in 1887 provided Oscar Medin (1847–1928), of Stockholm, with the opportunity of studying the disorder on a large scale.

Wickman's principal publications, appearing in the remarkably short period between 1905 and 1911,[4-9] represented both a masterly extension of previous work and a comprehensive description and analysis of almost every phase of the disease. Wickman first formulated a clear concept of the mode of spread of the infection based on extensive evidence, and gave the first detailed description of the symptomatology. His picture of the alimentary portal of entry, of the spread of virus along nerves, and of the histopathologic manifestations has required little revision, even after experimental methods were brought to bear upon these difficult problems of pathogenesis. Since he himself considered his work essentially completed in 1907, it was fortuitous that there soon followed the transmission of the disease to monkeys by Landsteiner and Popper in 1908.[10] Since then his classical monographs on the natural history of the disease[8,9] have served as a durable source for both experimentalists and clinicians. In his publication in 1910,[7] in which a bibliog-

raphy of the subject, including that on the "Landry form," is to be
found, Wickman dealt with the story of the nomenclature of the
disease: the prevalence of the use of the term "Heine-Medinsche
Krankheit," the recommendation by P. Krause that it be named

Portrait, courtesy of Prof. Folke Henschen, Stockholm, Sweden. (Taken in Strassburg, 1910.)

"akute epidemische Kinderlähmung," and his [Wickman's] reasons for calling it "Poliomyelitis acuta."

Wickman was born in Lund, Sweden, and received his medical education in Stockholm. In 1907 he was made Docent in neurology there. Between 1899 and 1903 he served as teaching assistant in infectious diseases and in medicine, and between 1907 and 1909 as a district medical officer in Stockholm. These experiences gave him the rare opportunity to deal with poliomyelitis as an infectious disease as well as a neurological one, and made possible the observations which gave overwhelming evidence in support of his theory of person-to-person spread of the disease. He confirmed Caverly's recognition in 1896[11] of abortive cases, and showed the role of healthy carriers as well.

Following his work on poliomyelitis, Wickman spent five years in Helsingfors, Berlin, Paris, Breslau and Strassburg, in studies intended to prepare him for the chair of pediatrics in Stockholm, soon to be relinquished by his teacher Medin. He returned to Sweden in 1914, but failed to be appointed. This was a blow which even the prospect of another professorship failed to cushion. A speech defect, which resisted all attempts at treatment, served to accentuate his unhappy position. He terminated a career of intense striving and great accomplishment by taking his own life at the age of 42.

BALTIMORE, MARYLAND   DAVID BODIAN

References

[1]*Beobachtungen über Lähmungszustände der untern Extremitäten und deren Behandlung.* Stuttgart, Köhler, 1840. (ed. 2: *Spinale Kinderläh-mung.* Stuttgart, Cotta, 1860.)   [2]C. rend. Soc. biol., 1863, 3.sér., 5: 187–192.   [3]Med.-Chir. Trans., Lond., 1868, 51: 249–262 (with Johnson). [4]*Studien über Poliomyelitis acuta; zugleich ein Beitrag zur Kenntnis der Myelitis acuta.* Berlin, Karger, 1905.   [5]Arb. Path. Inst. Helsingfors, 1905, 1: 109–292.   [6]Zschr. ges. Neur. Psychiat., 1911, 4: 54–66. [7]Deut. Zschr. Nervenh., 1910, 38: 396–437.   [8]*Beiträge zur Kenntnis der Heine-Medinschen Krankheit.* Berlin, Karger, 1907.   [9]Lewandow-sky, M., *Handbuch der Neurologie.* Berlin, 1911, 2: 807–910. (Engl. trans.: Nerv. Ment. Dis. Monogr., 1913, No. 16).   [10]Zschr. Immun-forsch., 1909, 2: 377–390.   [11]J. Am. M. Ass., 1896, 26: 1–5.

References to Biography: 1) Hygiea, Stockh., 1914, 76: 479–484 (Josef-son).   2) Zschr. ges. Neur. Psychiat., 1914, 26: 1–5 (Klotz).

IV

CLINICAL NEUROLOGISTS

WILLIAM JOHN ADIE (1886–1935)

*A*die was a son of Australia, that young, virile country which has given Burnet, Cairns and Florey to British medicine. He was born in Geelong, Victoria. As was common custom in the British Colonies at that time, he went to Edinburgh University, where he qualified in medicine. His interests were directed to neurology early in his medical career, and his intensive pursuit of the subject was naturally influenced by such great British neurologists of the day as Hughlings Jackson, Sir William Gowers, and Sir Byrom Bramwell. Awarded a postgraduate travelling scholarship, he spent two years in Munich, Berlin, Vienna and Paris. On his return to London, he was appointed resident medical officer to the National Hospital, Queen Square.

At the outbreak of World War I he "joined the colours" and was posted to the 1st Northhamptonshire Regiment, which was annihilated in the historic retreat from Mons. An attack of measles kept the young medical officer out of that battle, and subsequently he saw action as medical officer of the First Leicestershire Regiment in the great battles in France and Belgium in the first two years of the war. In April 1916 Adie was cited in Sir Douglas Haig's dispatches for gallantry in the field: he was responsible for saving a number of lives in one of the early gas attacks of the war by improvising a mask dampened with urine which enabled him to carry out his rescue work. Later, on withdrawal from the field, he served as consultant neurologist to the Second Army Centre for gunshot wounds of the head.

After the war he rejoined the staff of the National Hospital and subsequently was appointed physician to the Royal London Ophthalmic (Moorfields), Charing Cross, and Mount Vernon Hospitals. In 1926 he was elected a Fellow of the Royal College of Physicians, and, in the same year, the University of Edinburgh awarded him the gold medal for his M.D. thesis on *Idiopathic narcolepsy*.

Medical studies are naturally dictated by opportunities. Adie became interested in narcolepsy while in Germany. Subsequently the veritable spate of neurological maladies pouring into the outpatient department at "Queen Square" gave impetus to his investigation of the narcolepsies and the minor epilepsies. Migraine, from which he

231

William John Adie

himself suffered, also claimed his interest. Perhaps his outstanding contributions were on the subjects of dystrophia myotonica[1] and narcolepsy[2]—the maladie d'Adie of some French writers, though credit goes to Westphal[3] for the first account, to Jean B. E. Gélineau (1859–1907?)[4] for solidly establishing the disorder as an entity, to Gowers[5] for giving it its present-day perspective, and to Leopold Löwenfeld (1847–1924)[6] for clarifying its relation to cataplexy. (The term "cataplexy" was coined by Richard Henneberg, 1868–)[7]

It was while at Moorfields, with its great variety of neuro-ophthalmological diseases, that Adie wrote on the Argyll Robertson pupil,

Portrait, courtesy of Dr. Macdonald Critchley, London, England. (Photographer: Chesney, Ltd., London.)

disseminated sclerosis, and the syndrome of tonic pupils and absent reflexes.[8] He was not the first to write on this subject, but he described the syndrome in detail and was the first to delineate complete and incomplete forms. As a consequence the "Adie syndrome" became a familiar term in British literature. As pointed out by Wartenberg,[9] the lion's share of the credit for the initial description should go to Weill and Reys,[10] whose work antedated Adie's by six years. Injustice has been done by those who say that the disorder was first described by Strassburger[11] and by Saenger[12]: the tonic pupil was described by both, but neither made any reference to the absence of tendon reflexes.

Adie was closely associated with James Collier, who was his mentor, and it is interesting to note that these two were joint editors of the neurological section in Price's *Textbook of the practice of medicine,* so highly regarded by students of neurology in Britain.

Adie was naturally endowed with a wide and sympathetic outlook on life and a fine tolerance of his fellow men, no doubt amplified by long years of service among soldiers in the field. He was considerate and free of affectation–qualities which endeared him to students and colleagues. His teaching was clear, concise, and dogmatic to a degree ideally suited for students; and yet, in discussion, his was always an open mind, seeking new knowledge, and ready to consider with student or colleague some point of view which differed from his own.

Adie was indefatigable. He was fond of tennis and passed many strenuous holidays in Switzerland skating and skiing. A keen ornithologist, he spent long hours bird-watching at his country house on the Sussex Downs, and in his last years, while convalescing from coronary thrombosis at Majorca, he devoted much time to this hobby. It took courage for him to return to London to resume his activities, restricted though they were.

To one who knew him as "chief" in the days following his illness, Dr. W. J. Adie is remembered for the warmth and security of his personality, his tolerance, his fine teaching and outstanding clinical acumen: the complete neurologist, fortified with a sound knowledge of general medicine and a keen insight into human nature.

OTAGO, NEW ZEALAND   J. EGERTON CAUGHEY

References

[1]Brain, Lond., 1923, *46:* 73–127 (with J. G. Greenfield). [2]*Ibid.,* 1926, *49:* 257–306. [3]Arch. Psychiat., Berl., 1877, *7:* 622–635. [4]Gaz. hôp., 1880, *53:* 626–628 *et seq.* [5]*The borderland of epilepsy.* London, Churchill, 1907. [6]Münch. med. Wschr., 1902, *49:* 1041–1045. [7]Neur. Cbl., 1916, *35:* 282–290. [8]Brain, Lond., 1932, *55:* 98–113. [9]J. Am. M. Ass., 1951, *146:* 1152. [10]Rev. otoneur., Par., 1926, *4:* 433–441. [11]Neur. Cbl., 1902, *21:* 738–740 *et seq.* [12]*Ibid.,* 1902, *21:* 837–839 *et seq.*

References to Biography: 1) Brit. M. J., 1935, *1:* 624–625 (not signed). 2) J. Nerv. Ment. Dis., 1935, *81:* 726 (Jelliffe).

JOSEPH FRANÇOIS FÉLIX BABINSKI (1857–1932)

As political refugees, Babinski's parents fled in 1848 from Poland to Paris, where Joseph was born and grew up. He was graduated from the University of Paris in 1884. His thesis, of outstanding merit, dealt with multiple sclerosis. Under Charcot, he worked at the Salpêtrière, and from 1890 to 1927 headed the neurological clinic at the Hôpital de la Pitié. With Brissaud, Pierre Marie, Dejerine, Souques, and others, he founded the Société de Neurologie de Paris, to which he was profoundly devoted. The last years of his life were marred by paralysis agitans.

Babinski had a thorough training in general medicine before undertaking the study of neurology. His bibliography[1] contains 288 items, the first on typhoid fever (1882), the last on hysteria (1930). At a meeting of the Société de Biologie in 1896, he described his "cutaneous plantar reflex".[2] The report contained but 28 lines. Although this sign had been reported three years before by E. Remak, it was Babinski who first realized its diagnostic significance. In its simplicity, clinical importance, and physiological implications, Babinski's sign has hardly an equal in medicine. The number of works devoted exclusively to "Babinski" runs into the hundreds, yet in 1900 its diagnostic importance was declared to be "minimal." Among Babinski's most important papers are those on combined flexion of thigh and trunk,[3] Argyll Robertson pupil in cerebrospinal syphilis,[4] cerebellar symptomatology, particularly asynergia[5,6] and adiadokokinesis,[7] deep and superficial reflexes,[8] and reflexes of defense.[9] In 1902, with Nageotte, he reported the syndrome of a

unilateral bulbar lesion.[10]   The syndrome of dystrophia adiposo-
genitalis was outlined by him in 1900,[11] a year before Fröhlich's
description.   Many of his later papers were devoted to surgical
affections of the nervous system.   Babinski, the medical neurologist,
anticipated the approach of the neurosurgical era.   In 1922, he
localized the first spinal cord tumor to be removed in France.[12]   Six
days before his death he said that his best contribution was not his
sign, but the fact that he had showed the way to de Martel and Vincent, the founders of French neurosurgery.

His concept of hysteria, which he called "pithiatisme," was that

Portrait, courtesy of Dr. Maurice Genty, Académie de Médecine, Paris, France.

its manifestations were produced by suggestion and abolished by countersuggestion. Once, in 1926, he demonstrated this to me impressively. After a few words to a young hysteric he squeezed her right thumb, and a hysterical attack resulted; he squeezed her left thumb and it stopped abruptly.

While he lacked the dramatic trends of Charcot, his examinations were inspiring models of meticulous scrutiny, conscientiousness and patience. He was a genius in searching observation, a creative thinker of inexorable logic. His whole life work was characterized by absolute honesty and scientific integrity. He worked for neurology, not for the greater glory of Babinski. He made little use of laboratory and technical procedures; he was a clinical neurologist *par excellence*, guided by the maxim *Observatio summa lex*.

Some trends of modern neurology toward undue mechanization make one think that a plea "Back to Babinski!" would not be without justification.

SAN FRANCISCO, CALIFORNIA   ROBERT WARTENBERG

References

[1]*Oeuvre scientifique: recueil des principaux travaux* publié par les soins de Barré, Chaillous, Charpentier, et al. Paris, Masson, 1934 (contains bibliography). [2]C. rend. Soc. biol., 1896, 3: 207–208. [3]Bull. Soc. méd. hôp. Paris, 1897, 14: 1098–1103. [4]Bull. Soc. fr. derm. syph., 1899, 10: 347–352. [5]Rev. neur., Par., 1899, 7: 784–785. [6]Tr. Internat. Congr. Med., London, 1913. Section XI, Neuropath. pt. 1; p. 1–58. [7]Rev. neur., Par., 1902, 10: 1013. [8]Bull. méd., Par., 1912, 26: 929–936. [9]Rev. neur., Par. 1922, 38: 1049–1081. Brain, Lond., 1922, 45: 149–184. [10]Rev. neur. Par., 1902, 10: 358–365. [11]*Ibid.*, 1900, 8: 531–533. [12]*Ibid.*, 1912, 23: 1–4.

References to Biography and Works: 1) Arch. Neur. Psychiat., Chic., 1933, 29: 168–174 (contains partial bibliography; Fulton). 2) Bull. méd. (suppl.), 1934, 48: 1–8 (Charpentier). 3) J. Am. M. Ass., 1947, 135: 763–767 (Wartenberg).

ROBERT BÁRÁNY (1876–1936)

*B*árány was born and brought up in Vienna, and it was there that he received his university training. After graduating in medicine in 1900, he became assistant in the medical clinic of von Noorden in Frankfurt-am-Main, worked in neurology with Kraepelin in Heidelberg, and then went to Paris. In 1903 he returned to Vienna. Among his teachers was Sigmund Freud, of whom he liked to tell this story: Freud maintained that dreams are an expression of desire (Wunschträume). He said to his students: "If you cannot explain your dreams then come and see me." Bárány did so and described for Freud a dream which had nothing to do with *desire*. Freud said, "That is very simple. You had the *desire* to contradict me."

It was when he found a place in the ear clinic of Adam Politzer (later under Urbantschitsch) in Vienna in 1905 that Bárány was able to devote himself to the work for which he is best known. He was impressed by the rhythmic nystagmus produced by syringing the ears, a phenomenon which, as he discovered, was related to the temperature of the water. From his painstaking observations he was able to analyze the factors governing labyrinthine stimulation.[1-5] There was always a question in Vienna of priority in this field, for Bárány is said to have commenced working on the labyrinth after he had witnessed Spitzer's demonstration of labyrinthine nystagmus in experimental animals. The matter was even more discussed when, in 1914, Bárány received the Nobel Prize for his work on the physiology and pathology of the vestibular system.

Bárány was the first to arrive at a real understanding of recurrent labyrinthine vertigo, which previously had been confused with cerebellar disease, epilepsy, and a variety of other conditions. Recurrent labyrinthine vertigo was originally described by Prosper Ménière (1799–1862) in 1861,[6] but his case was a symptomatic form of the disorder (due either to leukemic hemorrhage into the labyrinth or to acute purulent labyrinthitis), not Ménière's disease as it is now known.

Bárány knew that altering the position of the head had a decided effect on labyrinthine stimulation, for he reported that the disagreeable sensations he had experienced while riding a scenic railway in a

Wien, April 1913

Dr Robert Bárány

Vienna amusement park were alleviated by flexing his head 90°,[7] but it was Quix who was the first to observe that the effects of changing the position of the head were due to an alteration in the relation of the otolith organs to the plane of motion[8] and to demonstrate that VIIIth nerve section renders animals insensitive to motion.[9] An-

Portrait, courtesy of the Army Medical Library, Washington, D. C.

other of Bárány's important observations was that neck muscles send proprioceptor impulses to the extraocular nuclei for the reflex control of eye movements.[10]   Because of his many contributions, Bárány may be regarded as a successor to such men as Purkinje, Goltz and Flourens, and, in the domain of motion sickness, a predecessor of Magnus and de Kleijn,[11] of Sjöberg (who, in a classical work, first demonstrated the indispensability of the labyrinths in the production of motion sickness),[12,13] of Spiegel,[14] and of Bard.[9]

Following the suggestion of Bolk that the cerebellum must be organized on a plan of somatomotor localization, Bárány set to work to test this view. He believed that the vermis is concerned with co-ordinated movements of the trunk, and the hemispheres with those of the extremities,[15] and that the floccular cortex influences eye movements.[16]

Bárány was made Privatdozent at the University of Vienna in 1908. Shortly before World War I he was appointed Professor Extraordinarius. During the war he served in the Austrian army until his capture by the Russians. He was still a prisoner in the fortress of Przmyzl when chosen for the highest honor of his career, the Nobel Prize for Physiology and Medicine in 1914. Prince Carl of Sweden at length prevailed upon the Czar to release Bárány, who then proceeded to Sweden for formal acceptance of the prize.

During this trip to Sweden, Bárány was invited to take the chair of otology in the University of Upsala, which he accepted in 1917, at first as Privatdozent and Titular Professor, and from 1926 as Ordinarius. He built up a great reputation as an aural surgeon, particularly in the surgical treatment of deafness, sinus disorders, and cerebral and cerebellar abscesses.

His explanation of the division of the granular layer of the visual cortex in mammals with binocular vision is well known.[17]   Perhaps it will not be long before his explanation of the mechanism of hearing will become general in application. His interpretation of neuroses as being the result of closed chain activity foreshadowed later utilizations of this theory by Kuhlenbeck,[18] Kubie, Hinsey and Ranson, de Nó, and Rosenblueth.

Bárány adapted himself well to his new country, Sweden, where his activities as philanthropist, pacifist and humanist brought him further prominence. It was upon his instigation that the International Academy of Politics and Social Science for the Promotion of World Peace was founded in Sweden in 1929. Besides being a prolific writer (his papers number almost 200), he found time to edit scientific journals.

Bárány was essentially a man of theory. He would develop a theory and then put it to the experimental test. A victim of insomnia, he would lie in bed until the early hours thinking, thinking, thinking. His dependence on theory is illustrated by the following story: While he was in Berlin in Oskar and Cécile Vogt's laboratory he and the Vogts were performing an experiment on a monkey. Oskar Vogt syringed cold water in one ear and simultaneously stimulated the cortex of the same side while Cécile Vogt and Bárány watched the direction in which nystagmus occurred. On cessation of the ocular movements Bárány declared that they were to the left, whereas Cécile argued that they were to the right. The argument grew more and more heated for the ensuing five minutes. The next day Bárány came into the laboratory and stated that during the night he had reconsidered the matter. He conceded that Cécile was right. He had allowed himself to be so influenced by theory that he failed in the observation. The same happened to Bárány several times in the Vogts' laboratory. The poorness of his memory for observation could well serve as an explanation for his forgetfulness of the work of Spitzer, referred to in the foregoing; there was no question but that he was most honest and upright.

Bárány died after having been afflicted with thalamic pain for a year and a half. Had he survived two weeks longer he would have witnessed an appropriate celebration of the anniversary of his 60th birthday. His death occurred 100 years after the birth of his teacher, Adam Politzer, of whom Bárány was a worthy successor.

NEW YORK CITY   FRED A. METTLER

References

[1]Arch. Ohr. &c. Heilk., 1906, 68: 1–30.   [2]Untersuchungen über den vom Vestibularapparat des Ohres reflektorisch ausgelösten rhythmischen Nystagmus und seine Begleiterscheinungen.   Berlin, Coblenz, 1906. [3]Physiologie und Pathologie (Funktionsprüfung) des Bogengang-Apparates beim Menschen. Leipzig, Deuticke, 1907.   [4]Verh. Deut. otolog. Ges., 1911, 20: 37–168 et seq. (with Wittmaack).   [5]Verh. Ges. deut. Naturforsch., 1913, 85 (I.Teil): 241–250.   [6]Gaz. méd. Par., 1861, 3.sér., 16:

29.   [7]Lewandowsky, M. H., *Handbuch der Neurologie,* Berlin, 1912,
Vol. 3, Specielle Neurologie.   [8]Arch. internat. laryng., Par., 1922, *28:*
16–25.   [9]Physiol. Rev., 1949, *29:* 311–369 (Tyler and Bard).   [10]Acta
otolar., Stockh., 1918, *1:* 97–102.   [11]*Körperstellung.* Berlin, Springer,
1924 (Magnus).   [12]Acta otolar., Stockh., 1929, *13:* 343–347.   [13]*Ibid.,*
suppl. 14, 1931.   [14]War Med., Chic., 1944, *6:* 283–290 (with Oppen-
heimer, Henny and Wycis).   [15]Wien. klin. Wschr., 1913, *26:* 277.
[16]Jahrb. Psychiat. Neur., Wien, 1941, *36:* 631–651.   [17]Riv. otoneuroft.,
1927, *4:* 141–149.   [18]*Vorlesungen über das Zentralnervensystem der
Wirbeltiere.*   Jena, Fischer, 1927; p. 249.

References to Biography: 1) Hygiea, Stockh., 1936, *98:* 241–248 (Ny-
lén).   2) Hospitalstidende, 1916, *58:* 1171–1174 (Schmiegelow).   3)
Das medizinische Wien. Geschichte. Werden. Würdigung. ed. 2.   Jena,
Urban & Schwarzenberg, 1947; p. 420–421 (Schönbauer).

HENRY CHARLTON BASTIAN (1837–1915)

*B*astian was born at Truro, Cornwall.   He studied at University
College, graduated from London University in 1861, and received the M.D. in 1866.   The next year, when only 30 years of age,
he became professor of pathologic anatomy at University College
where at the time the distinguished Sir J. Russell Reynolds held
sway in the teaching of neurology.   Gowers, eight years Bastian's
junior, was also at the University College, just having qualified in
medicine by taking his M.R.C.S. (1867).   Bastian later held the
chair in medicine, with neurology his special interest.   For many
years (1884–98) he was referee for the Crown in cases of question-
able insanity.

Bastian's activities and interests centered around two entirely different fields, in both of which he indulged frequently in philosophical
conjecture.   In his earlier years and again after his retirement, he
was concerned with the controversy as to the origin of life and
heterogenesis.[1,2]   His other chief interest was clinical neurology,
which at that time was emerging as an exact science.   As a teacher
in this discipline, he gained international recognition for his methods
of diagnosis and the sharpness of his intellect.   He was also a neuroanatomist of note, describing in 1867 a degenerating tract in the
spinal cord, which from 1880 on, however, became known as
"Gowers' tract."   Gowers did not appreciate this distinction for he

Very truly Yours
H. Charlton Bastian

was averse to eponymic designations. Bastian's volume on *The brain as an organ of mind* (New York, Appleton, 1880), translated into French and German, was an outstanding contribution; he himself felt it to be his greatest. This was followed by other books, all based on his studies and lectures at the University Hospital and at the National Hospital, Queen Square. He was much interested in the terms "hysterical" and "functional," and condemned the practice of using them synonymously. He maintained that if hysteria were defined as a neurosis in accordance with the views of Charcot and Briquet, then all the cases of functional spinal paralysis should be placed in some other category. In 1887 appeared his important

Portrait, courtesy of Dr. Maurice Genty, Académie de Médecine, Paris, France.

paper on *The "muscular sense"; its nature and cortical localization,*[3] discussed vigorously and on some points heatedly by Ferrier, Ross, Hughlings Jackson, Horsley, Crichton-Browne, and others. In crossing swords with Ferrier he was "compelled to point out" that Ferrier's doctrines "did not hang together at all well" and were "even made up of contradictory statements." Bastian also contended that "neither on physiological nor on psychological grounds was it needful to postulate the existence of motor centers in the cortex."

In 1897, Bastian delivered the Lumleian Lectures on aphasia and other speech defects, which formed the basis of a classical treatise on the subject.[4] He held that aphasia depends either on damage to one or the other of the four centers in the cerebral cortex which are concerned in the production of spoken and written language, or on interruption of the neural pathways connecting them. In 1869 he clearly delineated speech impairment[5] of the type described five years later by Wernicke as sensory aphasia, since known as "Wernicke's aphasia." His lectures and studies on aphasia were published in book form in 1898[4]; had he accomplished nothing else, these would have established him as a pioneer in neurology.

He was the first to show that in total transverse lesions of the upper spinal cord the reflexes below the level of the lesion are abolished and muscle tonus lost (Bastian's Law).[6] He was very critical of the excessive emphasis given by physicians of that day to "inflammation," and effectively opposed the practice of diagnosing as "myelitis" all kinds of transverse lesions of the cord.

Shortly after Bastian retired from University College (1897) he gave up the practice of neurology in order to resume his studies on biology. Contrary to the views of Pasteur and Tyndall, he denied that life always develops from pre-existing life, prepounding as an alternative the doctrine of abiogenesis. His painstaking experiments formed the basis of many articles and books, some of which were illustrated by his own photomicrographs. The firm beliefs he held in this realm were, however, not shared by others. He deeply resented the indifference, and even ridicule, with which his ideas were received, but he continued to hold fast to his faith until his death, which occurred at Chesham Bois, Bucks, when he was 75.

NEW YORK CITY   LOTHAR B. KALINOWSKY

References

[1]*The evolution of life.* London, Methuen, 1907.   [2]*Studies in hetero-genesis.* 2 vol. London, Williams & Norgate, 1901.   [3]Brain, Lond., 1888, *10:* 1–137; p. 119–120.   [4]*A treatise on aphasia and other speech defects.* London, Lewis, 1898.   [5]Brit. & For. M.-Chir. Rev., Lond., 1869, *43:* 209–236.   [6]Med.-Chir. Tr., Lond., 1890, *73:* 151–217.

References to Biography: 1) Lancet, Lond., 1915, *2:* 1220–1224 (contains bibliography; not signed).   2) Brit. M. J., 1915, *2:* 795–796 (not signed).

VLADIMIR MIKHAILOVICH BEKHTEREV (1857–1927)

*B*ekhterev (or Bechterew) was born in Sarali, a small village in the forests of Viatka Territory between the great bend of the Volga and the foothills of the Ural Mountains. There was a notable conformity in the physique and the personality of the man and the rugged austerity of the country whence he came. As seen in his middle 50's, Bekhterev was an arresting figure. Rather heavy-set, square-shouldered, with massive head slightly thrust forward, piercing black eyes under black, bushy brows, and clear-cut, characterful features framed by a silvery beard and grey locks of hair swept to one side, he could well serve as a prototype for a romanticized painting of a northern woodsman.

At the age of 16, Bekhterev entered the Imperial Medico-Surgical Academy at St. Petersburg, from which he was graduated in 1878. He remained at the Academy as assistant to the psychiatrist Merzheievskii (or Merjeievsky), a great teacher, widely traveled, who had been influenced by Magnan of Paris and by Darwin.

The last quarter of the 19th century was an heroic period in the history of neurology. The foundation of knowledge upon which the edifice of anatomy, physiology and pathology of the nervous system was later reared was being laid by the great men whose memory is honored in this volume. During that period the bed of the river of European civilization seemed rather definitely to shift toward the countries of central Europe. Those on the periphery of the cultural watershed fed generously into that common stream their youthful, creative energies. In 1884 Bekhterev received a traveling scholarship of approximately eighteen months. During the

winter of 1884–85 he worked under Flechsig, who was then applying his myelogenetic method to the study of nervous pathways. Young Bekhterev put his shoulder to the task with telling effect. It was while with Flechsig in Leipzig that Bekhterev described the superior vestibular nucleus[1] which bears his name. Among many subsequent contributions, the first descriptions of the central tegmental tract, the connections of the inferior olive, the component fibers of the cerebellar peduncles, and the nuclear complexes in the reticular formation of the tegmentum were made by Bekhterev.[2] Dur-

Portrait, courtesy of Prof. Hugo Spatz, Giessen, Germany.

ing his relatively brief scholarship abroad, Bekhterev also visited du Bois-Reymond, Meynert, Westphal, Charcot, and studied under Wundt. Yet it seems that Flechsig influenced him the most. Developmental momenta and myelogenesis remained the cardinal frame of reference in Bekhterev's scientific thought and method.

On returning to Russia in 1885, he was made professor at the University of Kazan. In 1893 he succeeded his old teacher, Merzheievskii, in St. Petersburg. During the following 21 years Bekhterev showed the full measure of his stature as a thinker, investigator, teacher, and organizer of research in neurology and social biology. Functional anatomy of the brain, experimental psychology, and clinical neurology were three fields in which Bekhterev carved out a place for himself somewhat as his ancestors must have cut the clearings in the primeval forest beyond the Volga. He was extremely versatile in his academic interests and fields of research, which embraced hypnosis and even psychosurgery (with Puusepp, or Pussep).[3,4] A contemporary and faculty colleague of Ivan Pavlov, he approached the problem of the relationship between the brain and behavior as an anatomist, experimental psychologist and clinician rather than a single-purposed physiologist, which Pavlov so eminently was. Bekhterev used the method of conditioned reflexes extensively in his work. As a pupil of Wundt and Flechsig, he called them "associative reflexes." Instead of the visceral response (salivation) which Pavlov employed as a natural development from his earlier studies on the physiology of the digestive tract and whose interest in "psychical secretion" led him to the study of higher nervous activity, Bekhterev chose to use the somatic response (skeletal movement). In this choice of the "indicator," Bekhterev probably put himself at a methodologic disadvantage, for a somatic motor response is less readily amenable to quantitation than a visceral response, such as drops of saliva. There was a keen and at times spirited competition between the two masters and their schools. In the long run, Pavlov came out the better of the two, but Bekhterev, although his work was publicly denounced,[7] made, nevertheless, a great contribution. In his elaboration of what he came to call "psychoreflexology,"[5] he and his pupils produced an impressive amount of factual data, many of which gained a peculiar relevance in application to present-day problems of neurology. For example, the cortical representation of visceral functions of blood pressure, of pupillary, gastrointestinal, urovesical and anorectal motility, and of glandular secretory activity, was intensely explored by Bekhterev during the period between 1890 and 1910.[2,5]

From 1913 on, he devoted most of his time to the Psychoneurological Institute in Leningrad, which he had founded in 1907. After 1905 the problems of abnormal social behavior, "mass" behavior and "collective" reflexology became his absorbing interests. Amidst his research and teaching activities, he was a widely sought practitioner and consultant. His close friend and pupil, Ludwig Puusepp (1875–1942),[6] able Estonian neurosurgeon, related that it was customary for Bekhterev to make appointments at his office as late as midnight or even in the small hours of the morning. Some of his former patients tell of the dramatic experience they had of being ushered into the heavily draped and carpeted library and beholding, behind a huge desk laden with books and manuscripts, the grey-locked, bearded head of a mystic-looking man who silently transfixed them with his glance as they approached him. He died at the age of 70, the day after his return from the All-Union Neurological Congress in Moscow, over which he presided as the last act of his many-sided and fruitful scientific life.

BOSTON, MASSACHUSETTS   PAUL I. YAKOVLEV

References

[1]Neur. Cbl., 1885, 3: 145–147.   [2]*Die Leitungsbahnen im Gehirn und Rückenmark; ein Handbuch für das Studium des Nervensystems.* Leipzig, Besold, 1894 (trans. by Weinberg from Russian original, 1877–78). [3]Arch. internat. neur., Par., 1912, 10.sér., 2: 1–17 *et seq.*   [4]*Die Funktionen der Nervencentra.* 3 vol. Jena, Fischer, 1908–11 (trans. by Weinberg from Russian original, 1903–07).   [5]*Objective Psychologie oder Psychoreflexologie: die Lehre von den Assoziationsreflexen.* Leipzig, Teubner, 1913.   [6]Walker (ed.), *A history of neurological surgery.* Baltimore, Williams & Wilkins, 1951 (biography on Puusepp, by A. F. Thomson); p. 270–271.   [7]Science, 1951, *114:* 227–233 (London).

Reference to Biography: Arch. Psychiat., Berl., 1928, 83: 677–886 (Pines).

MORITZ BENEDIKT (1835–1920)

Moritz Benedikt was born in Eisenstadt, Hungary, which at that time was part of the Austro-Hungarian Empire. He lived all his life in Vienna where he obtained his medical education under such celebrities as Hyrtl, Brücke, Skoda and Oppolzer. After graduation, Benedikt joined the army and participated in the military campaigns of 1859–61. On his return to Vienna, he was appointed Dozent to the University. In 1868 he became Extraordinarius, and in 1899 Ordinarius of electrotherapy.

Throughout his long life, Benedikt exhibited extraordinary activity as teacher, author, medico-legal expert, lecturer, clinician, traveler, and critic of art and drama. He was one of the founders of the General Poliklinik of Vienna and was greatly interested in sociological problems in connection with crime, tuberculosis and alcoholism. His work in criminology antedated that of Lombroso, for he had been interested in the criminal phases of anthropology (termed by Benedikt "criminal anthropology") since 1858. He boldly and ably maintained that a criminal is a sick individual, a degenerate possessing abnormal anatomic and physiologic traits. He based his views on extensive personal observations of inmates of prisons in various countries and on examinations of their skulls and brains.[1,2]

The contributions of Benedikt were varied and numerous in many other fields of neurology. Electrotherapy, for instance, was effectively popularized by him. In recognition of his activities in this field, the results of which are embodied in his two books on the subject,[3,4] he was promoted to Ordinarius. His work on the innervation of the choroid plexus[5] is of some historic interest; he described a nerve in the floor of the IVth ventricle which, according to him, originated in a special nucleus and supplied the blood vessels and the villi of the choroid plexus. This nerve, which he termed the XIIIth cranial nerve, was said to influence the circulation of various areas in the brain. Still widely quoted are his classic observations on the occupational neuroses, in which he distinguished three types: spastic, tremulous and paralytic.[3] He was the first to describe the syndrome of midbrain disease characterized by ipsilateral IIId nerve palsy and contralateral involuntary movements sometimes preceded

by hemiplegia,[6] and thus his name became an eponym alongside that of Sir Hermann David Weber (1823–1918), of London, who, in 1863, had set his stamp on the midbrain syndrome characterized by IIIrd nerve palsy on one side and hemiplegia on the other.[7] For an account of the many brain-stem syndromes the reader is referred to the monumental work by Claude and Lévy-Valensi.[8] Articles on the contributions of these two men have recently come into print.[13,14]

It should be emphasized that Benedikt lived in times of economic, political and scientific upheavals, when persons of exceptional ability and energy were needed to carry on the fight for progressive ideas

Portrait, courtesy of the Army Medical Library, Washington, D. C.

and to keep them alive. The activities of such a colorful person as Benedikt could not fail to arouse the admiration of many investigators. These included Ernest Julius Remak (1848–1911), whose work on lead poisoning[9] raised him above the rank and file, Wilhelm Griesinger (1817–68), Romberg's successor, noted for his work on pseudohypertrophic muscular dystrophy,[10] and Vladimir Aleksandrovitsch Betz (1834–94), of Russia, known for his studies of the giant cells of the motor cortex.[11,12] Benedikt's eloquent dissertations at local, national and international gatherings, where he was a familiar figure, exerted a leavening power not only on the medical profession but on human welfare as well.

CHICAGO, ILLINOIS   GEORGE B. HASSIN

References

[1]*Anatomische Studien an Verbrecher-Gehirnen für Anthropologen, Mediciner, Juristen und Psychologen bearbeitet.* Wien, Braumüller, 1879. (Engl. trans. by Fowler: *Anatomical studies upon brains of criminals.* New York, Wood, 1881.) [2]*Kraniometrie und Kephalometrie. Vorlesungen gehalten an der Wiener Poliklinik.* Wien u. Leipzig, Urban & Schwarzenberg, 1888. [3]*Electrotherapie.* Wien, Tendler, 1868. [4]*Nervenpathologie und Elektrotherapie.* Leipzig, Fues, 1874–76. [5]Virchows Arch., 1874, 59: 395–400. [6]Bull. méd., Par., 1889, 3: 547–548. [7]Med.-Chir. Tr., Lond., 1863, 46: 121–139. [8]*Maladies du cervelet et de l'isthme de l'encéphale (pédoncule, protubérance, bulbe).* Paris, Baillière, 1922. [9]Arch. Psychiat., Berl., 1875, 6: 1–56. [10]Arch. Heilk., 1865, 6: 1–13. [11]Zbl. med. Wiss., 1874, 12: 578–580 *et seq.* [12]*Ibid.,* 1881, 19: 193–195 *et seq.* [13]Encéphale, 1950, 39: 373–412 (Delay). [14]*Ibid.,* 1950, 39: 441–444 (Baruk).

Reference to Biography: *Aus meinem Leben. Erinnerungen und Erörterungen.* Wien, Konegen, 1906 (Benedikt).

DÉSIRÉ MAGLOIRE BOURNEVILLE (1840–1909)

*B*ourneville was the son of a small Normandy landowner in the little village of Garancières (Eure). He studied medicine in Paris. During a severe cholera epidemic in Amiens, in 1866, he volunteered his services and worked so tirelessly that at the end of the siege he was presented with a gold watch which bore an inscrip-

Désiré Magloire Bourneville

tion expressing the city's gratitude. This was his first official recognition.

During the Franco-Prussian War he volunteered as surgeon in the 160th Bataillon of the Garde Nationale. Later he became assistant medical officer at the field hospital of the Jardin des Plantes and finally—even though he was a well established physician—resumed his internship at the Pitié which then was covered by fire from German artillery. When Paris was under the Commune in 1871, the violent revolutionaries wanted to execute their wounded political enemies, but Bourneville, by virtue of his authority and with great courage effectively resisted their demands.

Bourneville's medical schooling and lines of thought were influenced by his close association with other leading physicians of his time, among them Noël Pascal, Claude Bernard, and the psychiatrist Delasiauve, who was his teacher. He began in 1872 the editing of Charcot's *Leçons sur les maladies du système nerveux faites à la Salpêtrière* (Paris, Delahaye, 1872–73). He founded *Le progrès*

Portrait from *Nos grands médecins d'aujourd'hui*, Paris, 1891; by H. Bianchon.

médical in 1873, and, under the patronage of Charcot, the *Archives de neurologie* in 1880. Most of Bourneville's papers were published in the *Recherches cliniques et thérapeutiques sur l'épilepsie, l'hystérie et l'idiotie*.

Bourneville's name is linked with our knowledge of tuberous sclerosis (Bourneville's disease), which he established as a morbid entity.[1,2] Almost simultaneously the disorder was described by Hartdegen,[3] who called it "glioma gangliocellulare cerebri congenitum." Bourneville also made a number of significant clinical contributions to the problems of myxedema and cretinism.[4,5] Stimulated by English work on mongolism, Bourneville, at the turn of the century, contributed a series of articles on this subject.[6] He was physician to the pediatric service of the Bicêtre from 1879 to 1905; after reaching the legal retirement age he remained in charge of the Fondation Vallée at the Bicêtre. He founded the first day school for special instruction of defective children in Paris, a movement which later took hold in many countries. On Saturdays he held open-house at the Bicêtre in which his charges performed exercises and dances to the accompaniment of a band composed of idiots, epileptics, and spastics; the trombonist had wooden legs.

No wonder that Bourneville was celebrated as the leading continental authority on all that concerned mentally abnormal children and was acknowledged as a great psychiatrist and scholar, whose modesty and brilliance commanded both love and respect.

Among French physicians Bourneville stands out as embodying fully the French ideal of *un homme des pensées et actions*. He combined the rare virtues of a thinker who adhered unswervingly to his convictions and a man who never hesitated to put his thoughts into action. He was councilman at Paris in 1876 and deputy in 1883. It is readily understandable that his reforming zeal involved him frequently in differences with his colleagues and exposed him to attacks by the clerical party. But when he died at the age of 69, his funeral was an occasion in which the profession, the Government and the people participated with equal mourning.

WAVERLEY, MASSACHUSETTS   CLEMENS E. BENDA

References

[1]Arch. neurol., Par., 1880, *1:* 69–91.   [2]Recherch. clin. thérap. sur l'épileps. [etc.], Par., 1882, *2:* 3–16 (with Bonnaire).   [3]Arch. Psychiat.,

Berl., 1880, *11:* 117–131.   [4]Recherch. clin. thérap. sur l'épileps. [etc.],
Par., 1901, *21:* 123–129.   [5]*Ibid.*, 1897, *17:* 144–178.   [6]*Ibid.*, 1902,
22: 136–147.

References to Biography: 1) Rev. philanthrop., Par., 1909, *25:* 174–180
(Thulié).   2) Progr. méd., Par., 1909, 3.sér., *25:* 293–295 (Noir).

SIR BYROM BRAMWELL (1847–1931)

*B*yrom Bramwell was born at North Shields, Northumberland,
where his father and grandfather were engaged in general practice. Educated at Cheltenham College and Edinburgh University,
he took his degree in 1869. The eminent neurologist, Laycock, then
professor of medicine in Edinburgh, thought so highly of him that
he awarded him the Medal in Medicine, and invited him, upon
graduation, to become his University assistant. Tempting though
this offer was, Bramwell felt it his duty to return to North Shields
and help his father with his busy practice. For five years Bramwell
was strenuously engaged in a large general practice and gathered
experience which in later years he frequently referred to as most
invaluable. His subsequent reputation was based essentially upon
his personal experience and characterized by exact observation, exceptional powers of logical inference, careful recording, and unusual clarity of expression.

Appointed in 1874, at the early age of 27, honorary physician and
pathologist to the Newcastle Royal Infirmary and lecturer on clinical
medicine in the Durham University School of Medicine (where
three years previously, while still in general practice, he had held
the appointment of lecturer on medical jurisprudence), he left North
Shields and commenced practice as a consulting physician in New-
castle-upon-Tyne. The *Transactions of the Durham and Northumberland Medical Society* of this time contain many of his early contributions.

Ambitious for a larger sphere for his activities, and probably
tempted by the opening of the new Royal Infirmary that year, he resigned his appointments at Newcastle and settled permanently as a
consultant in Edinburgh in 1879. A course of a hundred lectures on
medicine, which he gave each winter, and short courses on medical
diagnosis, which he instituted, made him a favorite with the students. In 1882 he was appointed pathologist and in 1885, assistant

Sir Byrom Bramwell

Portrait, courtesy of Dr. Edwin Bramwell, Edinburgh, Scotland.   (Photographer: Swan Watson, Edinburgh.)

physician to the Royal Infirmary. One morning a week he taught
in the out-patient department—this was the only opportunity the
assistant physicians then had of teaching clinically—and on this day
the students attended in such numbers that he had to obtain special
permission, a unique privilege, to hold his clinic in one of the large
clinical theatres. After 1897, when he became a full physician to the
Royal Infirmary, his Wednesday Clinics were always thronged. To
his disappointment and that of his many friends and admirers he was
not appointed to the chair of medicine on Sir Thomas Grainger
Stewart's death in 1900, an appointment which undoubtedly would
have been received with acclamation both at home and abroad.

Byrom Bramwell was a great general clinician, though his name
will perhaps be best remembered in connection with neurology.
Two of his books are classics: that on diseases of the spinal cord,[1]
which was widely translated, and that on intracranial tumors.[2] In
the latter, which was published in 1888, appears the significant
statement, which anticipated by many years the pioneering works
of Erdheim (1904) and Aschner (1912) on the functional significance of the hypothalamus: "Tumours of the pituitary body are in
many instances attended by an excessive development of the sub-
cutaneous fat, and in some cases with the presence of sugar in the
urine, or with simple polyuria (diabetes insipidus). Whether these
symptoms are due to the fact that the pituitary body itself is diseased, or whether, as seems more likely, to the secondary results
which tumours in this situation produce in the surrounding cerebral
tissue, has not yet been decided." Bramwell contributed *inter
alia* a monumental 3-volume atlas of clinical medicine[3] and a monograph on diseases of the blood-forming organs and endocrine
glands.[4] Eight volumes of the quarterly publication *Clinical studies*
(1903–11) carry a record of his teaching at the bedside and in the
clinic.

A man of particularly robust physique, of boundless energy and
great powers of concentration, a strenuous, untiring and thorough
worker, every moment of his day from early morning to bedtime
was, in his earlier years, fully occupied. Bramwell's activities were
at their height at a time when attention was focused upon the application of morbid anatomy to symptomatology, the differentiation of
clinical entities, and the significance of signs and symptoms. A pro-
fuse note-taker and coordinator, he was able to summarize and re-

view his personal experience upon the topic of the moment. He had no use for "the textbook clinician" nor for the man whose thoughts were always "in the air"; but for a great scientific thinker (and here Hughlings Jackson was his prototype) he had an admiration amounting almost to reverence. He took little interest in medical politics, and committee work did not appeal to him.

Honors naturally came to him and in 1925 he received a knighthood for "services to medicine." An honor, which as a neurologist he highly appreciated, was an invitation to deliver the Seventh Hughlings Jackson Lecture in 1927—the previous lecturers were Hughlings Jackson (1897), Hitzig (1900), Broadbent (1903), Horsley (1906), Gowers (1909), and Henry Head (1920)—but for reasons of health he was obliged to decline the invitation.

Although Bramwell's name is not attached to any disease, syndrome, physical sign or symptom, there are few aspects of neurology to the knowledge of which he did not significantly contribute. No one was more aware of Bramwell's greatness as a clinical neurologist than Harvey Cushing, who in his Lister Memorial Lecture in 1930[5] made this comment: "It has been said that if some unusual clinical condition turns up concerning which one seeks information, an account of it is likely to be found in Jonathan Hutchinson's Archives. To this I would like to add, particularly for the benefit of neurologists, that if Hutchinson fails, then try Byrom Bramwell."

EDINBURGH, SCOTLAND   EDWIN BRAMWELL

References

[1]*The diseases of the spinal cord.* Edinburgh, Maclachlan & Stewart, 1882. (ed. 2, Pentland, 1884). *Lectures on diseases of the spinal cord.* Edinburgh, Pentland, 1895. [2]*Intracranial tumors.* Edinburgh, Pentland, 1888. [3]*Atlas of clinical medicine.* Edinburgh, Constable, 1892–96. [4]*Diseases of the blood-forming organs and ductless glands.* Edinburgh, Oliver & Boyd, 1899. [5]Lancet, Lond., 1930, 2: 119–175.

References to Biography: 1) Brit. M. J., 1931, 1: 823–826 (Drummond, Hutchison, S. A. Kinnier Wilson *et al.*). 2) Lancet, Lond., 1931, 1: 1108 (Gulland). 3) Edinburgh M. J., 1931, n.s., 38: 444–447 (R.W.P.).

ÉDOUARD BRISSAUD (1852–1909)

*B*rissaud was a neurologist's neurologist. He grew up in the school of Charcot and Lasègue, wrote his thesis on the permanent contractures in hemiplegia, in which he showed that hemiplegia due to pontile lesions may occasionally be of the spasmodic type[1]; he rose steadily in the ranks from interne to agrégé, taking the chair of medicine in 1899 and of internal medicine the following year.

His interest in neurology and neuropathology was early excited by his work at the Salpêtrière, and both in the clinic and in the laboratory he toiled to cultivate the fields which Charcot planted. He described in detail the double innervation of the face, based upon the dissociation between the voluntary and mimetic expression as seen in cases of pseudobulbar palsy, and he contrasted this condition with the masked facies of parkinsonism.[2] Referring to the tremor of the tongue, mandible and lips in a patient with paralysis agitans, Brissaud used the unforgettable expression: He "murmurs an interminable litany."[3] He had the astuteness to conclude that "the localization of Parkinson's disease must be subthalamic or peduncular,"[3] and a decade or so afterward the lesions were found in these and at higher basal ganglion levels by Manschot,[4] Jelgersma[5] and Lewy.[6,7] Subsequently the pathologic study of paralysis agitans (a term coined apparently by Marshall Hall in 1841[8]) was rounded out by such authorities as C. and O. Vogt,[9] Bielschowsky[10] and Lotmar.[16]

Brissaud also described tics, spasms and torticollis, but rather on clinical than anatomical lines.[3,11–12] Tic without characteristic march, he said, consists of a series of fleeting movements without uniformity —a step, a shrug, frown, sigh, crack of the fingers, exclamation.[3] Brissaud also found time to publish a text on the anatomy of the human brain, illustrated by his own hand.[13] One of his major contributions to French neurology was the founding, with Pierre Marie, of the *Revue neurologique*.

Brissaud ventured into other fields: psychiatry, at the instigation of Lasègue; folklore in medicine[14]; hygiene for asthmatics.[15] In his medicolegal work he became known as the national expert on injuries in relation to conversion hysteria. Breaking with Charcot on the organic nature of hysteria, he aligned himself with Babinski, saying that one could always differentiate between organic and func-

Édouard Brissaud

tional disorders, but that the distinction between conversion hysteria and simulation was sometimes impossible. "A symptom that cannot be simulated is not a symptom of hysteria." Brissaud had a wide field for his expert testimony following passage of a compensation law in 1898.

Brissaud brought informality to the classroom and the laboratory. He even gave up the top hat, that symbol of professorial majesty.

Portrait, courtesy of Dr. Maurice Genty, Académie de Médecine, Paris, France.

His verbal sallies brought delight to students. At the same time he emphasized honesty and ethics. Work for him seemed altogether effortless. He was a target for the cartoonist, who embellished his generous paunch to overflowing. It was not hard to see that culinary art was one of his chief diversions.

Brissaud died of a brain tumor at the early age of 57. Horsley operated on him in Paris but it was too late. One of his last wishes, that he be buried without benefit of the church—for he considered himself a freethinker—was not granted.

WASHINGTON, D. C.   WALTER FREEMAN

References

[1]*Recherches anatomo-pathologiques et physiologiques sur la contracture permanente des hémiplégiques.* Thèse de Paris, 1880.   [2]*Leçons sur les maladies nerveuses.* Paris, Masson, 1895; p. 476.   [3]*Ibid.,* vol. 2, 1899. (Trans. of phrase by Wilson in his *Neurology,* 1940.)   [4]Psychiat. Neur. Bl., Amst., 1904, *8:* 597–775.   [5]Neur. Cbl., 1908, *27:* 995–996. [6]Lewandowsky, M. H., *Handbuch der Neurologie.* Berlin, 1902, *3:* 920– 933.   [7]Deut. Zschr. Nervenh., 1913, *50:* 50–55.   [8]*On the diseases and derangements of the nervous system.* London, Baillière, 1841.   [9]J. Psychol. Neur., 1920, 25, Erg. Heft 3: 279–462.   [10]*Ibid.,* 1922, *27:* 233–288.   [11]Rev. neur., Par., 1896, *4:* 417–431.   [12]Presse méd., 1908, 16: 234–236 (with Sicard).   [13]*Anatomie du cerveau de l'homme; morphologie des hémisphères cérébraux, ou cerveau proprement dit.* Paris, Masson, 1893.   [14]*Histoire des expressions populaires relatives à l'anatomie, à la physiologie et à la médecine.* Paris, Chamerot, 1888.   [15]*L'hygiène des asthmatiques.* Paris, Masson, 1896.   [16]*Die Stammganglien und die extrapyramidalmotorischen Syndrome.* Berlin, Springer, 1926.

References to Biography: 1) Rev. méd., Par., 1910, *24:* 1–3 (Ballet). 2) *Ibid.,* 1910, *24:* 195–200 (Dupré).   3) Rev. neur., Par., 1910, *18:* 1–4 (Souques).

PIERRE PAUL BROCA (1824–1880)

*B*roca was born in the town of Sainte-Foy-la-Grande, in the Gironde near Bordeaux. His parents were of old Huguenot stock. His father was an army surgeon noted for his "unflinching probity, courage and grave irony." His mother was a woman "of great intelligence and endowed with a prodigious memory." Paul's plenitude of gifts was already apparent in his undergraduate work. He entered the University of Paris at the age of 17 to study medicine. During the first 10 years after graduation his work was mainly on pathology.

Stimulated by the contributions of Geoffroy, Saint-Hilaire, Serres, and de Quatrefages, he shifted from pathology to anthropology and ethnography, and became distinguished for his craniometric and anthropometric studies. Huxley said that the mere mention of Broca's name filled him with a sense of gratitude for what he had accomplished in the field of anthropology, and Trélat once said of him that "he never wrote anything that came down to mediocrity."

In 1859 Broca founded the *Société d'anthropologie* and the *Revue d'anthropologie* and became a member of the *Institut Anthropologique*. Here he met his old friend Gratiolet, also a native of Sainte-Foy, and under his influence became interested in the anatomy and functions of the brain, particularly in problems of localization. His genius led him to build on the basis of a single case, which he had carefully observed clinically, the concept of the relationship of certain symptoms and circumscribed lesions, which opened the way to the discoveries and applications by Hitzig, Ferrier and Charcot.

It was a memorable day in 1861 when Broca demonstrated before the *Société d'anthropologie* in Paris—with his venerable father looking on in silent admiration—the lesion in the left frontal lobe of his patient who had suffered from *aphémie*[1,2] (renamed "aphasia" by Trousseau in 1861). From this and subsequent observations he concluded that the integrity of the posterior part of the third frontal convolution was indispensable to articulate speech, and therefore termed this region the *circonvolution du langage*. (Later Ferrier referred to it as "Broca's convolution.") Thus Broca brought to a head the smoldering idea promulgated some decades before in Paris by Franz Joseph Gall (1757–1828)[3] and Jean Baptiste Bouillaud (1796–1881) that frontal lobe lesions may cause speech disorders. Bouillaud was so firmly convinced that this was true that he offered (in 1825) to pay 500 francs to the person who could satisfactorily demonstrate that disorders of speech were not always associated with lesions of the frontal lobe.[4]

Broca's concept was not generally accepted and actually was opposed, particularly by Trousseau and Hughlings Jackson. At the now historic session of the British Association for the Advancement

Pierre Paul Broca

of Science held in Norwich in 1868,[5] the enthusiastic support of his view by the audience, coupled with their indifference to Jackson's part in the discussion, was a personal triumph for Broca, and from that time his basic idea dominated research on the brain cortex; the theory of circumscribed localization was considered to be established beyond doubt. His views took on even more importance when, in 1874, Wernicke localized the corresponding disturbance

Portrait, courtesy of Dr. Maurice Genty, Académie de Médecine, Paris, France.

in the sensory part of language, sensory aphasia, and elaborated his psycho-physical theory of brain function. However, Broca was not infallible: Pierre Marie, in the early 1900's sought out Broca's brain specimens in the old Musée Dupuytren and found that the very brain Broca described had parieto-temporal as well as frontal lesions.

The theory of circumscribed localization in the cerebral cortex is no longer so generally acknowledged. Broca's and Wernicke's ideas are giving way to Jackson's approach; but this does not lessen the fame of Broca or reduce the importance of his discovery, nor will it be forgotten that it was Broca, the meticulous observer, who insisted on the functional significance of the various areas in the cortex.

Broca was strongly built, with an expansive forehead and lustrous brown eyes. Benevolent and an excellent raconteur, he was adored by his associates, and it is said that those who were once his friends were his friends for life. Standing for many years at one corner of the Faculté de Médecine of Paris, until carted off by the German Army in the late war, was his statue, with that of Vulpian not far off. Here he could still survey the Paris of 1870–71, and reminisce how, as vice-president of the council of public assistance, he took his life in hand during the Commune to spirit 75 million francs from the treasury to Versailles for concealment. To do this he devised the bold scheme of hiding the bullion on an old wagon loaded with potatoes and driving it past the guarded gate of Paris. For this deed he received not so much as a vote of thanks from the French Government.

One of the greatest honors bestowed on him was his election in 1880 as a lifetime member of the Senate of the French Republic, representing science. He was in office, however, only six months when, still at the height of his powers, he suddenly died. The postmortem study served only to deepen the mystery of his sudden departure, the cause of death being written off as "cerebral exhaustion." The Musée Broca, in Paris, is only one of his enduring monuments.

NEW YORK CITY   KURT GOLDSTEIN

References

[1]Bull. Soc. anat. Paris, 1851, 2.sér., *36:* 330–357 *et seq.* [2]Bull. Soc. anthrop. Paris, 1861, *2:* 190–294 *et seq.* [3]Bull. Hist. M., 1947, *21:* 275–321 (Temkin). [4]*Essay on the cerebral cortex.* Springfield, Ill., Thomas, 1950 (von Bonin). [5]Bull. Soc. anthrop., Par., 1865, *6:* 377–393.

References to Biography and Works: 1) Rev. anthrop., Par., 1880, 2.sér., *3:* 577–608 (contains bibliography; Pozzi). 2)*Miscellaneous papers. 1882–1913,* Washington, D. C. (Fletcher). 3) Bull. Hist. M., 1947, *21:* 322–334 (Riese). 4) Rev. mens. méd. chir., Par., 1880, *4:* 746–764 (Reclus).

CHARLES ÉDOUARD BROWN-SÉQUARD (1817–1894)

*B*orn on the island of Mauritius of a French mother and an American father, Brown-Séquard spent much of his life travelling back and forth between Mauritius, Europe, and the United States. Like Claude Bernard, he first went to Paris in the heyday of the romantic movement with the intention of becoming an author, but he, too, was wisely advised to turn to the study of medicine. The clinician Trousseau and the surgeon Rayer influenced him strongly in his early days, but at first he preferred, like Claude Bernard, to continue his original physiological investigations rather than to settle down to a medical practice. He conducted private courses and eventually gave successful lectures in the United States and throughout the British Isles. He accepted professorships at the Medical College of Virginia and at Harvard and in the Geneva and Paris faculties of medicine, and served on the staff of the National Hospital in London. In 1878 he succeeded Claude Bernard as professor of medicine at the Collège de France. In the meantime, he founded three journals devoted to physiology and published hundreds of articles, mostly on the nervous system.

Brown-Séquard's first original work, his thesis for the M.D.,[1] foreshadowed the discovery with which his name is always associated, *viz.* the decussation of sensory tracts in the spinal cord, and the syndrome following hemisection of the cord. The ideas regarding the functions of the different parts of the spinal cord in vogue at that time were those of Sir Charles Bell in England, seconded by F. A. Longet in France, both of whom contended that all sensation was

carried in the dorsal columns. In his thesis, Brown-Séquard stated that after sectioning the dorsal columns of the cords of cold-blooded vertebrates, birds and mammals, sensation in every case persisted in the parts situated below the section. He also commented on the

Portrait, courtesy of the Army Medical Library, Washington, D. C.

ease with which he had found sensory impressions to be transmitted from one side of the cord to the other. The thesis was shortly followed by a series of papers in which he clearly established that after hemisection of the cord there was loss of sensation on the opposite side of the body, but retention and even increase of sensation on the same side—the now-familiar Brown-Séquard syndrome.[2]

His second important neurological observation completed Claude Bernard's discovery of vasomotor nerves, for Brown-Séquard was the first to show, in 1852,[3] that stimulation of the cervical sympathetic nerve in the rabbit causes blanching of the ear.

His practice as a neurologist began in earnest with the loan by Rayer of an electrical stimulator which he proceeded to apply to human patients with great skill. But on observing signs of epilepsy in the guinea pigs upon whose spinal cords he had performed various operations, his attention became fixed upon this peculiar neurological condition, and he spent the greater part of his life in the attempt to discover the causes and treatment of epilepsy. He was instrumental in introducing bromide for epilepsy, and by 1863 he was recognized throughout Europe and America as an authority on nervous disorders.

His inquiring mind early led him into another field, endocrinology. In 1856 he showed how fatal is the operation of adrenalectomy,[4] and at the end of his life he became uncritically enthusiastic over organotherapy, so that his career ended on a note of extravagant claims for the curative powers of testicular extracts that his results did not warrant.

His dynamic nature and sometimes explosive energy made of him a colorful character. He was both brilliant and ambitious, and his only outlet was his science. His influence was strong in Paris during the 1880's and he left an enthusiastic group of young workers, the best known of whom were d'Arsonval and François-Franck.

BERKELEY, CALIFORNIA   J. M. D. OLMSTED

References

[1]*Recherches et expériences sur la physiologie de la moelle épinière.* Thèse de Paris, 1846.   [2]C. rend. Acad. sc., 1850, *31:* 700–701.   [3]Med. Exam., Phila., 1852, n.s., *8:* 481–504 *et seq.*   [4]C. rend. Acad. sc., 1856, *43:* 422–425 *et seq.*

Reference to Biography: Charles-Édouard Brown-Séquard, a nineteenth century neurologist and endocrinologist. Baltimore, Johns Hopkins Press, 1946 (Olmsted).

Reference to Bibliography: Notice sur les travaux scientifiques. Paris, Masson, 1878 (Brown-Séquard).

JEAN MARTIN CHARCOT (1825–1893)

*A*mong the multitude of distinguished names which illumine the pages of French neurology of the nineteenth century, none shines with greater brilliance than that of Jean Martin Charcot. He typified French medical genius at its highest. Nature endowed him generously: he possessed an original mind, the quality of logical thinking, and the gift of lucid expression. There was much of the artist in him. He combined depth of knowledge with great industry. In an age of great teachers he was one of heroic stature. Few possessed more enthusiasm or éclat.

Jean Martin Charcot was born in Paris, the son of a carriage builder. For a time he wavered in his choice between medicine and art, then decided on a medical career. He passed his medical examinations with honor, became interne at the Salpêtrière in 1848, and for nine years worked in pathology and medicine under Rayer. During those years he devoted himself to clinical medicine and wrote on diseases of the heart, lungs and kidneys, and on rheumatism and gout. At the age of 37 he won his agrégation and was given a position at the Salpêtrière.

When Charcot entered the Salpêtrière he found thousands of unclassified and unrelated conditions which were a challenge to his industry and curiosity. Charcot possessed both. He observed, studied, described, and classified. He became a great neuropathologist, succeeding Vulpian to the chair of pathologic anatomy in 1872. As a clinician he was even greater. His *Leçons sur les maladies du système nerveux faites à la Salpêtrière* (Paris Delahaye, 1872–73) was a masterpiece which saw translations into English.[1] He wrote on cerebral localization, the while crossing swords with Brown-Séquard over the problem of localization in jacksonian epilepsy. His description of disseminated sclerosis embodied the triad which goes by his name.[2,3] He put his stamp on locomotor ataxia and described the arthropathies which now are called "Charcot joints." Amyotro-

Portrait, courtesy of Dr. Maurice Genty, Académie de Médecine, Paris, France

phic lateral sclerosis was first described and named by him in 1865,[4] and for a long time was known as Charcot's disease. Progressive bulbar palsy, first recognized by Duchenne de Boulogne in 1861 (he called it labioglossolaryngeal paralysis), was connected with amyotrophic lateral sclerosis by Dejerine in 1883.[5] Charcot's name is linked with that of Marie and Tooth in one of the neuropathies.[6] With Joffroy he formulated the concept that in poliomyelitis an "irritation" suddenly seizes many ganglion cells of the anterior horns and causes them promptly to lose their function, and he expressed the opinion that the interstitial inflammatory reaction is a secondary phenomenon.[7] Atrophy of anterior horns and their ganglion cells in poliomyelitis had been noted previously by Prévost,[8] but he did not comment on pathogenesis.

Famous internationally as a neurologist, Charcot became even more renowned for his studies of hysteria. To his lasting credit, he laid the solid foundation of psychopathology on which Janet and Freud, both his pupils, built so well. He made hypnotism respectable. There was artistry, if not histrionics, in his Tuesday and Friday morning lectures. The medical world rang with them, and enemies had opportunity to criticize. Disinclined to animal experimentation, he had inscribed over his door, "Vous ne trouverez pas une clinique des chiens chez moi." Charcot the artist is at his best in two graphic volumes, one on *Les démoniaques dans l'art* (Paris, Delahaye & Lecrosnier, 1887) and the other on *Les difformes et les malades dans l'art* (Paris, Lecrosnier & Babe, 1889), both written in collaboration with P. Richer. An impressive article on the artistic achievements of Charcot is that by Meige in the *Nouvelle Iconographie de la Salpêtrière*,[9] a journal which Charcot founded.

So great a teacher could not fail to inspire great pupils. Marie, Babinski, Souques, Marinesco, Bekhterev, Colin, and a host of others sat at his feet. Charcot was austere in public but gracious and kindly in his artistic home, open one evening a week to friends and pupils. Gifted also as a linguist, he spoke English, German, Spanish and Italian. While away on a vacation he died suddenly at the age of 68 of pulmonary edema, probably the result of coronary occlusion. His son, Dr. Jean Baptiste Charcot, became the dean of Antarctic explorers, and led the search for the lost Amundsen.

Of Charcot it may be said with truth that he entered neurology in its infancy and left it at its coming-of-age, largely nourished by his own contributions.

NEW YORK CITY   I. S. WECHSLER

References

[1]*Lectures on the diseases of the nervous system.* Philadelphia, Lea, 1879 (trans. by G. Sigerson). *Lectures on the nervous system.* London, New Sydenham Soc., 1881.   [2]Gaz. hôp., 1865, *38:* 93.   [3]C. rend. Soc. biol., 1868, *20:* 13–14.   [4]Gaz. hôp., 1868, *41:* 554–555 *et seq.*   [5]Arch. Physiol., Par., 1883, *2:* 180–227.   [6]Rev. méd., Par., 1886, *6:* 97–138 (with Marie).   [7]Arch. physiol. norm. path., 1869, *2:* 354–373 *et seq.;* p. 756.   [8]C. rend. Soc. Biol., 1865, 4.sér., *2:* 215–218.   [9]Nouv. Iconogr. Salpêtrière, 1898, *11:* 489–546.

References to Biography: 1) Bull N. York Acad. M., 1926, ser.2 (suppl.), *2:* 1–32 (Garrison *et al.*).   2) Ann. M. Hist., 1928, *10:* 126–132 (Beeson).   3) J. Neuropath., 1950, *9:* 1–17 (Hassin).   4) Bull. Acad. méd., Par., 1925, 3.sér., *43:* 573–603 (Marie, Marinesco, Christiansen). 5) Bull. méd., Par., 1900, *14:* 1389–1394 (Debove).

JAMES STANSFIELD COLLIER (1870–1935)

James Collier, whose vivid personality is a pleasant memory to many neurologists of the present day, was born in Cranford, near London, the son of a medical practitioner. His elder brother was a surgeon whose brilliant career ended prematurely. James was educated in London, and graduated Bachelor of Medicine in 1894, completing his M.D. in 1896. After house appointments at the National Hospital, Queen Square, he became pathologist to the hospital in 1901. He was appointed to the visiting staff of the National Hospital in 1902, and physician (in general medicine) to St. George's Hospital in 1903. The calls of hospital and private practice soon made it necessary for him to give up his appointment as pathologist, but he continued to show a lively interest in neuropathology throughout his career.

Apart from his profound influence as a teacher, the major contribution of Collier was undoubtedly his part in the first comprehensive description of subacute combined degeneration of the spinal cord and its relation to pernicious anemia, which was written in col-

James Stansfield Collier

laboration with J. S. R. Russell and F. E. Batten.[1] Ludwig Licht-
heim (1845–1915), of Bern, had already noted this association in
1887, and Gowers had provided a clinical description of the disorder
in 1886[2] under the designation "ataxic paraplegia," but the classical
description by Collier and his associates in 1900 was the first complete one, which has hardly been improved upon. His other contributions covered a wide range of subjects, chiefly clinical, of which
his views on cerebral diplegia,[3,4] Babinski's sign,[5] amyotonia congenita,[6,7] epilepsy,[8] aphasia, apraxia and agnosia,[9,10] intracranial
aneurysm,[11] and peripheral neuritis,[12] are the best known.

Portrait, courtesy of Dr. D. Denny-Brown, Boston, Massachusetts.

In the English school of neurology the memory of Collier is cherished as the last of the tradition of dramatic teachers in the manner of Charcot and Trousseau. The elegant phrases, falling to a whisper, as with the air and mannerisms of a magician he disclosed the climax to the clinical story, fascinated the large audiences which unfailingly crowded his Wednesday afternoon clinics. Inherent in such teaching is a dogmatism and overemphasis which occasionally crept into his writing. Few would accept his generalizations regarding the inherent defect in maturation of the pyramidal system in all cerebral diplegias, or his insistence upon the absence of infectivity of poliomyelitis after the onset of the paralytic phase. Yet by such categorical statements he continually stimulated further thought and investigation. There was some subtle quality by which he could demolish false dogma without setting up another equally false.

Without doubt Collier did more to mold medical opinion and contributed more to the betterment of clinical neurological ability of internists in general than any other man of his time.

BOSTON, MASSACHUSETTS   D. DENNY-BROWN

References

[1]Brain, Lond., 1900, 23: 39–110.   [2]Lancet, Lond., 1886, 2: 1–3 et seq. [3]Brain, Lond., 1899, 22: 374–441.   [4]Ibid., 1924, 47: 1–21.   [5]Ibid., 1899, 22: 71–99.   [6]Ibid., 1908, 31: 1–44 (with Wilson).   [7]Ibid., 1909, 32: 269–284 (with Holmes).   [8]Lancet, Lond., 1928, 1: 587–592 et seq. [9]Allbutt, T. C., and Rolleston, H. D., A system of medicine. London, Macmillan, 1910, 8: 385–446; Ibid., p. 447–451.   [10]Price, F. W., A textbook of the practice of medicine, ed. 1 to 3. London, Oxford Univ. Press, 1922–29.   [11]Brit. M. J., 1939, 2: 519–521.   [12]Edinburgh M. J., 1932, 39: 601–607 et seq.

Reference to Biography: Lancet, Lond., 1935, 1: 403–404 (not signed).

JOSEPH JULES DEJERINE (1849–1917)

" *A*t Paris, you always can advance yourself by work and enthusiasm. You don't need any 'relations.' You are the product of your work." These words of Jules Dejerine*—as he was known scientifically—were borne out by his career.

* The name is not Déjerine or Déjérine.

Joseph Jules Dejerine

The young Frenchman, born and raised in the provincial atmosphere of Geneva, Switzerland, hopefully set out in 1871 for Paris in a third-class compartment, with no more than a brief introduction to Vulpian. He arrived in the midst of the turmoil created by war and revolution, but unswervingly set out to reach his goal. Later he was to prove Vulpian's most distinguished pupil.

His career was punctuated by appointments to high position and by a succession of brilliant works. He was connected with both the

Portrait, courtesy of Mme. le Docteur Sorrel-Dejerine, Paris, France.

Salpêtrière and the Bicêtre, and as a climax to his career was elected, in 1910, Professeur de clinique des maladies du système nerveux à la Faculté de Médecine. His masterpieces include his studies on nervotabès périphérique,[1] progressive muscular dystrophy (with Landouzy),[2] Friedreich's disease (with André-Thomas),[3] progressive hypertrophic interstitial neuritis (with Sottas and André-Thomas),[4,5] olivopontocerebellar atrophy (with André-Thomas),[6] the thalamic syndrome (with Roussy),[7] and greatest of all, his *Anatomie des centres nerveux* (Paris, Rueff, 1890–1901) and his *Sémiologie des affections du système nerveux* (Paris, Masson, 1914). He was one of the pioneers in the study of localization of function in the brain, having first shown, with Vialet, that word blindness may occur as the result of lesions of the supramarginal and angular gyri.[8-11] Before his time Broca had connected the region of the operculum with motor aphasia (1861), Hitzig the precentral and postcentral region with hemiplegia (1874), Wernicke the superior temporal gyrus with word deafness (1874), Exner the 2nd convolution of the premotor cortex with agraphia (1881); and Henschen was soon to show that the region of the calcarine gyrus was the basis of hemianopia (1892). From the experimental side Fritsch and Hitzig elicited motor responses to electrical stimulation of the precentral gyrus (1870), Ferrier distinguished four centers in the region anterior to the central sulcus: a large one for tonic movements of the body, an oral one and a caudal one for the eyes, and a center for the ears (1874), Horsley and his co-workers found a fifth center for rhythmic movements of the mouth and its surrounding muscles (1886), and Sherrington and his co-workers confined most of the excitable motor cortex to the precentral gyrus (1896).

Although Dejerine is best known for his contributions in the field of organic neurology, his interest in functional disorders of the nervous system was also keen, and was greatly stimulated by his friendship with Paul Dubois of Bern. His vacations always brought him back to the land of his birth, to his place at Thalgut, near Bern, where his simple tastes and fondness for the rustic life found complete satisfaction. Robert Bing, in his warm-hearted tribute to Dejerine, tells that during this period Dejerine developed many of his ideas of psychotherapy which were applied by him with such remarkable success. Later on, Dubois's and Dejerine's views began to diverge, the latter insisting that the personality of the therapist was of extreme importance. He told his students: "It is rare that you will be able to use subtle logic; it is your heart that carries you along—if I may express myself thus— much more than your reason. In man, emotion is almost everything and reason very little."

In the wards made famous by Charcot, it was inspiring to me as to the others who were in his service in 1900–01 to note the earnest, simple, direct way in which Dejerine explained the basis of symptoms and the encouragement that he gave his patients. In the out-patient department he was equally effective. On one occasion, a young woman was being examined and her maladjustment to life was discussed with great frankness. The question of her relations with her lover, who was present with her, arose. She described one of her dreams, in which a phallic symbol played a prominent part. A certain slang word she used brought forth a hearty laugh from the audience. The professor was immediately indignant and with unaccustomed severity suppressed the laughter and informed the audience that they were not there to be amused.

Life with Dejerine and his group, which included André-Thomas and Bernheim, was always stimulating. At the meetings of the Société neurologique of Paris the presentations were terse and to the point, and the discussion at times tinged with biting sarcasm. There was no polite verbiage. All speakers had their gloves off.

Dejerine owed much to his wife, Augusta Klumpke (1859–1927), one of the brilliant sisters of a famous San Francisco family, whom he married in 1888. The bride was given away by Professor A. Hardy, with Professor Landouzy as her second witness. During the previous years she had studied medicine in Paris, and through intellect, courage and persistence, became the first woman to receive the title of "interne des hôpitaux" (1887). This distinction was, however, in the face of great opposition, finally overcome by Paul Bert, then Minister of Public Instruction. The Dejerines presented the rare spectacle of two intellectual giants collaborating and working together, each inspiring and helping the other throughout their married life. Only the Curies and the Vogts could boast of achievements of comparable magnitude. When Dejerine died during the dark hours of World War I as the result of having spent himself in exhausting service in neurology in an army hospital, it was his wife who carried on the bulk of his work both in practice and in research.

It was most fitting for the Fourth International Neurological Congress, which met in Paris in 1949, to celebrate the centennial of Dejerine's birth, to hear at the Sorbonne a discourse on Dejerine by one of his most distinguished pupils, André-Thomas,[12] to wear the medallion struck off in his honor, and to join with his daughter, Mme. le Dr. Sorrel-Dejerine, in laying a wreath on his grave.

NEW YORK CITY

EDWIN G. ZABRISKIE

References

[1]C. rend. Acad. sc., 1883, 97: 914–916. [2]Mém. Soc. biol., Par., 1886, 38: 478–481. [3]Rev. neur., Par., 1907, 15: 41–54. [4]C. rend. Soc. biol., 1893, 5: 63–96. [5]Nouv. Iconogr. Salpêtrière, 1906, 19: 477–509. [6]Ibid., 1900, 13: 330–370. [7]Rev. neur., Par., 1906, 14: 521–532. [8]C. rend. Soc. biol., 1891, 43: 167–173 (Dejerine). [9]Ibid., 1892, 44: 61–90 (Dejerine). [10]Ibid., 1893, 45: 790–791 (Dejerine and Vialet). [11]Les centres cérébraux de la vision et l'appareil nerveux visuel intra-cérébral. Paris, Alcan, 1893 (Vialet). [12]C. rend. IVe Congrès Neurologique International, Paris, 1949. Vol. 3. Paris, Masson, 1951; pp. 450–469.

References to Biography: 1) Schweiz. Arch. Neur. Psychiat., 1918, 2: 314–315 (Bing). 2) Encéphale, 1938, 23: 75–88 (André-Thomas). 3) Le Professeur J. Dejerine 1849–1917. Paris, Masson, 1922 (contains bibliography; Gauckler). 4) Éloge de Madame Dejerine-Klumpke, 1859–1927 Paris, Lahure, 1927 (Roussy). 5) Paris méd., 1917, 23: 90–91 (Camus).

GUILLAUME BENJAMIN AMAND DUCHENNE (1806–1875)

Duchenne was born in the town of Boulogne-sur-Mer. For generations his forebears had been fishermen, coastwise traders, and ship captains. His father, a member of the famous group of "corsaires boulonnais," had commanded a vessel which gave such a good account of itself in the war between France and England that he received, in 1804, the Croix de la Légion d'honneur by order of Napoleon Bonaparte. Men who go down to the sea in ships draw their lonely strength from their struggle with the implacable elements. Duchenne de Boulogne, as he signed himself in order not to be confused with Duchesne of Paris, carried into his medical career the strong qualities of the folk from whom he sprang.

Guillaume Benjamin Amand Duchenne

Having passed, at the age of 19, his baccalaureate at Douai, Duchenne went to Paris (in 1825) to study medicine. Among his teachers were Cruveilhier, Dupuytren, Velpeau and Laennec, the latter just retiring from the scene of his activities. After graduation in 1831 he returned to Boulogne and became a general practitioner. He soon entered into a happy marriage, cut short after two years by the death of his wife during childbirth. In his grief he forsook his

Portrait, courtesy of Dr. Maurice Genty, Académie de Médecine, Paris, France.

practice, preferring to read, play the violin, and linger on the water-front conversing with the fishermen. His indolence invited reproach from the family of his deceased wife and in time his son, listening to the vicious tongues of the relatives, became alienated from him; and thus, after 11 years in Boulogne, Duchenne decided to return to Paris to resume the work on the electrical stimulation of muscles which he had commenced some time previously.

As Lhermitte tells us, he brought to the capital little else than "sa pile et sa bobine," and with them "des réserves inépuisables de confiance, d'indépendance et de courage." He had at that time no powerful friends in the medical world. He was regarded as an uncouth interloper. But, like his sailor forebears, he had set his course and he followed his star. Undaunted by the rebuffs and contempt of the "monarchs" who reigned over the wards, he worked daily in the crowded clinics and followed patients into their homes. Even the Revolution of 1848, the siege of Paris, and the rise and fall of the Paris Commune failed to influence his activities to any appreciable degree.

Without his two great friends in Paris, Trousseau and Charcot, much of Duchenne's work would never have been published, for he was absent-minded and inarticulate in the expression of his ideas. Duchenne's first publication of importance was on the electrical stimulation of muscles by the faradic current.[1] The third edition of this work,[2] much amplified, contains all his observations on electrical stimulation of muscle, the elucidation of the mechanism of facial expression, and a complete review of muscular function as determined by stimulus of the muscle itself.

Duchenne's painstaking observations on muscle physiology led him to the understanding of neuromuscular disease. He gave accurate descriptions of progressive (spinal) muscular atrophy,[3] poliomyelitis,[4] locomotor ataxia,[5] pseudohypertrophic muscular dystrophy[6] and glossolabiolaryngeal paralysis,[7,8] the latter first recognized by Louis Duménil (1823–90) in 1859,[9] and subsequently called progressive bulbar paralysis by Wachsmuth in 1864.[10] While he was not the first to write of some of these disorders, his accurate clinical descriptions and his meticulous work on muscle function built up clear-cut clinical entities. In his monograph on pseudohypertrophic muscular dystrophy[6] he announced a novel method of examining small bits of muscle taken from living patients, referred

to subsequently by Gowers as Duchenne's "histological harpoon."
Thus, the science of biopsy was created.

The disease with which Duchenne's name is most closely associated is progressive (spinal) muscular atrophy. He made observations of this soon after he came to Paris. François-Amilcar Aran
(1817–61), then physician to the Hôpital Saint-Antoine, disseminated the knowledge of Duchenne's work by publishing his cases
in 1850,[11] and acknowledging his pioneer work in these words: "I
owe a thousand thanks to my friend Duchenne (of Boulogne) who
freely put at my disposal all his material, and without officious intervention . . ." After the description of progressive (spinal) muscular atrophy it was logical for him to understand bulbar paralysis.
His clinical description of this disease has never been surpassed.

Before Duchenne, poliomyelitis was called "paralysie essentielle
de l'enfance," a term provided by Rilliet. Duchenne renamed it
"paralysie atrophique graisseuse de l'enfance." Struck by the similarity in the clinical features of poliomyelitis and traumatic lesions
of the spinal cord, Duchenne, in 1855,[1] formulated the hypothesis
that the lesion was in the spinal cord: "En raisonnant par analogie,
j'ai été conduit à penser que le point de départ de ces paralysies
graves de l'enfance pouvait résider dans le système nerveux spinal."
Duchenne also clarified the various forms of lead palsy and established their electrical reactions.[2]

Duchenne's work was done without benefit of hospital appointment or academic chair. The Académie de Médecine and the Institut de France passed by his name, but he received recognition
outside his native country, being elected corresponding member
of the academies in such far-flung capitals as Rome, Madrid, Stockholm, St. Petersburg, Geneva and Leipzig. His work took on even
more luster when his estranged son joined him in Paris in 1862 to
take up the study of neurology. He devoted himself to his son and
the son did well; life was again on an even keel. But not for long,
for in 1871 his son died of typhoid fever. This was a blow from
which Duchenne never recovered. Four years later he suffered a
cerebral hemorrhage which in a few weeks brought him everlasting
quiet.

In the Salpêtrière there is a simple monument on which a bas-relief
depicts a doctor leaning over a patient while he applies the elec-

trodes of a simple apparatus. Above the bas-relief is a plaque on which is engraved:

1806–1875

A. Duchenne (de Boulogne)
Électrisation localisée
Physiologie des mouvements Neuropathologie

CHARLESTON, SOUTH CAROLINA OLIN B. CHAMBERLAIN

References

[1] *De l'électrisation localisée, et de son application à la pathologie et à la thérapeutique.* Paris, Baillière, 1855. (ed. 2, 1861.) [2] *Ibid.,* ed. 3, 1872. [3] C. rend, Acad. sc., 1894, *29:* 667–670. [4] Arch. gén. méd., Par., 1864, 6.sér., *2:* 28–50 *et seq.* [5] *Ibid.,* 1858, 5.sér., *12:* 641–652 *et seq.* [6] *Ibid.,* 1868, 6.sér., *11:* 5–25 *et seq.* [7] *Ibid.,* 1860, 5.sér., *2:* 283–296 *et seq.* [8] *Ibid.,* 1870, 6.sér., *15:* 539–547. [9] Gaz. hebd. de méd., 1859, *6:* 390–392. [10] *Über progressive Bulbärparalyse (bulbus medullae) und die Diplegia facialis.* Dorpat, Gläser, 1864. [11] *Ibid.,* 1850, 4.sér., *24:* 1–35 *et seq.*

References to Biography: 1) Bull. Acad. méd., Par., 1946, *130:* 745–755 (Lhermitte). 2) Bull. N. York Acad. M., 1948, *24:* 772–783 (Viets). 3) *Duchenne de Boulogne.* Thèse de Paris, 1936 (contains bibliography; Guilly). 4) Arch. gén. méd., Par., 1875, 6.sér., *26:* 687–715 (Lasègue and I. Straus). 5) Med. Rec., N. Y., 1908, *73:* 50–54 (Collins). 6) Kagan (ed.), *Victor Robinson Memorial Volume. Essays on history of medicine.* New York, Froben, 1948 (Kaplan); p. 177–192. 7) Med. Rev. of Rev., 1931, *37:* 641–656 (Robinson).

WILHELM HEINRICH ERB (1840–1921)

*E*RB, one of the greatest of clinical neurologists, was born in the Bavarian Palatinate at Winnweiler, the son of a forester. He studied medicine at Heidelberg, Erlangen and Munich, receiving his doctorate in Munich in 1864. At first, as Privatdozent, he became an internist at Heidelberg (1865), only to be led into neurology in 1867 by Nikolaus Friedreich, who exemplified the advantage of integrating pathological observations with clinical studies. In 1869 Erb became Extraordinarius at Heidelberg, in 1880 Ordinarius for special pathology and therapy and director of the medical polyclinic at Leipzig, and from 1883 on, Ordinarius at Heidelberg.

All his important work on structural neurology was done at Heidelberg.

Friedreich's views were uppermost in the scientific work of Erb, first on peripheral nerves and later on diseases of the spinal cord and medulla oblongata—273 publications altogether. To Erb, we

Portrait, courtesy of the Library, Northwestern University School of Medicine, Chicago, Illinois.

owe the delineation, in part, of progressive muscular dystrophy,[1,2] spastic spinal paralysis (Erb-Charcot disease),[3] the brachial plexus syndrome (Duchenne-Erb paralysis),[4] and myasthenia gravis (called Erb-Goldflam-Oppenheim disease, though Thomas Willis first described it in 1672[5] and Gowers reported the features of a typical case in his *Manual* in 1886–88). The most dramatic recent development in this field was the discovery by M. B. Walker[6,7] that neostigmine constitutes an effective treatment of myasthenia gravis.

Erb recognized the syphilitic origin of tabes as early as 1892,[8] i.e., some 14 years before the establishment of the relationship by Schaudinn and Wassermann. Stimulated by the studies of Duchenne, he became interested in the diagnostic and therapeutic aspects of electricity and devised the electro-diagnostic test of reaction of degeneration which bears his name.[9] Increased electrical irritability of motor nerves in tetany was first demonstrated by him (Erb's phenomenon).[10] He held high hopes for the therapeutic value of electrical current in mental diseases, and it was to him a bitter disappointment when, despite valiant efforts, he found the method of little avail.

Of great importance were his contributions as a teacher, his development of a systematic examination of the nervous system for clinical evaluation of signs and symptoms, and his insistence on neurology as an important part of the curriculum of medical schools. It was Erb who established neurological instruction as an integral part of the medical curriculum at Heidelberg. With Fr. Schultze he founded the *Deutsche Zeitschrift für Nervenheilkunde* in 1891.

Erb may well be called the father of clinical neurology, for he led the way to recognition of this branch of medicine in both hospital and school and made it an acceptable medical specialty; he was to Germany what Charcot was to France and Gowers to England— her leading neurologist. Of his many students, which included E. Remak, Fisher, Eisenlohr and Fr. Schultze, the most outstanding was Nonne, who carried on the Erb tradition to the present generation.

Erb had the appearance of a cultured gentleman; he was always immaculately dressed and kept his professorial beard trimmed to the last hair. There was an air of detachment about him: neither he nor anyone else forgot that he was the Herr Geheimrat. He could lose his temper and he often did so; his language on occasion was not that customarily heard in academic circles. He was noted for his benevolence, as reflected, for instance, in the equal care he gave to all patients—peasant or aristocrat—in his large international practice. The title of *Seine Excellenz* was conferred on him by the Grand Duke of Baden. His 70th birthday was an occasion for a celebration in Heidelberg. A bronze statue of him was unveiled in the park near the Akademisches Krankenhaus, and a street was named after him.

In his latter years Erb was a broken man; two of his four sons had died, and a third was killed at the front during World War I. His end came shortly after a heart attack, which occurred while he was listening to Beethoven's *Eroica*.

BOSTON, MASSACHUSETTS   HENRY R. VIETS

References

[1]Arch. Psychiat., Berl., 1879, 9: 369–388 (with Fr. Schultze).   [2]Deut. Arch. klin. Med., 1884, 34: 467–519.   [3]Berl. klin. Wschr., 1875, 12: 357–359.   [4]Verh. naturhist. med. Verein. Heidelberg, 1877, 1: 130–136. [5]*De anima brutorum* . . , 1672.   [6]Lancet, Lond., 1934, 1: 1200–1201. [7]Proc. R. Soc. M., Lond., 1935, 28: 759–761.   [8]Samml. klin. Vortr., n.F., 1892, No. 53 (Inn. Med., No. 18); p. 515–542.   [9]Deut. Arch. klin. Med., 1868, 4: 535–578 *et seq.*   [10]Arch. Psychiat., Berl., 1873, 4: 271–316.

References to Biography: 1) Deut. Zschr. Nervenh., 1922, 73: i–xvii (Fr. Schultze).   2) Zschr. ges. Neur. Psychiat., 1922, 47: i–x (Nonne). 3) Penfield (ed.), *Neurological biographies and addresses.* London, Oxford Univ. Press, 1936 (Torkildsen and Erickson); p. 115–119.   4) Deut. Zschr. Nervenh., 1911, 41: 169–171 (Oppenheim).

EDWARD FLATAU (1869–1932)

*F*latau, Poland's most famous neurologist, was born in Plock. During the course of his studies at the University of Moscow, from which he received the M.D. in 1892, a lasting impression was made on him by the neurologist Kozhevnikov and the psychiatrist Korsakov. His postgraduate work and assistantship at the University of Berlin under Mendel, Waldeyer, Jacobsohn and Goldscheider (until 1899) were extremely fruitful. While associated with Kurt Mendel, he completed, at the early age of 25, a large *Atlas des menschlichen Gehirns und des Faserverlaufes* (Berlin, Karger,

Edward Flatau

1894), which was received with such acclaim that it was soon translated into English, French, Russian and Polish.

Flatau became interested in the neuron theory, and with Johannes Karl Goldscheider (1858–1935) he published on the structure of nerve cells and their changes under mechanical, thermal and toxic influences.[1-3] This work, in which the normal and pathologic anatomy of the Vth, VIIth and VIIIth (cochlear) cranial nerves was included,[3] created much discussion and was adversely criticised by Nissl, who opposed the neuron theory. About 1896 Flatau restudied Bastian's Law concerning the loss of function following spinal cord injury and on the basis of clinical observation discovered that the greater the length of the fibers in the spinal cord the closer they are situated to the periphery (Flatau's Law).[4,5]

Portrait, courtesy of Dr. George Schumacher, Bellevue Hospital, New York City. (Photographer: A. Gürtler, Warsaw.)

In Waldeyer's laboratory in Berlin he worked intensively on comparative anatomy of the central nervous system, producing with L. Jacobsohn, with whom he had contracted a deep friendship, an important monograph on the subject.[6] By the time he was 29 his reputation as a clinical neurologist and investigator was world-wide. The University of Buenos Aires offered him the chair of neurology but he rejected the call and returned instead, in 1899, to Poland.

Even though his achievements were acknowledged in his native country, he was not immediately appointed to an official position, but worked as a consultant in neurology. To satisfy his investigative mind, however, he developed a private neuropathological laboratory. In 1907 he became associated with the Jewish Hospital at Warsaw, and began a very fruitful teaching career. Many clinicians and neuroanatomists accompanied him on his rounds. Later, in 1912, he was instrumental in founding the Neurobiological Institute of Poland.

His contributions in Lewandowsky's *Handbuch der Neurologie* (vol. 1 & 2, 1914) were drawn from his many studies on tumors of the spinal cord and on motor and sensory segmentation of the cord. With Sterling he was among the first to describe progressive torsion spasm in children.[7] He wrote a classical treatise on migraine,[8] a disorder from which he suffered many years. Tuberculous meningitis was also one of his fortes.[9] Another significant offering was his experimental production of neoplasms of the central nervous system by chemical and physical means,[10] but modern work on this problem was initiated by Weil[11] and Seligman and Shear.[12]

Among the outstanding contributions which came from his Neurobiological Institute were his experimental work with Handelsman on epidemic cerebrospinal meningitis[13] and his studies on the permeability of the meningoencephalic barrier.[14,15] The excellence of his work in the latter field, in which the effect of a great variety of substances on the barrier was tested, made him a worthy contemporary to such pioneers in the field as Hauptmann, Mestrezat, Goldmann, Doerr, Cestan, L. Stern, H. Spatz, Friedemann, Kafka and F. K. Walter.[16] Flatau's last important contributions were those on disseminated encephalomyelitis (Flatau-Redlich's disease)[17] and encephaleukopathia scleroticans[18]—one of the many synonyms of Schilder's disease (encephalitis periaxialis diffusa), as brought out by

François Lhermitte in his recent *Les leuco-encéphalites* (Paris, Éd. Méd. Flammarion, 1950).

Flatau was the creator of neurobiologic and neuropathologic science in Poland. An unselfish scientist, he always took the greatest interest in his students; he eagerly followed their careers and frequently surprised them by knowing their publications better than they did themselves. He used to quote to them time and again a saying of Nothnagel which constituted his medical *confessio fidei:* "Only a good man can be a good physician." A fervent Polish patriot, he nevertheless withstood all temptations to enter politics and considered it his duty—even in the turbulent days of 1918—to "carry on" at his laboratory.

By a strange irony of fate, Flatau, who contributed so much to our knowledge of intracranial neoplasms, died from a brain tumor.

MADISON, WISCONSIN   HANS H. REESE

References

[1]*Normale und pathologische Anatomie der Nervenzellen auf Grund der neueren Forschungen.* Berlin, Fischer, 1898. [2]Arch. mikr. Anat., 1895, *45:* 158–162. [3]Zschr. klin. Med., 1897, *32:* 280–301. [4]Neur. Zbl., 1896, *15:* 147–154. [5]Zschr. klin. Med., 1897, *33:* 55–152. [6]*Handbuch der Anatomie und vergleichenden Anatomie des Zentralnervensystems der Säugetiere.* Berlin, Karger, 1899. [7]Zschr. ges. Neur. Psychiat., 1911, *7:* 586–612. [8]*Die Migräne.* Berlin, Springer, 1912. [9]Encéphale, 1921, *16:* 283–288. [10]Rev. neur., Par., 1921, *28:* 987–999. [11]Arch. Path., Chic., 1938, *26:* 777–790. [12]Am. J. Cancer, 1939, *37:* 364–395. [13]Zschr. ges. Neur. Psychiat., 1916, Orig., *31:* 1–156. [14]Rev. neur., Par., 1926, *33:* 521–540. [15]*Ibid.*, p. 5–10. [16]For references, see *Die Blut-Liquorschranke, eine physiologische und klinische Studie.* Leipzig, Thieme, 1929 (Walter), and Physiol. Rev., 1942, *22:* 125–145 (Friedemann). [17]Encéphale, 1929, *24:* 619–660. [18]*Ibid.*, 1925, *20:* 475–499.

Reference to Biography: Schweiz. Arch. Neur. Psychiat., 1933, *31:* 165–168 (Simchowicz).

CHARLES FOIX (1882-1927)

Charles Foix, the son of a physician, was born at Salies-de-Béarn, near Bayonne, France. He embarked on the study of medicine in Paris and became interne in 1906, médecin des hôpitaux in 1919, and agrégé in 1923. During his Salpêtrière days he was a pupil of Pierre Marie. Later he gave courses at Guillain's clinic at the Salpêtrière and at Achard's at the Hôpital Beaujon, always distinguishing himself by his wide knowledge and rational approach.

When Foix died at the age of 45, France lost one of her finest neurologists. He had approached the problem of focal lesions of the brain by a novel method, namely, the arterial supply. Instead of designating lesions by topographic location, he established syndromes that were due to thrombosis of specific arteries. He studied in detail the syndromes produced by occlusion of the posterior[1] and anterior[2] cerebral arteries and their branches and of the pontile arteries,[3] describing among the latter the syndrome of the lateral artery of the bulb,[4] which up to that time was thought due exclusively to occlusion of the posterior inferior cerebellar artery. He was at work on the much larger field of infarction in the regions supplied by the middle cerebral artery when his life was cut short. From a vast material gathered at the Salpêtrière and later at Ivry he compared in minute detail the findings during life and those after death. His clinical perception was swift and sure, and with an almost photographic memory for detail he could draw from past experience the knowledge to fit the case under discussion.

While vascular lesions were his particular domain, he was also deeply interested in those most difficult regions of the brain, the midbrain and the interbrain, and with Nicolesco published a volume dealing with the anatomy of those regions.[5] He and his colleagues established in 1921[6] the location of the specific lesions in parkinsonism, finding them above all in the substantia nigra, whereas at that time and for many years to come the German school of neuropathologists contended that the specific lesions were in the globus pallidus. Clinical studies in connection with these anatomical demonstrations led him into the field of muscle tonus, reflexes of automatism, postural reflexes, and synkinetic pathways in the production of spasticity, and revealed many new clinical tests. Years were to pass,

Charles Foix

however, before the mystery surrounding the delayed occurrence of parkinsonism was to be solved, and then by Hallervorden[7] through his observation that the cells of the substantia nigra undergo the Alzheimer neurofibrillary change and then disappear.

Foix described intracerebral centrolobular sclerosis at about the same time that Schilder's work on the subject appeared, so that in some quarters the disorder became known as Schilder-Foix disease. His and Alajouanine's introduction of subacute necrotic myelitis[8] attracted much attention, although their view that endomesovasculitis is the cause is certainly open to question.

Another disorder which bears the imprint of Foix is rhythmic myoclonus of the palate, larynx, pharynx and other brain-stem-innervated structures. Described originally by Kupper[9] and by Spencer,[10] and shown post mortem by Klien[11] to be associated with a

Portrait, courtesy of Dr. Maurice-Levy, Paris, France.

lesion of the cerebellar hemisphere, Foix and his associate Hillemand[12,13] hit upon a case in which there was degeneration of the
central tegmental tract and the reticular formation and pseudohypertrophy of the inferior olivary nucleus.   Papers in collaboration
with Tinel[14] and Chavany[15] appeared soon afterward.   Subsequently, van Bogaert[16,17] raised the question whether one and the
same disorder may not arise from lesions at different sites, the
genesis of the myoclonus depending on the interruption of functional systems having synapses either in the inferior olivary or in the
dentate nucleus.   He and Bertrand[18] came a step nearer the solution
in their report of a case in which the inferior olivary and dentate
nuclei were degenerated and the tract and formation as well.   This
concept introduced, it was but a short step for Guillain and Mol-
laret[19] to provide the necessary evidence that a break in any part of
the olivo-dentato-rubro-olivary triangle could produce the disorder.
The importance of the pseudohypertrophy of the inferior olivary
nucleus in causing the myoclonus was later stressed by Lhermitte
and Trelles.[20]

To return to Foix: He was a versatile individual.   Although primarily interested in neurology, he was placed in charge of a tuberculosis service after World War I and acquitted himself well.   When
the time came for his inaugural lecture, he was given four hours in
which to prepare a discourse on the splenic anemias, and did so
brilliantly.   Outside the field of medicine his chief interest was
poetry, and some of his longer poems dealing with classical subjects
ranked well with those of his literary contemporaries.   Even better
were his lyrics, which preserved for posterity a certain grace of expression that stamped the author as a man of understanding, sympathy and poetic vision.

He was of medium height, with mobile expression and dancing
eyes.   He let his hair grow in ringlets over the left side of his head,
and would sweep the unruly locks away from his face when bending
over a patient.   His voice was warm, vibrant, and captivating.
Gentleness and kindness endeared him to his friends and students.
Some of them imitated his brisk walk, his staccato speech, and his
quick responses which, although they seemed superficial in others,
were exact and to the point in Foix.

WASHINGTON, D. C.   WALTER FREEMAN

References

[1]Presse méd., 1923, *31(1)*: 361–365 (with Masson). [2]Encéphale, 1925, *20*: 209–232 (with Hillemand). [3]Rev. méd., Par., 1926, *43*: 287–305 (with Hillemand). [4]Rev. neur., Par., 1925, *1*: 160–179 (with Hillemand and Schalit). [5]*Anatomie cérébrale; les noyaux gris centraux et le région mésencéphalo-sous-optique; suivie d'un appendice sur l'anatomie pathologique de la maladie de Parkinson.* Paris, Masson, 1925. [6]Rev. neur., Par., 1921, *28*: 593–600. [7]Klin. Wschr., 1933, *12*: 692–695. [8]*Ibid.*, 1926, *33*: 1–42. [9]Arch. Ohrenh., 1873, *1*: 296–297. [10]Lancet, Lond., 1886, *2*: 702. [11]Neur. Cbl., 1907, *26*: 245–254. [12]Rev. neur., Par., 1924, *1*: 451–452 *et seq.* [13]*Ibid.*, 1924, *2*: 501–503. [14]*Ibid.*, 1924, *2*: 503–506. [15]*Ibid.*, 1926, *1*: 942–956. [16]*Ibid.*, 1925, *2*: 189–200. [17]*Ibid.*, 1926, *1*: 977–988. [18]*Ibid.*, 1928, *1*: 203–214. [19]*Ibid.*, 1931, *2*: 545–566. [20]Encéphale, 1933, *28*: 588–600.

References to Biography: 1) Rev. neur., Par., 1927, *34*: 441–446 (Roussy). 2) Aesculape, Par., 1927, *17*: 243–251 (Vinchon).

NIKOLAUS FRIEDREICH (1825–1882)

*F*riedreich was born in Würzburg, and it was there that he had most of his undergraduate and medical training. At the age of 31 he succeeded Virchow, as Extraordinarius, in the chair of pathological anatomy at Würzburg, where his father and grandfather had been on the medical faculty before him. The following year he accepted a call to Heidelberg as chief of the medical clinic, where he worked until his death 25 years later.

Early in his career, Friedreich had profited by his contacts with von Kölliker, and had served as first assistant under the blind clinician Marcus, but the prime molding influence on his life was Virchow. His particular strength lay in his broad grasp of pathology as applied to clinical problems. His first work of importance (1853), a Habilitationsschrift dealing with intracranial tumors, demonstrated the great capacity he had for supporting original clinical observations by means of exact pathological descriptions.

Adept in pathology as he was, Friedreich's foremost talent lay in clinical medicine, with an especial flair for the techniques of physical diagnosis. All his work was remarkable for its volume, excellence and versatility. He was an authority in almost all branches of internal medicine, but his main interest was in neurology.

Dr N. Friedreich,

The most elaborate of his writings was a monograph on progressive muscular atrophy.[1] This publication, dedicated to Virchow, contributed much to the early understanding of muscular dystrophy; but Friedreich fell into the error of regarding all muscular atrophy as myopathic, and this marred the value of the work. His studies of hereditary spinal ataxia, however, are justly regarded as classics.[2,3] They were pioneer achievements which laid the groundwork for all subsequent knowledge of hereditary degenerations of the spinal

Portrait, courtesy of Yale Medical Library, New Haven, Connecticut. (Photographer: Lange, Heidelberg.)

cord, brain stem, and cerebellum. Details have been added or changed and some of the physiologic interpretations proposed by Friedreich are no longer tenable, but the main clinical and pathologic observations and ideas are sound and enduring. Among Friedreich's gifts to neurological lore his original description of paramyoclonus multiplex,[4] so named by him, remains standard.

Friedreich was not only an investigator but also an assiduous teacher, and not the least of his contributions was the training he gave to his many gifted pupils and assistants, among whom were Adolf Kussmaul, Fr. Schultze, and especially, Wilhelm Erb.

The rest of his busy life was occupied by much attention to the administration of his clinic, to university affairs, and to one of the largest consulting practices in Europe. There was not time for other interests: for him, medicine was everything. His only diversion came from the joys of his family life. Though loyal to his friends, of whom he had many, he was inclined to be sensitive and even mistrustful of others, and was bitterly vindictive to his open enemies. His drive for work was tremendous. The whole direction of that work is best expressed in his own words, written in a prefatory dedication to Virchow: ". . . die Prinzipien cellular-pathologischer Anschauungen in mich aufzunehmen, welche für meine klinische Tätigkeit mir sichere Leitsterne geworden sind in dem Labyrinthe pathologischer Vorgänge."

CHICAGO, ILLINOIS   RICHARD B. RICHTER

References

[1]*Über progressive Muskelatrophie, über wahre und falsche Muskelhypertrophie.* Berlin, Hirschwald, 1873.   [2]Virchows Arch., 1863, *26*: 391–419 *et seq.*   [3]*Ibid.,* 1876, *68*: 145–245; 1877, *70*: 140–152.   [4]*Ibid.,* 1881, *86*: 421–430.

References to Biography: 1) *Heidelberger Professoren aus dem 19.Jahrhundert.* Vol. 2. Heidelberg, Winter, 1903 (Erb).   2) *Verdienste deutscher Ärtze um die Erkenntnis der Neuro-Pathologie.* Inaug.-Diss., Düsseldorf, 1936 (Kleinjohann).

SIR WILLIAM RICHARD GOWERS (1845–1915)

Gowers was one of a brilliant group who, in the latter part of the past century, were the glory of British neurology and indeed of British medicine. Hughlings Jackson, David Ferrier, Victor Horsley, and William Gowers led knowledge and the methods of knowledge to new heights and into unexplored territory. Their pupils, who often became their colleagues, have maintained the march they led. Of these four, Gowers, the clinician, deepened the foundations of neural medicine; Ferrier and Horsley, experimental investigators, physician and surgeon, raised its pillars strongly; and Jackson, the neurological philosopher, erected flying buttresses for its perpetual strength.

Gowers' life was spent in London, at University College and especially at "Queen Square." It was spent with a diversity of interest and a thoroughness of energy which brought to him all honour and to all of us, education. We should be better doctors, better teachers, better writers, if we from time to time read Gowers' *Clinical lectures on diseases of the nervous system* (Philadelphia, Blakiston, 1895), his *The borderland of epilepsy* (London, Churchill, 1907), his occasional papers such as that *On special sense cortical discharges from organic disease,*[1] and *On syringal haemorrhage into the spinal cord,*[2] and thereby learn somewhat the art of perfect observation and perfect precise description, written in easy simple prose. His textbook,[3] which wore his health, was written when he was surrounding 40. It used to be called "The Bible of Neurology," and can still give light on diagnostic problems, difficult for us. He illustrated it himself. His drawing was as clear and simple as was his writing and vastly better in instruction than our photographs which embarrass by their views of the unessential. Such was his gift in paint, draughtsmanship and imagination that his pictures were "hung" regularly by the Royal Academy of Arts. This gift allowed him to publish in 1904 his famous *Manual and atlas of medical ophthalmoscopy* (London, Churchill, 1904) which has not since been bettered even through the craft of retinal photography.

Once at dinner he said to me,—"I'm not sure what I shall do this summer. Last year I studied—British grasses, so perhaps this year I'll study—clouds." This zest in diversity made him, as it must make

Portrait, courtesy of Dr. Foster Kennedy, New York City.

all wise physicians, a philosopher with a view of life,—and of life universal. Some quotations from one of his lectures show the modern quality of his thought: "The energy of the Universe is only perpetual motion"; "Atomic motion along nerve fibrils," when discussing neural impulse transmission; "We must accept the fact of discontinuity of structure and continuity of function,"—this in *The dynamics of life* in 1894 (Philadelphia; Blakiston) when most of us elders were small boys, or as unborn as were then wireless transmission and radar! He added here the warning that "words have a strong tendency to cause opacity if they be numerous," and made a half-apology for his speculative thoughts: "Who is there that does not feel that an earnest effort to perceive that which is unseen leaves him on a higher level,—and that if he be still at his old standpoint he has a better view?"

He was a passionate man in his beliefs and zests. He thought obsessionally about shorthand and to the last day would tuck up the skirts of his frock coat, and sit on the edge of the bed taking shorthand notes of the case,—it was a life habit. He was once seen,—and it probably happened often,—to stop his coachman in crowded Southampton Row, having fastened his eye on a likely-looking young man hurrying on his lawful occasions along the pavement. Gowers climbed out of his carriage, white beard waving, stumbled up to him,—his gait was unsteady,—clutched him by the arm, and glaring at him with his frightening flaming fierce blue eyes said, "Young man, do you write shorthand?" To which the shocked man answered, "No, I don't." Whereupon Gowers dropped his arm, saying bitterly, "You're a fool, and will fail in life." He then clambered abruptly back into his carriage.

However, no picture of Gowers can be appreciated without at the same time having in the mind's eye his look of being a combination of one of the Wise Men of the East and the Ancient Mariner, and hearing too his harsh loud staccato voice speaking in sardonic humorous invective against the errors of the world.

Such were the "Original" spirits who led our Profession half a century ago. The Gods have departed. "Leadership" now lies with the "Deans' Executive Committees" compounded of medical mediocrities or with the lay bureaucrats of Socialized Medicine! Having lost Men to lead us, we shall surely dwindle into a necessary "City Service,"—like the Department of Sanitation. We shall cease to be a learned profession and shall become instead a Union of Slick Gadgeteers,—of proletariat proclivities and level!

NEW YORK CITY   FOSTER KENNEDY

References

[1]Brain, Lond., 1909, 32: 303–326 (Hughlings–Jackson Lecture). [2]Lancet, Lond., 1903, 2: 993–997.   [3]A manual of diseases of the nervous system. 2 vol. London, Churchill, 1886–88.

Reference to Biography: Sir William Gowers, 1845–1915. A bibliographical appreciation. London, Heineman, 1949 (contains complete bibliography) (Critchley).

WILLIAM ALEXANDER HAMMOND (1828–1900)

*H*ammond, a native of Maryland and the son of a physician, entered the U. S. Army Medical Department as assistant surgeon early in his career (1849). His first tour of duty was in the Southwest, where he took part in many campaigns against the Indians. After a few years an illness brought him extended sick leave which he spent in Europe making an intensive study of military hospitals. On his return a friendship with Weir Mitchell was kindled by their mutual interest in arrow and ordeal poisons and snake venoms, on the latter of which they published an account in 1859 in the *American Journal of Medicine*. Hammond's academic interests were the cause of his resignation from the army in 1860 to accept the chair of anatomy and physiology at the University of Maryland.

At the outbreak of the War Between the States he re-entered the army as an assistant surgeon, and from the standpoint of future promotions was placed at the bottom of the list. But his accomplishments as inspector of camps and hospitals were of such merit that despite his youth—he was then 34—he received from President Lincoln the appointment of Surgeon General (1862). His tenure was notable for many important accomplishments. Among them was the founding in 1862 of the Army Medical Museum, known more recently (1949) as the Armed Forces Institute of Pathology. In the same year he began with his distinguished associates J. H. Brinton, J. J. Woodward and G. A. Otis the work of compiling and preparing for the press those weighty and invaluable tomes compris-

William Alexander Hammond

ing the *Medical and surgical history of the War of the Rebellion*,[1] of which Rudolf Virchow stated (1874): "Whoever takes in hand and examines these comprehensive publications will continually have his astonishment excited anew by the riches of the experience purchased at so dear a price, which is there recorded . . ."[7]

Portrait, courtesy of the Army Medical Library, Washington, D. C.

The strained personal relations and constant friction between General Hammond and Secretary of War Stanton—the former of keen intellect and indomitable spirit and, to some, pompous and arrogant, the latter autocratic, of irascible temper, unrelenting in his prejudices—came to a climax in 1863 when General Hammond was ordered on an extended, apparently permanent, inspection tour, a situation which caused him to demand the restoration of the pre-rogatives of his office or trial by court-martial. Tried by a "packed court" on the charge of irregularities incident to the purchase of medical supplies, General Hammond received a verdict of guilty. He was dismissed from the army in 1864, but more than a decade later (1878) by Act of Congress he was vindicated and his former rank of Brigadier General restored. It was some years later that he donned his resplendent dress uniform to sit for his portrait, shown herewith.

Shortly after the trial, Hammond went to New York where he established a practice of neurology. Ultimately he became professor at the University of the City of New York (1874), and at Bellevue Hospital Medical College (1876), and at the peak of his career was earning well over fifty thousand dollars a year. He was among those who founded the American Neurological Association. In 1888 he returned to Washington, where some years later he died of a cardiac ailment.

Hammond shares with Weir Mitchell the distinction of having se-cured for neurology its place in the orbit of American medicine. What raised him most above the rank and file was his observation in 1869 of a bizarre unilateral muscular affliction, for which he coined the term "athetosis" (from the Greek, "without fixed position"). In his report of two cases, published in 1871 in his *Treatise on diseases of the nervous system* (New York, Appleton; ed. 6, 1876)—a volume announced as "the first textbook on nervous diseases in the English language"—he predicted that the responsible lesion would be found in the striatum; and post-morten examination of one of the patients some twenty years later (1890) proved him to be correct. In the meantime, however (1876), Gowers[2] had performed an autopsy in a case of hemiathetosis—the first such reported—and he had found a puckered scar in the contralateral thalamus. Involuntary, slow, grotesque flexion and extension movements of the fingers in associa-tion with spastic hemiplegia had been described by Cazauvielh[3] as early as 1827 in his famous study of cortical hemiatrophy, but it was Hammond who forcibly emphasized that athetosis is an entity. His suggestion that the terms "spasmoparalysis" and "spastic-contracture" be replaced by "athetosis" was not followed by his good friend Weir Mitchell, who referred to post-hemiplegic movements as "hemichorea,"[4] nor by Gowers, who used the term "mobile spasm."[2] Charcot[5] also was critical of Hammond's definition, and stated that athetosis is nothing else than a variety of chorea. Greidenberg[6] seems to have been the first to have given Hammond due credit. When, in time, Hammond's definition of athetosis was broadened, the term finally was adopted.

Hammond was an uncommonly tall and large man with a voice so powerful that it could be heard up-wind in a hurricane. As lecturer, playwright and novelist he had the opportunity of exercising to the full his penchant for theatrical action. There was a substantial dash of Paracelsus in him. Not only was he an outstanding leader and talented organizer, but he was also an aristocrat among the laborers in the neurological field. He remains a "brave figure of the past, a reminder of the days when words were plain and men were men" (Ducan).

WASHINGTON, D. C.   WEBB HAYMAKER

References

[1]By Woodward and Otis, under direction of the U. S. Surgeon General. 2 vol. in 6. Washington, D. C., Govt. Printing Office, 1870–80.   [2]Med.-Chir. Soc. Tr., 1876, 59: 271–326.   [3]Arch. Gen. Med., 1827, 14: 5–33 et seq.   [4]Am. J. M. Sc., 1874, 68: 342–352.   [5]Lectures on the diseases of the nervous system. Philadelphia, Lea, 1879 (trans. by Sigerson); p. 390.   [6]Arch. Psychiat., Berl., 1886, 17: 131–216.   [7]Die Fortschritte der Kriegsheilkunde, besonders im Gebiete der Infectionskrankheiten. Berlin, Hirschwald, 1874; p. 7.

References to Biography and Works: 1) Mil. Surgeon, 1929, 64: 98–110 et seq. (Ducan).   2) Army Med. Bull., 1940, 52: 42–46 (Phalen). 3) Chiefs of the Medical Department, United States Army, 1775–1940. Biographical sketches. Washington, D. C., privately printed, 1940 (Phalen).   4) Disease of the basal ganglia and subthalamic nuclei. New York, Oxford Univ. Press, 1946 (Denny-Brown).   5) Arch. Neur. Psychiat., Chic., 1950, 63: 875–901 (Carpenter).   6) Neurology, 1951, 1: 1–17 (Pearce Bailey).

SIR HENRY HEAD (1861–1940)

*H*enry Head came of an old Quaker family of Stamford Hill in
England. In 1880 he was elected to a scholarship at Trinity
College, Cambridge, where, with Langley and Sherrington, he was
strongly influenced by the physiologists Gaskell and Michael Foster.
After graduating B.A. with honors in natural science he spent two
years in the German University of Prag and the University of Halle.
He is reputed to have introduced the game of association football to
Prag, where it has since assumed the popularity of a national pastime.

Head's first paper was on the action potential of nerve. From
Hering's laboratory in Halle in 1889, he published a masterly treatise
on the respiratory effects of the vagus nerve. Head then graduated
in medicine following study in University College Hospital, London.
His M.D. thesis in 1892, *On disturbance of sensation, with special
reference to the pain of visceral disease,*[1] was of outstanding merit.
At the instigation of Hitzig, Head's studies on disturbance of cutaneous sensibility resulting from visceral disorders were brought out in
book form in German.[2]

Head's study of pain referred from deep structures led him to
study zona (herpes), from which his investigation of the dermatomes
naturally evolved.[3] It was typical of his enthusiasm that he lived
in a mental hospital for two years in order to obtain firsthand information on the herpes that was then common in paretics. Foerster
called attention to the remarkable accuracy of Head's observations
when compared with the method of section of nerve roots. In 1898
Head was elected assistant physician to the London Hospital and
was occupied in hospital and private practice to the time of his retirement in 1925.

Following his study on dermatomes, Head's investigations were
devoted almost wholly to the sensory system, to every division of
which his stimulating thought and refinement of clinical method
brought order out of chaos. With Rivers' assistance, he made many
observations on himself in 1903 after sectioning the superficial ramus
of his own radial nerve. He undertook this auto-experiment because
of his annoyance when his patients became weary after an hour's ex-
ploration of a restricted skin area. He further states in his account
of the experiment that for two years before the experiment began

Sir Henry Head

he had given up smoking, and that he abstained from alcohol in this period, except on holidays!

Pre-eminent was his paper with Gordon Holmes in 1911 on sensory disturbances from cerebral lesions.[4] His collected papers on sensation appeared in 1920.[5] His postulate of two separate sensory

Portrait, courtesy of the Army Medical Library, Washington, D. C.

systems—protopathic and epicritic—to explain the different susceptibilities of sensation, did not survive more detailed quantitative studies. It nevertheless served a valuable immediate purpose in throwing into high relief the important practical implications of the new knowledge of sensory dissociation. The clinical facts which Head and his collaborators established remain the basis for the greater part of clinical investigation of sensation today, and one has only to review the knowledge of sensory disorders before Head's investigations to realize the magnitude of his contribution. His extensive study of the reflex functions of the spinal cord also brought new light and abundant stimulus to this problem. His contribution to aphasia[6] was no less monumental, for his originality of thought brought new definition to the more complex aspects of disorders of speech and their relation to intellect. The full implications of this work are even yet not generally recognized. Russell Brain, in his *Diseases of the nervous system* (ed. 3, London, Oxford Univ. Press, 1947), has provided a resumé of Head's views on aphasia in the light of previous contributions. Head's other writings include a volume of attractive verse.[7]

Head was editor of *Brain* from 1910 to 1925, and the honor of knighthood was conferred on him in 1927. He became fluent in German and French, so much at ease in these languages that at the customs barriers the officials were often in doubt as to his nationality. A man of great patience, humility, and profound learning, he was fated to endure, for the last twenty years of his life, the prolonged physical discomfort and incapacity brought about by paralysis agitans. Even in this period his lively mind and indomitable enthusiasm immensely stimulated the fortunate few who were privileged to enjoy his conversation.

BOSTON, MASSACHUSETTS   D. DENNY-BROWN

References

[1]Brain, Lond., 1893, *16*: 1–133; 1894, *17*: 339–480; 1896, *19*: 153–276.
[2]*Die Sensibilitätsstörungen der Haut bei Visceralerkrankungen* (trans. by Seiffer, with foreword by Hitzig). Berlin, Hirschwald, 1898.
[3]Brain, Lond., 1900, *23*: 353–523.   [4]*Ibid.*, 1911, *34*: 102–271.   [5]*Studies in neurology.* 2 vol. London, Oxford Univ. Press, 1920.   [6]*Aphasia and kindred disorders of speech.* 2 vol. Cambridge, Univ. Press, 1926.
[7]*Destroyers, and other verses.* London, Oxford Univ. Press, 1919.

References to Biography: 1) Brit. M. J., 1940, 2: 539–541 (not signed).
2) Brain, Lond., 1940, 63: 205–208 (contains bibliography; not signed).
3) Arch. Neur. Psychiat., Chic., 1941, 45: 698–702 (Kennedy).

JAMES RAMSAY HUNT (1872–1937)

R amsay Hunt was born in Philadelphia, received his academic
education in that city, and obtained his medical degree from
the University of Pennsylvania in 1893. After studying in Paris,
Vienna and Berlin, he settled in New York City to practice medicine.
Very early he evinced great interest in neurology. Although he
made his chief contributions in this field, toward the end of his
career he became interested in the relationship of neurology and
psychiatry, or what is today euphemistically called psychosomatics.
After serving from 1900 to 1910 as assistant instructor at Cornell
University Medical School under Charles Loomis Dana (1852–
1935), he was made associate professor of nervous diseases to the
College of Physicians and Surgeons of Columbia University, then
professor (1924). He was associated with the Montefiore Hospital
and with the New York Neurological Institute, and served as neurological consultant to numerous hospitals. He was president of the
New York Neurological Society (1909–10) and the American Neurological Association (1920). His alma mater conferred upon him the
D.Sc. *honoris causa* in 1931. During World War I he served over-
seas as lieutenant colonel in the Medical Corps of the United States
Army.

Hunt published numerous articles on a variety of neurological subjects, but his main contributions dealt with the seventh cranial nerve,
more particularly the geniculate syndrome, which bears his name,
and with the basal ganglia. His initial paper on herpetic inflammation of the geniculate ganglion appeared in 1907.[1] Two years later
Hunt published a study of the sensory system of the seventh nerve
and its symptomatology,[2] and it was at about this time that L. P.
Clark and A. S. Taylor, of New York, performed their historic operation for the relief of peri-otitic tic douloureux, which consisted of
transection of the root of the facial nerve, the nervus intermedius,
and the upper fasciculus of the acoustic nerve.[3,4] Then followed
his study of the symptom-complex of the "acute posterior poliomyelitis" of the geniculate, auditory, glossopharyngeal and vagal

James Ramsay Hunt

ganglia,[5] and in 1915 he announced further disclosures concerning the sensory field of the seventh nerve.[6] Thirty years after his first paper on the sensory aspects of the seventh nerve had appeared, he brought together in a masterly and detailed exposé[7] the many data on geniculate neuralgia which he had accumulated. This article included a review of the literature and a series of superb illustrations on the anatomy concerned.

Following Kinnier Wilson's epoch-making contribution on lenticular degeneration in 1912, neurologists the world over became inter-

Portrait, courtesy of Dr. I. S. Wechsler, New York City. (Photographer: Blackstone Studios, New York City.)

ested in the basal ganglia and extrapyramidal motor system, a field hitherto little explored. In 1916, Hunt wrote a detailed review of dystonia musculorum deformans,[8] and in the same year he completed a monograph on progressive atrophy of the globus pallidus, regarded by him as "a system disease of the paralysis agitans type characterized by atrophy of the motor cells of the globus pallidus mechanism."[9] This monograph carried a chapter on the anatomy of the corpus striatum and another on juvenile paralysis agitans, on which he wrote a more detailed account in 1918.[10] The subject of atrophy of the large motor cells of the corpus striatum was pursued further in 1917 in an exposition of the presenile type of paralysis agitans[11-13]; and in 1920, in his presidential address before the American Neurological Association, he summed up his views in a discussion of the static and kinetic systems of motility.[14]

Hunt best typified the neurologist who is single-minded in the pursuit of one or two subjects. His scholarship, though wide, was reflected chiefly in the two fields he plowed so thoroughly. Whereas subsequent investigations of the extrapyramidal motor system have called into question some of Hunt's concepts, the geniculate syndrome has remained a permanent contribution.

Hunt was a superior and outstanding person. He possessed a fine character, an imposing appearance, and the manner of a true gentleman. He had deep intelligence, marked by its best index—a genuine sense of humor. It was a real privilege to work with him, as this writer can recall with pleasure from an association over many years.

NEW YORK CITY   I. S. WECHSLER

References

[1]J. Nerv. Ment. Dis., 1907, 34: 73–96.   [2]Ibid., 1909, 36: 321–350.   [3]J. Am. M. Ass., 1909, 53: 2144–2146.   [4]J. Nerv. Ment. Dis., 1910, 37: 242–243.   [5]Arch. Int. M., 1910, 5: 631–675.   [6]Brain, Lond., 1915, 38: 418–446.   [7]Arch. Neur. Psychiat., Chic., 1937, 37: 253–285.   [8]J. Am. M. Ass., 1916, 67: 1430–1437.   [9]Tr. Am. Neur. Ass., 1916, 42: 104–170. [10]Neur. Bull., N. Y., 1918, 1: 237–242.   [11]Tr. Ass. Am. Physicians, 1917, 32: 567–570.   [12]Brain, Lond., 1917, 40: 58–148.   [13]J. Nerv. Ment. Dis., 1917, 44: 437–442.   [14]Arch. Neurol. Psychiat., Chic., 1920, 4: 353–369.

References to Biography: 1) Tr. Ass. Am. Physicians, 1938, 53: 12–13 (Cobb, Draper, Meyer).   2) Tr. Am. Neur. Ass., 1938, 64: 219–222 (Jel-

liffe).   3) Arch. Neur. Psychiat., Chic., 1938, *39:* 600 (not signed).
4) *Semi-Centennial anniversary volume of the American Neurological
Association, 1875–1924.* Albany, N. Y., Boyd, 1924.

GEORGE SUMNER HUNTINGTON (1850–1916)

George Huntington was born in East Hampton, Long Island, New
York. His grandfather, Dr. Abel Huntington, had settled in
East Hampton in 1797, and his father, Dr. George Lee Huntington,
spent many years in the practice of medicine in that locality.

After receiving preliminary training from his father, Huntington
attended the College of Physicians and Surgeons of Columbia University, graduating in 1871. He returned to East Hampton to assist
his father in practice, and was able to observe further the cases of
hereditary chorea which he had first seen with his grandfather and
father. It was here that in all probability he began his paper on
chorea, as his father's correctional marks have been found on the
original manuscript. Later in the same year he moved to Pomeroy,
Ohio, and on February 15, 1872, he read his paper, *On chorea,*[1] before the Meigs and Mason Academy of Medicine in Middleport,
Ohio. In 1874 he moved to New York, and aside from two years
in North Carolina, spent the remainder of his life in the practice of
medicine in Dutchess County. He retired in 1915.

Huntington's one major scientific contribution dealt with the
subject of chorea in general, but it included his description of the
hereditary form which he had observed in East Hampton. He
stressed as marked peculiarities of the disease its hereditary nature,
its occurrence only in adult life, and the tendency for patients so
afflicted to become insane and sometimes suicidal. Speaking before
the New York Neurological Society on December 7, 1909, he stated
that without the facts and observations imparted to him by his grandfather and father he could never have formulated a picture of the
salient characteristics of the disease. From personal memories he
recounted: "Over fifty years ago, in riding with my father on his
professional rounds, I saw my first case of 'that disorder,' which was
the way in which the natives always referred to the dreaded disease.
It made a most enduring impression upon my boyish mind, an impression every detail of which I recall today, an impression which
was the very first impulse to my choosing chorea as my virgin con-

tribution to medical lore. We suddenly came upon two women, mother and daughter, both tall, thin, almost cadaverous, both bowing, twisting, grimacing. I stared in wonderment, almost fear. What could it mean? My father paused to speak with them and we passed on. Then my Gamaliel-like instruction began; my medical instruction had its inception. From this point on my interest in the disease has never wholly ceased."

Portrait, courtesy of Dr. Edwin G. Zabriskie, New York City.

Even though it has since been shown that previous workers had described the same condition, Huntington, by his lucid, concise and accurate account of the disease, deserves the credit of having been the discoverer of the disorder which bears his name. But the study of this family did not rest with Huntington's description of it. Jelliffe[2] and Tilney[3] took up the task of tracing the ancestry of the families concerned, a study concluded some years later by Vessie (1932),[4] who found that they stemmed from two brothers and their families who left Bures (in Essex) for Suffolk, England, and then sailed to Boston Bay in 1630. During the intervening three centuries about 1,000 descendents of the original settlers were known to have come down with the disease. Not a few of these unfortunate persons were tried for witchcraft in the Colonial courts, and in other ways, too, they were persecuted because their involuntary movements were interpreted as "a derisive pantomine of the sufferings of the Saviour during crucifixion." Among the pioneers in the study of the pathologic changes in the basal ganglia in this disease were Jelgersma,[5] Alzheimer,[6] Pfeiffer,[7] Marie and Lhermitte,[8] and C. and O. Vogt.[9]

Huntington was a general practitioner of medicine; his major interests were his patients and their problems. No faculty appointments came his way, nor did he perform any significant research. Because of his attractive personality, keen intellect, ready wit, and sense of humor, he was widely admired and respected. He had a great fondness for music and often played the flute to his wife's accompaniment. Moreover, he was an ardent student of nature and a devotee of the rod and gun. Drawing was one of his lifetime interests and he often made sketches of game birds during his trips through the woods. Here, then, was a man who enjoyed life to the full, and who, because of his insight and imagination, gained a place in neurological history.

ANN ARBOR, MICHIGAN   RUSSELL N. DE JONG

References

[1]Med. & Surg. Reporter, Phila., 1872, 26: 317–321.   [2]Neurographs, 1908, 1: 116–124.   [3]Ibid., p. 124–127.   [4]J. Nerv. Ment. Dis., 1932, 76: 553–573.   [5]Verh. Ges. Deut. Naturf., 1908, 80, 2.Teil, 2.Hälfte; p. 383–388. [9]Neur. Cbl., 1911, 30: 891–892.   [7]Brain, Lond., 1913, 35: 276–291. [8]Ann. méd., Par., 1914, 1: 18–47.   [9]J. Psychol. Neur., Lpz., 1920, 25, Erg. Heft: 627–846.

References to Biography and Works: 1) Ann. M. Hist., 1937, n.s., *9:* 201–
210 (DeJong).   2) *Diseases of the basal ganglia and subthalmic nuclei.*
New York, Oxford Univ. Press, 1946 (Denny-Brown).   3) *Historical introduction: the basal ganglia and their diseases.* In *The diseases of the basal ganglia.* Ass. Research Nerv. & Ment. Dis., Proc., 1942, *21:* 1–20
(Lewy).

JOHN HUGHLINGS JACKSON (1835–1911)

O ne of five children, Jackson was born of a farmer father at Providence Green, Hammerton, Yorkshire, England. He had only a grammar school education and his medical training was not impressive. After qualifying for medicine at the age of 21, he worked under Laycock at the York Dispensary. Attracted by the writings of Herbert Spencer, Jackson returned to London in 1859 ready to abandon medicine in favor of philosophy. Sir Jonathan Hutchinson, himself a York man, took credit for dissuading Jackson from this course in favor of medicine. Given an appointment at the Moorfields Eye Hospital, Jackson's interest in the nervous system was stimulated by his peephole view of it through the ophthalmoscope, invented by Helmholtz 10 years before. In 1860 the National Hospital, Queen Square, London, was founded, with Brown-Séquard as physician-in-chief, and in 1862 Jackson became a member of the staff of this hospital where he worked for the next 45 years. His early interest in seizures was doubtless sustained through his many years by the fact that his cousin-wife experienced what we now call jacksonian epilepsy.

W. Russell Brain[1] makes this cogent observation: "The discoverer of a substantial thing, such as a bacillus, an extract or a disease, achieves more certain immortality than one who discovers a principle, for permanently valid principles soon become part of current thought and in time appear so obvious as to have needed no discovery." The name of Jackson is embedded in our everyday medical vocabulary, for at the suggestion of Charcot, seizures that on anatomic grounds might have been termed rolandic, are called jacksonian. However, the man's importance does not rest on his description of a certain seizure pattern, but on his formulation of concepts or principles that explain paroxysmal seizures of all sorts. "Epilepsy is the name for occasional, sudden, excessive, rapid and

local discharge of the gray matter." Far-reaching conclusions regarding neurophysiology were based on meticulous study of a few selected patients, supplemented whenever possible by gross examination of the brain, but without the aid of animal experimentation or the microscope.[2-7]

Jackson postulated three evolutionary levels of the sensorimotor

Portrait, courtesy of the Army Medical Library, Washington, D. C.

mechanism: the lowest, cord, medulla and pons; the middle, the rolandic region; the highest level, the prefrontal lobes.[8] He described an evolution from automatic to purposive movements and a dissolution from the purposive to the automatic. Excessive discharge of grey matter is followed by its exhaustion. Discharges from a lower center might result from a loss of inhibition from the highest center. An excessive discharge of the "epileptogenous focus" is a consequence of instability of nerve cells, due in turn to their malnutrition, possibly the result of a defective blood supply.

Many of Jackson's approximately 300 publications appeared in obscure journals. Because of his meager education or his philosophic and meticulous cast of mind, his writing is involved and repetitious, its continuity broken by qualifying statements. He made no use of illustrations, diagrams or statistical data and shirked the task of writing a book. This defect has been made good in part by the volume of *Selected writings* (London, Hodder & Stoughton, 1931), edited by James Taylor. Although Jackson carried on an active practice, his writings reflect no interest in the patient as a person or in his treatment.

Jackson was quiet, unassuming, serious and hobbyless. He was easily fatigued, restless, could not endure boredom, and suffered from vertigo and migraine. Sir Hugh Cairns tells the story that on one occasion Sir Henry Head emerged from "Queen Square" jubilant over a new observation he had made, and spying Jackson standing quietly on the corner, came up to him to relate his find. Jackson interrupted him with the remark: "Don't bother me now, Head. I'm making some observations on my own migraine." Childless, he lived alone for 35 years after the early death of his wife from cerebral thrombosis. He died of pneumonia at the age of 76. He joined Ferrier, Bucknill and Crichton-Browne as editors of *Brain* when that great periodical was established in 1878. "Father of British Neurology," he was foremost of the brilliant staff that made "Queen Square" a center of world neurology. Best of all, he subjected the ancient ill of epilepsy to the genius of his scrutiny, and thereby opened a door of hope on this hitherto hopeless disease.

BOSTON, MASSACHUSETTS   WILLIAM G. LENNOX

References

[1]Postgrad. M. J., Lond., 1935, *11*: 145–149.   [2]Med. Times Gaz., 1864, *50*: 166–167.   [3]*Ibid.*, 1864, *50*: 167.   [4]Trans. St. Andrew's Med. Grad. Ass., 1870, *3*: 162–207.   [5]Brit. M. J., 1875, *1*: 773–774.   [6]Brain, Lond., 1888, *11*: 179–207 *et seq.*   [7]Brit. M. J., 1890, *1*: 703–707 *et seq.* [8]Lancet, Lond., 1898, *1*: 79–87.

References to Biography: 1) Postgrad. M. J., Lond., 1935, *11*: 145–149 (Brain).   2) Bull. N. York Acad. M., 1935, *11*: 479–480 (Kennedy). 3) Brit. M. J., 1911, *2*: 950–954 *et seq.* (Hutchinson).   4) *Ibid.*, 1912, *1*: 85 (Mercier). 5) Brain, Lond., 1903, *26*: 305–366 (Broadbent). 6) *Ibid.*, 1915, *28*: 1–190 (Head).

SERGEI SERGEIVICH KORSAKOV (1853–1900)

*T*he first great psychiatrist of Russia, Korsakov ranks high among *The founders of neurology* through his many contributions to the knowledge of organic psychoses.   He was born on the Gus estate (Vladimir Province), a locality known for its glass factory, of which his father was the manager.   He studied medicine at the University of Moscow, and upon graduating in 1875 became physician to Preobrazhenskii Hospital.   From 1876 to 1879 he was on Kozhevnikov's staff in the clinic for nervous diseases.   His thesis on "alcoholic paralysis"[1] won him the M.D. in 1887.   In the following year he received the title of Privatdozent, and in 1892 he became superintendent to the newly opened University Psychiatric Clinic and Professor Extraordinarius.   During this time he visited Vienna where he was a pupil of Meynert.

The general recognition of Korsakov as an original thinker is largely due to his description of the disorder which bears his name. In 1887[2] and again in 1890[3] he drew attention to several cases of alcoholic polyneuritis with distinctive mental symptoms: faulty retention of impressions, amnesia, disorientation in time and place, and confabulation.   "This mental disorder," he said, "appears at times in the form of sharply delineated irritable weakness of the mental sphere, at times in the form of confusion with characteristic mistakes in orientation for place, time and situation, and at times as an almost pure form of acute amnesia, where the recent memory is most severely involved, while the remote memory is well preserved ... Some have suffered so widespread memory loss that they literally

forget everything immediately."[4]   In another paper in 1890[5] he emphasized, as he had in his previous publications, that this amnestic-confabulatory syndrome, which he called "cerebropathia psychica toxaemica" could occur in a great variety of disorders other than alcoholism and even without neuritis.   In time it became customary to apply the term "Korsakov's psychosis" only when the mental disorder was accompanied by neuritic symptoms.   Jolly[6] introduced that eponymic term and full credit for this contribution was given Korsakov by others as well,[7] though he himself[5] accorded priority to Magnus Huss.

Portrait, courtesy of Dr. Maurice Genty, Académie de Médecine, Paris, France.

But Korsakov's reputation was not based on a single observation: He struck out into the whole field of psychiatry with telling effect, orienting psychiatry to medicine, and bringing his efforts to bear on the social factors in psychiatry. He is credited with establishing the concept of paranoia ("paranoia hyperphantasica," as he called it)[8]; his textbook on psychiatry[9] compared favorably with the best contemporary works in other languages; his classification of mental diseases[8] offered distinct advantages over that of Krafft-Ebing, which was more generally accepted; and his elaboration of memory disturbance in alcoholism, described in Bumke's *Handbuch*,[10] added further to his fame. He was responsible for freeing mental patients from straitjackets and other restraints. The "no-restraint" principle was not popular with the hospital personnel for, as Korsakov remarked, "The less restraint for the patient, the more restraint for the doctor," that is, he must give "more attention, affection and devotion to the patient."[8] Another new therapeutic measure advocated and practiced by Korsakov was the family care of psychotic patients—transferring them from psychiatric institutions to families on farms, under close hospital supervision. He raised the question "whether rest cure, indiscriminately used might not be apt to inhibit the energies and the guiding forces of the intellect," and in regard to narcotics, he warned that their use should be solely for the purpose of calming the patient.[7]

Korsakov was deeply respected by his colleagues and students. His humanitarianism may be traced to his boyhood: when only eleven he wrote, "Help others. When the occasion presents itself to do good deeds, do them. Withdraw from evils." To this principle he remained true. He deplored the fact that students had to waste their energies obtaining the bare necessities of life when they should be concentrating on their studies, and as chairman of "The Society for Aid to Needy Students," he did much to alleviate their financial difficulties. But he also clearly indicated what he expected of students: "First of all I wish that all students recognize the absolute necessity of education; that they deeply love science and knowledge, and that they despise ignorance ... For the great privilege of being educated, students must be ready to sacrifice, even to pay with their lives if necessary, for the good of the Country and for the ideals of mankind." One of Korsakov's pupils was Serbskii, who at a meeting of Russian psychiatrists, in 1911, achieved fame for his attack on the government for its disregard of the social services. Reforms soon followed.

An able organizer, Korsakov was instrumental in founding in 1890 the Moscow Society of Neuropathologists and Psychiatrists. In his opening address, he laid down as the basic principle for each member, "to further scientific knowledge without being concerned who will be first to reach a scientific achievement."

A high point in his career was the organization of the 12th International Medical Congress, which was held in Moscow in 1897. He then set out to achieve a lifelong ambition: namely, to establish a Russian Association of Psychiatrists and Neurologists which would have national scope. He worked out the constitution in all details, but worn by the intensity of his striving he died, at the age of 46, just before the Association came into being. The warmth of his heart and his many contributions left an indelible mark on the scientists of his time. By acclamation the *Zhurnal neuropatologii i psikhiatrii* was named after him. He is to be counted among such "moral geniuses" as Pinel and Charcot.

WASHINGTON, D. C.   S. KATZENELBOGEN

References

[1]*Ob alkogolnom paralichie.* Moskva, Kushnerev, 1887. [2]Arkh. Psikhiat. Nevrol., 1887, 9, No. 2: 16–38; No. 3: 1–14. [3]Arch. Psychiat., Berl., 1890, 21: 669–704. [4]Trans. from Bull. Johns Hopkins Hosp., 1942, 70: 467–487 (Gantt and Muncie). [5]Allg. Zschr. Psychiat., 1890, 46: 475–485. [6]Charité Ann., Berl., 1897, 22: 580–612. [7]Sovremennaia psikhiat., 1911, 5: 16–51 (Geiner). [8]Vopr. filosof. psikhol., 1901, 12: XIII–XXXVIII (Serbskii). [9]*Kurs psikhiatri.* Moskva, Kushnerev, 1893. (ed. 2, Moskva, Rikhter, 1901). [10]Bumke, O., *Handbuch der Geisteskrankheiten,* Berlin, 1928, 7 (Spez. Teil III): 271–285 (in chapter by Meggendorfer).

References to Biography and Works: 1) Med. obozrenie, 1900, 53: 948–951. 2) Zh. nevropat. psikhol. imeni Korsakova, 1900, 1: 1–40 (Rot). 3) Vopr. filosof. psikhol., 1901, 12: I–XII (Rot). 4) Sovremennaia psikhiat., 1911, 5: 1–10 (Melnikov-Razvendenskov). 5) *Ibid.,* p. 10–15 (Ferkhmin). 6) Vopr. filosof. psikhol., 1900, 11: V–XIX (Lopatin *et al.*). 7) Am. J. Psychiat., 1939, 95: 887–899 (Tarachow).

ALEKSEI YAKOVLEVICH KOZHEVNIKOV (1836–1902)

*K*ozhevnikov (or Kojevnikoff, Kogevnikoff, Koschewnikow, etc.) was born in Ryazan, where he early proved himself a brilliant student. He entered the University of Moscow in 1853, and received the M.D. in 1860. His doctoral dissertation, presented in 1865, was on progressive locomotor ataxia.

The interest that Kozhevnikov had shown in nervous diseases prompted the state to send him abroad, in 1866, for further study, principally to Germany, and also to England, Switzerland and France. In Charcot's laboratory in Paris he showed that in amyotrophic lateral sclerosis the nerve degeneration in the form of *corps granuleux* could be followed up to the motor cortex, a most important contribution to the pathology of this morbid condition.

Upon his return to Russia he was named Dozent in nervous and mental diseases at the Novo-Ekaterininskii Hospital. He became the first neuropathologist and the first alienist of the Moscow faculty. For three years, starting in 1871, he had charge of a course in general pathology and therapeutics. Later he was invested with the newly created chair in nervous and mental diseases in Moscow. He initiated the reconstruction of the psychiatric clinic, which his brilliant young pupil Korsakov, who later was Kozhevnikov's assistant, built into the Moscow school of psychiatry. His interest in psychiatry went much further than the scientific aspects: he was also motivated by a great humanitarian interest in championing the protection of the insane throughout the Russian empire. Kozhevnikov also founded the neurological clinic in Moscow, establishing in the latter a neurological museum, financed largely by himself. In conjunction with his students, he also founded the Moscow Society of Neurology and Psychiatry, over which he presided for several years.

Kozhevnikov's earlier work was mainly in the field of neuroanatomy, in which he was concerned especially with the nerve fiber connections in the cerebellar and cerebral cortices.[1,2] He is perhaps best known for his description of an atypical form of convulsive seizure[3,4] of cortical origin, which has generally been referred to as epilepsia partialis continua (Kozhevnikov's epilepsy). When he reported the condition to the Moscow Society of Neurology and Psychiatry, Nil Filatov, the famous Russian pediatrician, commented

Aleksei Yakovlevich Kozhevnikov

that this was an observation ranking in importance with that made by Hughlings Jackson on another seizure pattern, called cortical epilepsy. His work on lathyrism[5] is regarded as a classic. He described progressive familial spastic diplegia,[6] and wrote on the neuropathology of nuclear ophthalmoplegia,[7] myasthenia, and bulbar paralysis. His textbook on nervous diseases[8] was a popular manual because of its brevity and lucidity. He was editor of the *Zhurnal nevropatologii i psikhiatrii* (Korsokav's journal).

Kozhevnikov was a man whom nature favored with a kindly spirit, great industry, and a high degree of intelligence. His ability as a speaker, his critical judgment and his quiet dignity won for him a position of leadership in all his endeavors. On the occasion of the 25th anniversary of the completion of his doctoral thesis, his friends and pupils, as a mark of devotion, published in book form his many

Portrait, courtesy of the Armed Forces Institute of Pathology, Washington, D. C. (From portrait in *Méd. mod., Par., suppl.*, 6: 357, 1895.)

papers.[9] Although a Russian patriot, Kozhevnikov was not a nationalist: he had a profound respect for the advances made in other countries, giving credit where it was due. Minor, in referring to him, said that in his passing—he died of cancer after a long illness—Russian science had lost a creator, and western Europe an earnest, forceful and true friend.

NEW YORK CITY   DOROTHY GOODENOW

                                                FRED A. METTLER

References

[1]Arch. neur., Par., 1883, 6: 356–376.   [2]Arch. mikr. Anat., 1869, 5: 332–333.   [3]Tr. Obshch. nevropat. Mosk., 1893–94; p. 30.   [4]Neur. Cbl., 1895, 14: 47–48.   [5]Latirizm-boliezn obuslovlennaya upotrebleniyem v pishtshu govokha; lathyrus. St. Petersburg, Stasyulevich, 1894.   [6]Med. obozr., Mosk., 1895, 43: 329–366.   [7]Ibid., 1887, 27: 148–159.   [8]Kurs nervnikh bolieznei; lekstsii. Moskva, Volchanimov, 1892.   [9]Sbovnik statei po neuropatologii i psikhiatri. Moskva, Kushner, 1890.

References to Biography: 1) Med. obozr., Mosk., 1902, 57: 342–352 (contains bibliography; Pribytkov).   2) Arch. Psychiat., Berl., 1902, 35: 874–875 (Minor).   3) Méd. mod., Par., 1895, suppl., 6: 357–358 (not signed).

LOUIS THÉOPHILE JOSEPH LANDOUZY (1845–1917)

*L*andouzy was a native of Reims, where his father held a chair in the school of medicine. Upholding the family tradition, he began his professional studies in Reims and continued them in Paris. Here he obtained the M.D. on the basis of his thesis entitled *Contribution à l'étude des convulsions et paralysies liées aux méningo-encéphalites fronto-pariétales* (Thèse de Paris, 1876). Under the tutelage of Charcot he worked on tuberculous meningitis and on diphtheritic paralysis, both reported in *Des paralysies dans les maladies aiguës* (Thèse de Paris, 1880).

Landouzy held places of high position and was accorded numerous honors. He was appointed assistant professor of the faculty of medicine in 1877, became professor in the medical clinic in 1901, and was elected dean of the faculty of medicine in 1901, a position which he held the remainder of his life. Near the end of his career

Louis Théophile Joseph Landouzy

he was awarded the Médaille des Épidémies in recognition of his services in preventive medicine, especially tuberculosis. He was editor-in-chief of the *Revue de médecine* and scientific director of the *Presse médicale*.

From the beginning he was occupied with neurological questions. In 1879 appeared his important work on conjugate deviation of the eyes.[1,2] Prévost's[3] observation in 1868 that in cerebral apoplexy the eyes are deviated temporarily toward the affected side was supplemented by Landouzy, who found that the same occurred after de-

Portrait, courtesy of Dr. Maurice Genty, Académie de Médecine, Paris, France. (Photographer: Henri Manuel, Paris.)

struction of the cerebral cortex. Grasset noted in the same year (1879)[4] that lesions of the pons may also cause conjugate ocular deviation, but toward the unaffected side. Knowledge of convergence movements of the eyes was to come later. Perlia, of Frankfurt, described his now well-known nucleus in 1889,[5] but it was not until the work of Brouwer in 1928[6] that this nucleus was finally conceded to control ocular convergence.

In 1885 Landouzy described, with Dejerine, the disorder with which his name has been linked—a type of progressive muscular dystrophy in infants which begins in the face and is unaccompanied by lesions of the spinal cord or the nerves (atrophic myopathy, type Landouzy-Dejerine).[7] Other outstanding contributions included a study on blepharoptosis of cerebral origin,[8] and a medical glossary (with F. Jayle).[9] Also he described a classical case of unilateral athetoid movements lasting for 30 years in which a calcified mass in the opposite lenticular nucleus was ultimately found.[10] A crowning achievement was his book with Leon Barnard on *Éléments d'anatomie et de physiologie médicales* (ed. 2, Paris, Masson, 1921).

He was greatly interested in physiotherapy, particularly balneotherapy, and was highly successful in making the virtues of the French spas known. He will best be remembered for his work on tuberculosis. We owe to him the demonstration of the tuberculous nature of acute pleurisy, the delineation of the frequency of the various forms of tuberculosis in children, and the description of a type of acute tuberculosis which he characterized as *typho-bacillose*, in which the ordinary morbid changes of tuberculosis failed to make their appearance. Later he showed that serum from the lesions of erythema nodosum produces tuberculosis when injected into guinea pigs. He worked unstintingly in his fight against tuberculosis, and in the beginning of World War I he never ceased to plead the cause of soldiers discharged from the army because of tuberculosis. He proved himself a great leader at several international congresses on tuberculosis.

Although Landouzy had a brusque, authoritative manner, he was beloved by his students and associates for his intellectual honesty. His outstanding facility in physical examination and his unusual clearness of verbal expression and special flair for using new terms and epigrams made him a highly successful teacher. His interests extended far beyond the realm of medicine; he was a judge of fine art, a bibliophile, and a confirmed traveler. He married a daughter of A. Richet, a distinguished surgeon, but had no children.

He is assured a place of honor in the annals of neurology, but his greatest merit lay in the field of tuberculosis, where he was pre-eminent as therapist, epidemiologist, and sociologist.

PHILADELPHIA, PENNSYLVANIA   BERNARD J. ALPERS

References

[1]*De la déviation conjuguée des yeux et de la rotation de la tête par excitation ou paralysie de 6ᵉ et 11ᵉ paires.* Paris, Delahaye, 1879.   [2]*Progr. méd.,* Par., 1879, 7: 698–701 *et seq.*   [3]*De la déviation conjuguée des yeux et de la rotation de la tête dans certains cas d'hémiplégie.* Thèse de Paris, No. 30, 1868.   [4]*De la déviation conjuguée de la tête et des yeux; contribution à l'étude des localisations cérébrales.* Montpellier, Coulet, 1879.   [5]Arch. Ophth., Berl., 1889, 35 (4):287–308.   [6]Zschr. ges. Neur. Psychiat., 1928, 40: 152–193.   [7]C. rend. Acad. sc., 1884, 98: 53–55. [8]*De le blépharoptose cérébrale.* Paris, Asselin, 1877.   [9]*Glossaire médical.* Paris, Naud, 1912.   [10]Progr. méd., Par., 1876, 6: 79–81 *et seq.*

References to Biography: 1) Rev. méd., Par., 1916, 35: 281–284 (Lépine).   2) Presse méd., Par., 1917, 25: annexes, 281–287 (Helme). 3) Progr. méd. Par., 1917, No. 21; p. 178 (Loeper).   4) Paris méd., 1917, 23: 185–186 (Gilbert).

JEAN BAPTISTE OCTAVE LANDRY DE THÉZILLAT
(1826–1865)

*L*andry was born and brought up in Limoges, France. His uncle, Dr. de Thézillat, a neurologist and psychiatrist of Limoges, did much to influence him in his decision to study medicine. He went to Paris, and in 1850 became externe des hôpitaux. When, at this time, cholera swept into the Département de l'Oise, decimating its population, Landry volunteered his services and distinguished himself in the face of great difficulties. Not until the epidemic had died down did he consent to return to Paris, where a medal commemorating the gratitude of the people of the Oise was struck for him.

Back in Paris he again pursued his medical education, becoming interne under Sandras and Gubler at the Hôtel-Dieu and Hôpital Beaujon. While interne in 1852 he brought forward evidence that movements, both passive and active, are dependent on afferent im-

pulses from muscles—"sens de l'activité," as he called it[1]; and thus his work anticipated the similar studies of Duchenne by three years and Bellion's[2] by two, as has been brought out so well by Bastian.[3] His description in 1855[4] of ataxia in posterior column disease was as graphic and true as Romberg's in 1851.

Landry's celebrated memoir on ascending paralysis appeared in 1859,[5] simultaneously with the first volume of his *Traité complet des paralysies* (Paris; Masson). The memoir dealt with ten cases of this

Portrait, courtesy of Charles Martin de Thézillat, Paris, France.

mysterious malady, five of which had been under his care. The greatness of Landry's report consisted not only in the precision of his observations and the clarity with which he set them down, but in his contention that the disorder could manifest itself in three ways: as an ascending paralysis without sensory signs or symptoms, as an ascending paralysis with concomitant ascending anesthesia and analgesia, and as a progressive generalized polyradiculoneuritis. Landry's concept was lost sight of in the subsequent heated controversy on the nature of the form characterized only by ascending paralysis—whether it was a disease entity affecting the spinal cord or constituted a polyneuritis—until gradually Landry's name came to be associated solely with this form. More recently, however, his concept in its entirety has found complete confirmation.

Although Landry did not determine the nature of the pathologic changes in this disorder, mentioning only that the spinal cord was free from change macroscopically, his contribution helped set the stage for the brilliant work of Louis Duménil (1823–90)[6] on neuritis a few years later (1864 and 1866), and it was the forerunner of a report in 1916[7] on polyradiculoneuritis in two French soldiers by Guillain, Barré and Strohl. This report was significant from the standpoint that the spinal fluid was found to contain an immense amount of protein and no increase in cells. André Strohl, who now is professor in charge of the Laboratoire de Physique Médicale of the Faculté de Médicine of Paris, performed the electrical reactions in these two cases.

Although Landry had opened the door on a fresh new vista, he went no further. There were circumstances to account for this. In 1857 he had married a young lady, Claire Giustigniani (1832–1901), "d'une grande beauté, d'une distinction suprême, mais beaucoup plus riche de noblesse que d'argent," and at about this time his father died, leaving the family in straitened circumstances. To make an adequate livelihood he took charge of the Établissement hydrothérapeutique at Auteuil for the treatment of nervous diseases, and as a result of his unbounding energy achieved financial success and considerable prominence.

Once again Landry's career was interrupted by an epidemic of cholera, which reached the environs of Paris. Oblivious to personal danger he attended the destitute victims unceasingly until he himself contracted the infection. Charcot and Guéneau de Moussy were at his bedside when, a few days later, he died.

Landry had the mark of gentility. He was affable, unusually generous and possessed of *une grande simplicité*. His life was a very full one. Like his father, he was a distinguished violoncellist. He had the voice of a professional singer and was an expert dancer. His elegance was the talk of the salons of Paris. He moved in the circle of artists, and sat for E. Corbet in 1864. Also he was a fervent alpinist, an accomplished horseman and hunter, and a geologist and crystallographer *passioné*.

He had spent his thirty-nine years generously, and although the common people would remember him, he left no impression on his professional colleagues. The *Gazette des hôpitaux* and the *Gazette médicale de Paris*, in obituary notices, devoted a few perfunctory lines to him, and the *Gazette hebdomadaire*, in whose pages his now famous work had appeared six years earlier, even fewer. Apparently none of the obituary writers was aware that a few months previously, Pellegrino-Lévi, in an important paper on descending paralysis, had recognized that Landry had broken new ground.

WASHINGTON, D. C.   WEBB HAYMAKER

References

[1]Arch. gén. méd., 1852, *29:* 257–275 *et seq.*   [2]Thèse de Paris, 1853. [3]Brain, Lond., 1888, *10:* 1–137.   [4]Gaz. hôp., 1855, *28:* 262.   [5]Gaz. hebd. méd., Par., 1859, *6:* 472–474 *et seq.*   [6]Rev. méd. Normandie, 1900, *1:* 195–198 (Halipré).   [7]Bull. Soc. méd. hôp. Paris, 1916, *40:* 1462–1470.

Reference to Biography: Presse méd., Par., 1933, *41:* 227–229 (Remlinger).

ERNEST CHARLES LASÈGUE (1816–1883)

*L*asègue was born in Paris. During his student days he and Claude Bernard roomed together in the Latin Quarter, and often so many of their francs went for the purchase of guinea pigs and rabbits with which to experiment that they did not have enough left to pay their rent. Lasègue had embarked on the study of philosophy, but on listening one day to a lecture by Trousseau at the Hôpital Necker, decided in favor of clinical medicine. Subsequently he

became Trousseau's favorite pupil and frequent collaborator, and on the occasion of Trousseau's death in 1867, he delivered a eulogy which remains to this day one of the finest orations in the French language.

He registered at the Faculté de Médecine in 1839. On obtaining the M.D. in 1847 he was sent by the French government to study the cholera epidemic then raging in southern Russia. In 1853 he won his agrégation on the basis of a thesis on general paralysis,[1] which dealt with a large group of chronic cerebral disorders, comprising

Portrait, courtesy of the Library of the College of Physicians and Surgeons, Philadelphia, Pennsylvania.

several pathological entities. In the same year—he was then 37—he was made, with Valleix and Follin, co-editor of the *Archives géné-rales de médecine*. He became physician to many hospitals in Paris, among them the Salpêtrière, the Necker, and the Pitié. From 1852 to 1854 he was Trousseau's *chef de clinic*.

Lasègue published 115 works. Although he wrote on a wide variety of subjects, psychiatry was his forte. In this field he is best known for his studies on hysteria,[2] dipsomania,[3] delusions of persecution, "folie à deux," catalepsy, and exhibitionism. He was forever after malingerers, varying his tests and traps; and when confronted by a psychotic individual he would give to his listeners the following advice: "Go back in the history of the patient, and if you search carefully you will find the 'ictus' which suddenly destroyed his mental balance. From then on, the brain is like a piano from which certain keys have been removed and which, therefore, produces only imperfect and dissonant chords."

His joust with Virchow was a classic. He had criticized Virchow's *Cellularpathologie* (1858), stating that the disease of cells was only a fragment of pathology. Virchow replied that the only critics he worried about were competent ones, and that thus far he had not heard from them, whereupon Lasègue answered ironically that innovators such as Virchow are like knights who feel that they are fast in the saddle just because they have sharp spurs.

Among his publications in neurology was his classic work on *Les cérébraux*, dealing with vascular disorders of the brain, in which he said that those who have lost their "cerebral virginity" are thereby predisposed to future accidents. Astruc has related in his inimitable way the story of Lasègue's discovery of the sign which bears his name: "On one Sunday morning he thinks of the question which he had been asked by Inspector General Dujardin-Baumetz: how to discover the malingerer simulating sciatica. He promised to study the question; it is ever present in his thoughts. While smoking his pipe, he sees Mme. Lasègue seated at the piano while his son-in-law, Cesbron, is tuning his violin. Is not the string stretched over the bridge like the sciatic nerve which is made taut on the ischium when the lower extremity is elevated? Undoubtedly as he listens to the classical music he has formulated the answer to the Inspector General's question. Tomorrow he will look for the sign in his clinic . . ." In his widely quoted *Considérations sur la sciatique*[4] a description of his sign does not, however, appear. As brought out by Wartenberg,[5] it was only years later that his pupil Forst[6] put the sign on record. Lazarevič, Serbian neurologist, described the sign fully and accurately in 1884,[7] independently of Forst.

Versatile in almost every field of medicine, Lasègue was, indeed, a "universal specialist." His work in neurology which made his name an eponym was but a minor phase of his remarkable career. He was a friend of the arts and a man free of all outward formalities, who in his speech could pass readily from Gallic witticisms to the highest form of eloquence. In defending a broad education based on the humanities, he stated that the time given to these studies is like that which the soldier spends on making his armor shine. Ritti described him at the Infirmerie Spéciale, in a dreary room where daylight hardly ever entered, as "urging, begging, ironical, good-natured, even endearing, permitting the patient to express himself freely or on other occasions asking him innumerable questions, but never tiring until he was sure to have obtained all possible information." When he died of diabetes at the age of 67, France lost one of an illustrious group of physicians which had raised French medicine to its pinnacle.

SAN FRANCISCO, CALIFORNIA   ROBERT AIRD

References

[1]*De la paralysie générale progressive.* Thèse de Paris, 1853.   [2]Arch. gén. méd., Par., 1864, 6.sér., *1:* 385–402.   [3]*Ibid.,* 1882, 7.sér., *10:* 257–271.   [4]*Ibid.,* 1864, 6.sér., *2:* 558–580.   [5]Arch. Neur. Psychiat., Chic., 1951, *66:* 58–60.   [6]Thèse de Paris, 1881.   [7]Allg. Wien. med. Ztg., 1884, *29:* 425–426 *et seq.*

References to Biography and Works: 1) *Essai sur Ch. Lasègue, 1816–1883.* Thèse de Paris, 1908 (Streletski).   2) Biogr. méd., Par., 1934, *8:* 33–64 *et seq.* (Astruc).   3) Ann. médico-psychol., Par., 1885, 7.sér., *2:* 88–121 (Ritti).   4) *Études médicales du Professeur Ch. Lasègue.* 2 vol. Paris, Asselin, 1884 (contains complete works).

HUGO KARL LIEPMANN (1863–1925)

*H*ugo Liepmann was born in Berlin, the son of a Jewish family of culture and wealth. He first studied philosophy and acquired his Ph.D. with a thesis on the atomistic doctrine of Leucippus and Democritus. Later he published a paper on Schopenhauer. He had a deep interest in philosophical problems, but the solutions which he

Hugo Karl Liepmann

found did not satisfy him. He was looking, as one of his friends wrote, for the real and certain things, and as a consequence shifted to natural science and medicine. It has been told that he literally threw the work of a famous Neo-Kantian philosopher into the corner and went to the great anatomist Waldeyer to ask him for an anatomical specimen. But the ardor for philosophy never left him. It later became apparent in his deep interest in the psycho-physical problem of the classification of the processes of thinking and the role ideation plays in action, which found its special reflection in his concept of apraxia.

Liepmann passed his medical examination in 1894, was for a short time assistant of the psychiatrist Jolly, and studied anatomy with Weigert. Then he went to Breslau and came under the influence of Wernicke. He considered himself primarily a pupil of his highly ad-

Portrait, courtesy of the Armed Forces Institute of Pathology, Washington, D. C. (From portrait in *Mschr. Psychiat. Neur.*, 54: frontispiece, 1923.)

mired teacher though he later deviated from his teachings, even op-
posing him on essential points.

He returned in 1899 to Berlin as psychiatrist of the municipal
mental institution of Dalldorf. Here he did the work on apraxia
which made his name famous. In 1901 he became Privatdozent at
the University of Berlin. He was never appointed Ordinarius. According to Oskar Vogt, he was told by faculty members of the
University of Berlin that if he would change his name and adopt
Protestantism a place for him was assured. Although he had no
strong religious convictions in regard to the Jewish faith he decided
not to accept the suggestion. As he was an excellent teacher he
greatly regretted losing this opportunity to exercise his pedagogic
skill to the full. Later he was director of the mental institution at
Herzberge, a position which he was forced to relinquish because of
paralysis agitans. When he could no longer endure the hardships of
this disease he ended his life by taking an overdose of poison. He
had the reputation of being a man of the highest ethical standards, as
exemplified during the blockade of Germany in 1915/16, when he
voluntarily underwent starvation (he lost 60 pounds), refusing to
eat more food than his patients.

Liepmann's earliest paper dealt with alcoholic delirium.[1] In it he
showed for the first time that hallucinations may be evoked arti-
ficially. Then followed studies on word deafness, visual agnosia,
and echolalia—all of which showed his excellent capacity to combine
clinical observation and scientific interpretation. His paper, *Das
Krankheitsbild der Apraxie,* which appeared in 1900,[2] secured for
him at once a place among the eminent men of his profession. The
great merit of this paper was the clarification of the structure of human action ("Bewegungsformel") and of the relation of its single
parts to psychological processes. He distinguished the learned motor
automatisms from the processes which bring them into action, the
ideation. The problem of ideation led him to become preoccupied
with the phenomena of will and recognition. His psychological
analysis of the thinking process in a book entitled *Ideenflucht* (Halle
a.S., Marhold, 1904) is one of the finest representations of this topic
in the literature. He tried to bring all phenomena into relation to
physiological processes. This made possible the separation of different forms of disturbance of action, the recognition of various

types of apraxia, which he illustrated by clinical observations.
He followed, in general, Wernicke's ideas, but went much further
and deeper into psychological and physiological analysis. From his
careful clinical observations came the important discovery of the
dominance of the left hemisphere,[3,4] and it was he who found that
isolated apraxia of the left side of the body is a sign of involvement
of the corpus callosum.[5] He was a theoretical neuroanatomist. One
does not find any patho-anatomical contributions in his papers. The
brains from his patients were sent to his friend, Oskar Vogt, in Berlin-
Buch, who examined them in detail. The Liepmann collection, consisting of about 26 brains and histories, is now at the Vogts' *Institut
für Hirnforschung* in Neustadt/Schwarzwald.

Liepmann's work will remain one of the landmarks in the progress
of our knowledge of the function of the brain. He is a worthy
representative of a great creative epoch in neurology.

NEW YORK CITY   KURT GOLDSTEIN

References

[1]Arch. Psychiat., Berl., 1895, 27: 172–232.   [2]Mschr. Psychiat., 1900, 8:
15–44 *et seq.*   [3]Münch. med. Wschr., 1905, 52: 2322–2326 *et seq.*
[4]*Über Störungen des Handelns bei Gehirnkranken.* Berlin, Karger, 1905.
[5]Med. Klin., Berl., 1907, 3: 725–729 *et seq.*

References to Biography: 1) Psychol. & Med., Stuttg., 1925–26, *1:* 257–
277 (Niessl von Mayendorf).   2) Mschr. Psychiat., 1925, 59: 225–232
(Kramer).   3) Zschr. ges. Neur. Psychiat., 1923, 83: 1–16 (Isserlin).
4) *Ibid.,* 1925, 99: 635–650 (Isserlin; contains bibliography).

PIERRE MARIE (1853–1940)

*P*ierre Marie was born into a wealthy bourgeois family of Paris.
He first studied law but soon turned to medicine. In 1878 he became interne in the hospitals of Paris, where he came under the influence of Charcot, then at the height of his career. Marie was appointed chef de clinic and chef de laboratoire under Charcot, and in
1889 became médecin des hôpitaux and professeur agrégé. During
this period he gave his famous lectures on the intrinsic diseases of
the spinal cord,[1] and published his classical descriptions of new
clinical entities which he not only isolated but christened—progressive muscular atrophy (with Charcot) in 1886,[2] acromegaly in

1886,[3] hypertrophic osteoarthropathy in 1890,[4] cerebellar heredo-ataxia in 1893,[5] spondylose rhizomélique in 1898.[6] This period of sustained creative activity gave him an international reputation.

In 1897 he transferred his activities to the Hospice de Bicêtre and established there a neurological service which attracted pupils from all over the world. During the ten years he remained there he became interested in the problems of aphasia, and his documentation of the subject (reported in detail in the thesis of Moutier) was the

Portrait, courtesy of Dr. Percival Bailey, Chicago, Illinois.

basis of a devastating critique on the previous work.[7] Not only did he attack the ideas of Broca, using as the provocative title for his paper "The third left frontal convolution has no special role in the function of language," but he even examined Broca's original specimen to prove how erroneous was his observation, and in the process swept away many old prejudices. In his fondness for controversy, Marie drew in Babinski and the Dejerines, setting neurologists at each other's doctrines so that they took sides and debated vigorously. Marie's work on aphasia was extended later by his pupil, Charles Foix. In 1907, in the midst of the controversy over aphasia, Marie took the chair of pathologic anatomy in the faculty. Here he did much to improve the teaching but added little to the subject itself. Again his work was continued by a brilliant pupil, Gustave Roussy, when the latter succeeded Dejerine to the chair of clinical neurology at the Salpêtrière.

At 65 years Marie finally assumed the chair of neurology which had been created for Charcot and occupied since his tenure by Raymond, Brissaud and Dejerine. This was in 1918 toward the end of a destructive war. There were no longer the facilities or the means to continue the painstaking laboratory studies of the Dejerine school, nor did Marie's interests incline him in that direction. In collaboration with Meige, Foix, Chatelin and Bouttier he published interesting studies of the neurological lesions caused by the war,[8] but his great productive period was over.

In October 1921, I entered his clinic as foreign assistant, too late to feel the full impact of his creative personality. I remember him as a dignified old gentleman, who came regularly about 10:00 A.M. to the little building called the Pavillon de la Grille where patients were brought to him for examination. Only rarely did he enter the wards and never the laboratory, for he was very sensitive to formalin and would look at fixed brains only through a window, and there dictate his description. He was at his best in clinical consultation, in which his discussions were short and pithy. His teaching seems always to have been simple, clear, plain exposition. He was very kind to me and courteous to everyone, including the patients. His agrégé at that time was Foix, a brilliant lecturer, whose early death was a great loss to French neurology.

By 1925 Marie withdrew from his professorship and retired to his estate on the Côte d'Azur, taking his leisure seriously. He returned to Paris rarely except to attend meetings of the Comité de Direction of the *Revue neurologique,* which he and Brissaud had founded in 1893 and of which he was very proud. His later years were saddened by the loss of his wife and his only son. After several months of painful illness, he, too, died.

Pierre Marie's influence in the Parisian medical world was immense. His great wealth made him independent; his honesty made him respected; his innate courtesy and dignity made him friends and disarmed his opponents; and his creative intelligence spread his reputation throughout the world. He is a good example of the best in French medicine.

CHICAGO, ILLINOIS   PERCIVAL BAILEY

References

[1]*Leçons sur les maladies de la moelle.* Paris, Masson, 1892.   [2]Rev. méd., Par., 1886, *6:* 97–138.   [3]*Ibid.,* 1886, *6:* 297–333.   [4]*Ibid.,* 1890, *10:* 1–36.   [5]Sem. méd., Par. 1893, *13:* 444–447.   [6]Rev. méd., Par., 1893, *18:* 285–315.   [7]Sem. méd., Par., 1906, *26:* 241–247.   [8]*Travaux et mémoires.* 2 vol. Paris, Masson, 1926–28.

References to Biography: 1) Rev. neur., Par., 1939–40, *72:* 533–543 ("Le Comité"). 2) *Ibid.,* 1928, 35 (1): 691–694 (Guillain).

SILAS WEIR MITCHELL (1829–1914)

*W*eir Mitchell in his prime was a tall, vigorous, alert man with deeply chiselled features and an expression denoting clear aims and dominating ambition. His distinctive appearance was enhanced by the grey cap he wore and by the long grey cape which hung from his shoulders. His erudition and versatility brought him friends by the score—such men as Phillips Brooks, William Osler, Oliver Wendell Holmes, William James, Walt Whitman and Andrew Carnegie. He made a point of cultivating younger men in whom he sensed the spark of brilliance: John Shaw Billings, Hideyo Noguchi, W. W. Keen. The last of these once wrote of Mitchell, "Never have I known so original, suggestive, and fertile a mind. I often called him a yeasty man. His mind was ever fermenting, speculating, alert, and overflowing . . . An hour in his office set my own mind in a turmoil so that I could hardly sleep." He has been regarded, indeed, as "the most versatile American since Franklin."

Portrait, courtesy of Dr. Loyal Davis, Chicago, Illinois. (Painted by Frank Hall, engraved by T. Johnson.)

Mitchell was born to an inheritance of refinement and culture, the seventh physician in three generations. During his early years as a student at the University of Pennsylvania, which he entered when he was 15, his record was a poor one, for he had an aversion to such subjects as mathematics. He preferred to daydream, write poetry, steal peaches and melons from Jersey farmers, and make a general nuisance of himself in the classroom. "You are wanting in nearly all the qualities that go to make a success in medicine," he was told by his father, the distinguished Dr. John Kearsley Mitchell, when he suggested that he study medicine. Nevertheless Weir was enrolled at Jefferson Medical College in 1848, and received the M.D. in 1850. Forthwith he boarded a clipper ship for a year in Europe. In Paris, as is related in the biography of Mitchell by Earnest (from which the quotations in the present biographic sketch stem), he did not permit the legendary distractions from making too many inroads on his scholarship. The person who influenced him most in Paris was Claude Bernard.

On his return to Philadelphia he plunged into research, one of his interests being snake venoms, on which he worked with Hammond and later with W. W. Keen. Soon after the outbreak of the War between the States he became "contract surgeon" to a 400-bed hospital in Philadelphia, created for him and Dr. George R. Morehouse by Surgeon General Hammond. W. W. Keen soon became an associate. Together they collected thousands of pages of notes on wounded soldiers, which culminated in Mitchell's masterpiece: *Gunshot wounds and other injuries of nerves* (Philadelphia, Lippincott, 1864) in which the entity known as "causalgia" was given its place in medicine. *Reflex paralysis* was another brilliant outgrowth of the researches of Keen, Morehouse and Mitchell. As time passed, Mitchell made other important contributions, including those on erythromelalgia,[1] post-paralytic chorea,[2] the "rest cure,"[4] and the functions of the cerebellum, in which he confirmed Rolando's view that the cerebellum augments and reinforces movements initiated by the cerebrum.[3]

In spite of his growing fame he failed in 1863 to receive the vacated chair of physiology at Jefferson Medical College or the chair in the same field at the University of Pennsylvania. Important persons wrote in his behalf, among them Hammond, who on learning of the second failure, wrote: "I am disgusted with everything and can only say that it is an honor to be rejected by such a set of apes!" Mitchell was turned down again for the chair at Jefferson in 1868.

From the early 1880's Mitchell turned his major efforts to literary pursuits, using almost every form of literary expression: novel, short story, essay, drama and verse.[5,6] His verses were his earliest and his last utterances. His *Ode on a Lycian tomb* is said to be the finest elegiac poem written in America. *Westways*, a novel written when he was past 80, reflects the indelible impression left upon him by his visit to Gettysburg shortly after the battle—"a most horrible memory." The belief that he was more interested in writing poetry and novels than in medicine became general among his colleagues, causing him to write under a number of pseudonyms. His attitude toward the practice of his profession can be expressed in no better way than was stated in his novel, *Hugh Wynne: free Quaker* (New York, Century, 1879): "No man knew better than he how to use his intellect to apologize to himself for lack of strict obedience to the moral code by which his profession justly tests the character of its own labor."

In his 80's, Mitchell, now "the sage," continued to write at full speed and to enjoy the company of the brilliant men he had long cultivated. At 84 his powers were such that he "bombarded Osler with questions about rare books he was seeking and about some letters of William Harvey." Not long afterward he was stricken with influenza. Nonetheless he took this occasion to read the proof of his dramatic poem, *Barabbas*, but had not gotten far when he lapsed into a delirium in which he again found himself at Gettysburg, operating on the wounded. Soon afterward he was gone.

WASHINGTON, D. C.   WEBB HAYMAKER

References

[1]Am. J. M. Sc. 1878, 76: 17–36.   [2]*Ibid.*, 1874, 68: 342–352.   [3]*Ibid.*, 1869, 57: 320–338.   [4]*Fat and blood, and how to make them.* Philadelphia, Lippincott, 1877.   [5]*Selections from the poems of S. Weir Mitchell.* London, Macmillan, 1901.   [6]*Hephzibah Guinness.* Philadelphia, Lippincott, 1880.

References to Biography: 1) Brit. M. J., 1914, *1:* 119–121 (Osler). 2) Nature, Lond., 1914, *92:* 534–535 (Brunton). 3) Boston M. & S. J., 1914, *170:* 821–825 (Putnam). 4) J. Nerv. & Ment. Dis., 1914, *41:* 65–74 (Mills). 5) *S. Weir Mitchell, novelist and physician.* Philadelphia, Univ. Pennsylvania Press, 1950 (Earnest). 6) *History of the American Physiological Society Semicentennial 1887–1937.* Baltimore, 1938 (Howell, Greene); p. 1–128.

CONSTANTIN VON MONAKOW (1853–1930)

*V*on Monakow was born on the family estate Bobretzovo, in Vologda, north of Moscow. His Polish mother died when he was four years old. His father, Ivan Monakow, a wealthy, well-educated nobleman, was censor of the political press during the reigns of Nicolas I and Alexander II. In 1863 he sold his estates with some dispatch and emigrated with his two sons and daughter to Dresden. Three years later the Austro-Prussian war caused the family to move to Paris. After a year in Paris, then in the glittering period of the Second Empire, the forebodings of the Franco-Prussian war which was to come in 1870 must have influenced the elder Monakow to look for a more peaceful place in which to rear his family. They moved to Zürich, where, in 1869, they became naturalized.

According to von Monakow's autobiographical notes as retold by Minkowski, it appears that he was mediocre as a student and frequently at odds with his teachers. His father became more and more annoyed with him, until finally he bade him—he was then 17—to leave the paternal home. Against his father's wishes he took up medicine. In 1876, while still a candidate for the M.D., the search for work led him to the famed Hitzig, then director of Burghölzli Asylum near Zürich. Hitzig sent him to survey the administration of asylums in Germany. This brought him to von Gudden in Munich. Von Gudden showed him the microtome—his invention—and sections of the brain of an adult rabbit in which the superior colliculus had undergone atrophy after removal of the contralateral eye at birth. Von Monakow was impressed. In 1877 he returned to Munich, and then went to Würzburg for further study, but a pressing need for money forced him to look for a job. After a trip to Brazil as ship's doctor, he obtained the position of ward physician in the Cantonal Asylum St. Pirminsberg, near Ragaz. It was here,

in 1879, that von Monakow removed the occipital lobes in two new-born rabbits and, after keeping them alive for more than a year, he found that the lateral geniculate nuclei were completely degenerated, while the rest of the thalami was intact. This was a significant discovery and the beginning of his *exegi monumentum.* In

Portrait, courtesy of Dr. Paul I. Yakovlev, Boston, Massachusetts.

1885, after a three-month sojourn in Berlin, where he attended the clinics and lectures of Westphal, Oppenheim, Virchow, du Bois-Reymond, and especially Munk, he returned to Zürich, where he set up a private research laboratory and became an active practitioner. In 1894 his Hirnanatomisches Institut was incorporated with the University of Zürich, and he was appointed Extraordinarius.

Judging by the picaresque stories told about him, he must have been an eccentric figure. A huge man, his high-pitched voice contrasted oddly with his monumental stature and heavily-bearded countenance. To his more gracile Swiss compatriots he represented the generalized prototype of that forensic abstraction—a Russian— *ein russischer Mensch*.[1] To him, however, Switzerland was the mother country or, as he put it, his "cradle."[2] In his younger days he is said to have been a boisterous *bon vivant* and a devotee of the *Bierstube*. In his maturity he became and remained an abstemious man devoted to family life. Many of his students remember the pleasure of weekly *soirées musicales*, during which his friends and pupils gathered at his home to hear concerts played by members of his family and some musically adept guests.[3] He was a prodigious worker, a copious writer, and an omnivorous reader. His *Gehirnpathologie* contains over 3,000 references, compiled by himself. He was an impetuous and at times an irascible man: there is a certain door in the laboratory of his Institute which once he attempted to open, unaware that it was locked—he pulled the handle and the door yielded with the frame.[3] Faculty affairs did not seem to interest him. It is said that he is known to have attended only one faculty meeting during the many years he was its member, and then it was to sponsor the candidature of his son for a faculty appointment. There are those who can remember the Russian-style blouse and the great long boots he wore on that unique occasion.[4]

The War of 1914–18 and the Russian Revolution of 1917 made a deep impression on him. He reread Russian classics avidly.[3] During the later years of his life he became deeply absorbed in problems of philosophy, religion and biological sources of the forces of ethics and morality (the values) in human affairs.[5]

His was one of the most forceful and original personalities in neurology at the turn of the century. The qualification *eccentric* may not accurately describe the temper of his character, but its picturesque uncommonness made him a fit subject for a biography in the form of a novel, *Begegnung am Abend* (Stuttgart, Deutsche Verlagsanstalt, 1933), written by the poetess Maria Waser.

He retired in 1928 at the age of 75. His health began rapidly to decline. He was a recalcitrant patient and refused medical care. An enlarged prostate, which caused retention-uremia, was established at autopsy as the cause of his death.[4] Had he been in a position to be present, the old man would probably have frowned into his beard upon learning that his spinal cord had been lost, for in his will he had requested that the pathologist search a certain level for the alterations responsible for the longstanding atrophy of his thenar eminence.[4]

With the work of his younger and living contemporary, Kurt Goldstein, that of von Monakow will remain an outstanding contribution to the empirically-founded theory of neurology. Von Monakow's scientific life and work may be divided into three overlapping periods, one rising above the other like tiers of a pyramid: the first from 1880 to the publication of his *Gehirnpathologie* (Wien; Hölder) in 1897; the second from about 1900 to the publication in 1914 of his greatest work, *Die Lokalisation im Grosshirn und der Abbau der Funktion durch kortikale Herde* (Wiesbaden; Bergmann); and the third period, deeply philosophical, from World War I to his death in 1930. This last period in the development of his thought is epitomized in his book with Raoul Mourgue, *Introduction biologique à l'étude de la neurologie et de la psychopathologie* (Paris; Alcan), published in 1928.

During the first period, inaugurated with the classical studies of visual and acoustic pathways, von Monakow laid the foundation upon which the present knowledge of developmental and functional unity of the thalamus and cortex securely rests. During the second period he elaborated the concept of *diaschisis*, and brought forth the fundamental distinction between the *geometric* localization of symptoms (e.g., paralysis, aphasia) and the *chronogenic* localization of functions (e.g., locomotion, language). He thus introduced concepts which make clinical neurology a truly biological science of organismal dynamics of human behavior. In this orientation of thought, von Monakow's work reveals many interesting parallels with the contemporary work in this country of the Herrick brothers and of Coghill, which made so meaningful the comparative neurobiology of vertebrate behavior. In the last period of his life he made a sublime effort to delineate ethical and moral values in terms of the neurobiological frame of reference which he had created. His three lectures on *Emotions, morality and the brain* were published in this country in English, but unfortunately the translation was grossly inadequate. In the orginal German text,[5] involved as it is, these lectures are a noteworthy example of penetrating empirical generalization. Von Monakow's Promethean thoughts have not yet been fully appraised.

On October 19, 1930, at the age of 77, as he was preparing a manuscript on *The value of life,* he put down his pen and lay on the couch to rest. A peaceful end came. The last words jotted on the sheaf of manuscript were "Angemessenes Handeln ..." The context which was to follow is not given us to know, but the words are a fitting epitaph for the pyramid of his life and work. Indeed, from the relevant foundation of the measurable truth, his understanding rose above the misty clouds which veil the vision of lesser minds, and from that lonely pinnacle he reached for the immense.

BOSTON, MASSACHUSETTS   PAUL I. YAKOVLEV

References

[1]Erich Katzenstein (personal communication to P.I.Y.).   [2]Schweiz. Arch. Neur. Psychiat., 1931, *27:* 1–63 (Minkowski).   [3]Eugen Frey (personal communication to P.I.Y.).   [4]E. A. Uehlinger (personal communication to Webb Haymaker).   [5]*Gefühl, Gesittung und Gehirn.* Arb. Hirnanat. Inst., Zürich, 1916, Heft X; p. 115–213.

Additional Reference to Biography: Arch. Neur. Psychiat., Chic., 1931, *25:* 389–390 (Adolf Meyer).

SIR FREDERICK WALKER MOTT (1853–1926)

M ott was born in Brighton, England. After completing his medical studies at the University College, London, in 1881, he remained there to study neuroanatomy under E. A. Schäfer (later Sharpey-Shaffer).* In 1883 he was appointed assistant professor

---

* The change of name came as the result of the death of his son, Sharpey, during World War I. There had been a great affection between the two, which caused Schäfer to adopt his son's name and anglicize his own.

Sir Frederick Walker Mott

of physiology at Liverpool, and a year later received a lectureship in physiology at the Charing Cross Hospital. Soon thereafter, in 1895, he became pathologist to the London County Council Asylums and director of the newly established laboratories at Claybury Asylum.

For many years Mott was a close friend of Dr. Maudsley and it was at Mott's suggestion that Maudsley bequeathed a large sum to endow a hospital for the study and treatment of psychoneuroses. After considerable delay the London County Council, who were nominated under Maudsley's will, consented to build and equip the Maudsley Hospital at Denmark Hill.

Mott had long desired to have his laboratory transferred to London from Claybury, and it was the building of the Maudsley

Portrait, courtesy of Sir Allen Daley, Maudsley Hospital, London, England. (Photographer: Barr, London.)

Hospital that made it possible for the Central Pathological Laboratory to be located in the London area. He succeeded in convincing
the London County Council that his laboratory should be converted
into a central institution to serve as a headquarters of the pathological and research services of the London mental hospitals. Mott
and the staff of the Central Pathological Laboratory remained independent while the laboratory, which occupied a wing of the Maudsley Hospital, acted as a research centre for all the mental hospitals
in the London County Council.

After his retirement from the Maudsley staff in 1923, Mott continued with his teaching and research duties at Birmingham. He
was engaged in these activities until his death, at 72.

Mott had a distinguished career of amazing versatility. He was
equally at home at the bedside and in the laboratory. His earlier
studies dealt with problems of neurophysiology and neuroanatomy.
With Sherrington he was the first to study the consequences of dorsal root section in monkeys.[1] He was a pioneer in the field of cerebral localization of the sense of vision.[2] He also demonstrated the
thalamic connections of the medial lemniscus,[3] contributed to our
knowledge of the anatomy of the spinothalamic and spinocerebellar
systems, and showed that the pathway for the projection of impulses
from one ear was to both sides of the brain.[4] He was the first in
England to establish the relationship between syphilis and general
paresis by demonstrating the spirochete in the brains of general
paralytics (1913). He anticipated the organic basis of many mental
illnesses and published numerous articles on the influence of alcohol,[5]
and in this connection observed degeneration of cortical tangential
fibers in Korsakov's disease.[6] His work on trypanosomiasis encephalitis also was outstanding.[7]

During World War I, Mott led in the study of shell shock,[8,9] and
with keen insight distinguished between physical and emotional factors in this disorder. After the war, he turned his attention to dementia praecox and manic depressive insanity, attempting to corre-
late their clinical manifestations with the morphological, microchemi-
cal, chemical and endocrine changes. He was a pioneer in the study
of the central nervous system in hypothyroidism.[10] His foresight
was probably best demonstrated in his ability to perceive the limita-
tions of physiological and anatomical methods in the study of the
nervous system, for he was convinced that the future of neuropath-

ology lay largely in the biochemical and in the chemical fields.

Mott was an indefatigable worker. In both public and private life he was the embodiment of the traditional John Bull. He combined stout common sense with irreproachable honesty and fairmindedness. His loyalty to tradition earned him a reputation for conservativism. Like so many biologists of his generation he had spent most of his life in conditions where scientific research facilities were almost absent and he never quite acclimatized himself to the newer conditions which have transformed neurological research methods. He knew how to fight for what he conceived to be his rights and those of his subordinates, and at the same time he showed considerable ability in dealing with the Committees of Management of the London County Council. He was made Knight of the British Empire in 1919.

MINNEAPOLIS, MINNESOTA   A. B. BAKER

LONDON, ENGLAND   F. GOLLA

References

[1]Proc. R. Soc., Lond., 1895, 57: 481–488.   [2]Arch. Neur., Lond., 1907, 3: 1–117.   [3]Brain, Lond., 1892, 15: 215–229.   [4]Brit. M. J., 1907, 2: 310–315.   [5]Practitioner, Lond., 1924, 113: 244–263.   [6]Brit. M. J., 1910, 2: 1403–1408.   [7]Proc. R. Soc., Lond., 1905, ser.B., 76: 235–242.   [8]The effects of high explosives upon the central nervous system. London, Harrison, 1916.   [9]War neuroses and shell shock. London, Frowde, Hodder & Stoughton, 1919.   [10]Arch. Neur. Psychiat., Path. Lab., Lond., 1918, 7: 51–59.

References to Biography: 1) Birmingham M. Rev., 1926, n.s., 1: 221–231 (Graves).   2) J. Ment. Sc., Lond., 1926, 72: 317–320 (Starling).

HERMANN OPPENHEIM (1858–1919)

Oppenheim was born at Warburg, Westphalia. After graduation from the Gymnasium in 1876 he studied medicine at the Universities of Göttingen, Berlin, and Bonn. During the years 1880–82 he was especially interested in physiology and, under the guidance of Zuntz, published three papers on the metabolism of urea, which formed the basis of his doctoral dissertation in 1881. Shortly afterward he became assistant at the psychiatric clinic Maison de Santé in

H. Oppenheim

Berlin, and later (1883) at the neurological and psychiatric clinic of
the Charité, a part of the University of Berlin.   Here he soon became
the favorite assistant of Westphal, whose support enabled him to
become established as Privatdozent in 1886 and as Titular Professor
in 1893.

His first publications dealt with tabes dorsalis, bulbar paralysis,
and neuritis associated with lead intoxication and with alcoholism.

Portrait, courtesy of Library of Northwestern University School of Medicine, Chicago, Illinois.

During 1887–88 there followed studies on syphilis, disseminated sclerosis, and chronic anterior poliomyelitis. The first publication of his monograph on traumatic neuroses, which appeared in 1889,[1] started a never ending flow of acrimonious debate. Oppenheim's contention was that the psychic disturbances following trauma originate in an actual organic disturbance of the brain (molecular changes), and that the altered psyche continued to perpetuate the neurosis. His theory was vigorously opposed by Charcot, Mendel, Nonne and others, who did not accept the idea of organic changes, and especially during World War I this debate, which concerned also hysteria and malingering, became very heated.[2] Oppenheim seems to have been very sensitive to such opposition and considered it a personal affront. His sensibility may have been conditioned by a previous experience: During Westphal's protracted illness prior to his death in 1890, Oppenheim conducted his clinic, and despite being unanimously nominated by the Berlin medical faculty as Professor Extraordinarius to succeed Westphal, the nomination was not confirmed by the Prussian Secretary of Education, who acted in the spirit of intolerance of that period. As a consequence, Oppenheim had to leave the Charité.

In 1890 he opened his own private clinic, which later was to become the international center of clinical neurology in Berlin. This year marked the beginning of a veritable flood of publications which inspired neurologists the world over. The last decade of the 19th century was a fertile period for clinical neurology. Charcot, Westphal, Erb and others had done the primary investigation and left it to their successors to collect cases, analyze the findings, and classify them. One can hardly understand now the enthusiasm with which Oppenheim, together with his associates, R. Koehler, M. Borchardt and F. Krause, reported single cases of successfully diagnosed and verified brain tumor. Oppenheim's neurosurgical experiences on brain tumors were collected in book form in 1896[3] and again in 1907.[4] It was on the basis of Oppenheim's diagnosis that the first surgical removal of a brain tumor was performed by Koehler.[5] Important monographs which he published included those on syphilitic diseases of the brain[6] and encephalitis.[7] He provided the term "dystonia musculorum deformans" in his paper on the subject in 1911;[8] four cases were described and the characteristic "dromedary gait" emphasized. Other pioneers in this particular field were Schwalbe[9] and Ziehen.[10] The disorder has been called "Oppenheim-Ziehen's disease," but Schwalbe deserves credit for the original description.

Although primarily an expert clinical diagnostician, Oppenheim did not neglect therapy—surgical, pharmacologic and psychic—limited though it was at that time. The volumes on brain surgery have been mentioned. He was one of the first to try Ehrlich's salvarsan in the treatment of syphilis of the nervous system (1910). A monograph on peripheral nerve lesions appeared in 1917, *Die ersten Zeichen der Nervosität im Kindesalter* (Berlin; Karger) in 1904, and *Psychotherapeutische Briefe* (Berlin; Karger) in 1906. The latter had three editions. Oppenheim attacked therapeutic charlatanry in his article, *Zum Nil Nocere in der Neurologie.*[11]

Lasting monuments to the fame of this veteran neurologist were his description of amyotonia congenita,[12] called "Oppenheim's disease," and the seven German editions of his *Lehrbuch der Nervenkrankheiten* (Berlin, Karger, 1894), which was translated into English three times, and into Russian, Spanish and Italian.

NEW YORK CITY   ARTHUR WEIL

References

[1]*Die traumatischen Neurosen nach den in der Nervenklinik der Charité in den letzten 5 Jahren gesammelten Beobachtungen.* Berlin, Hirschwald, 1889. (Ed. 2, 1892; ed. 3, 1918.)   [2]See Bumke in Arch. Psychiat., Berl., 1925, 76: 58–67.   [3]*Die Geschwülste des Gehirns.* Wien, Hölder, 1896. (Ed. 2, 1902.) (Also in Nothnagel, H., *Specielle Pathologie und Therapie.* Wien, 1896. 9.Bd., 1.Theil, 3.Abth., 1.Lfg.)   [4]*Beiträge zur Diagnostik und Therapie der Geschwülste im Bereich des zentralen Nervensystems.* Berlin, Karger, 1907.   [5]Berl. klin. Wschr., 1890, 27: 677–681.   [6]Nothnagel, H., *Specielle Pathologie und Therapie.* Wien, 1897, 9.Bd., 1.Theil, 3.Abth., 2.Lfg.   [7]*Ibid.*, 1897, 9.Bd., 2.Theil. [8]Neur. Cbl., 1911, 30: 1090–1107.   [9]*Eine eigentümliche tonische Krampfform mit hysterischen Symptomen.* Inaug. Dissert.—Berlin, 1907. [10]Neur. Cbl., 1911, 30: 109–110.   [11]Berl. klin. Wschr., 1910, 47: 198–201. [12]Mschr. Psychiat., 1900, 8: 232–233.

Reference to Biography: Berl. klin. Wschr., 1919, 52: 669–671 (Cassirer)

ALBERT PITRES (1848–1928)

Pitres was born in Bordeaux. After having been interne des hôpitaux (1866) in his native city, ranking highest among his fellow internes, he departed in 1871 for Paris. Here he became interne in 1872 and chef de clinique of Charcot in 1877–78.

Préparateur and chef de laboratoire to the great histologist, Ranvier of the Collège de France, Pitres worked in Marey's laboratory with the physiologist François-Franck. Together in 1877 they began a series of investigations on the electrical excitability of the brain of the dog, the study of which had been initiated in 1870 by Fritsch and Hitzig. Soon they confirmed the existence of a motor mechanism at the level of the prerolandic convolution.[1-3] Pitres was ever intent on passing to the clinic the information that he had gained experimentally, and day by day he would go to the wards of Charcot at the Salpêtrière to put his data to the test. The outcome was in the form of three memoirs with Charcot which left no doubt of the existence of cortical motor centers in man (1877,[4] 1878, 1883). During this time he also made significant observations on jacksonian epilepsy.[5]

In 1877 Pitres submitted as his Paris thesis a study on the pathology of the centrum ovale. It was in this work, published also in book form,[6] that he announced a method for sectioning the brain which became widely known as "les coupes de Pitres."

In 1878 he returned to the University of Bordeaux. After teaching histology for three years, he became, at the age of 33, professor of medicine (1881). He held this chair during the subsequent 38 years. As dean of the Faculté de Médecine of Bordeaux for more than two decades, he proved a gifted administrator; he was the first in France to add to the medical curriculum such specialities as biochemistry, pediatric surgery, and tropical diseases. Among his students were Lieur, Vaillard and De Fleury.

Although Pitres' activities in the field of neurology were far-flung, his favorite subject was aphasia. He remained faithful to Broca's concept of aphasia, continuing to defend it against the onslaughts of Pierre Marie, and in the process, consolidated his doctrines of cerebral localization of function. His description of agraphia[7] has become famous, as have also his observations on amnesic aphasia,[8]

D⁄ A. PITRES
Prof. à l'Université de Bordeaux
Associé N^{NAL} de l'Académie de Médecine

aphasia in multilingual persons,[9] and paraphasia,[9] his exposé of the last-named being among his greatest contributions. An appraisal of his work on aphasia is to be found in the Bordeaux thesis of Moreau (1945).

His 2-volume *Leçons cliniques sur l'hystérie et l'hypnotisme* (Paris, Doin, 1891) bears the same mark of his talent. Based on

Portrait, courtesy of Prof. Paul Delmas-Marsalet, Bordeaux, France.

clear-cut observations, which were painstakingly verified pathologi-
cally over a long period of time, many of his views still ring as true
today as they did 60 years ago. He saw in Babinski's "pithiatisme"
no more than a fleeting work of imagination without substantial
roots, but in crossing swords with Babinski, Pitres fared none too
well. Later, Pitres' views gained more widespread acceptance.

Many aspects of peripheral neuritis also were elucidated by Pitres:
diabetic neuritis with palsy of all four limbs,[10] peripheral neuritis
in tuberculosis[11] and in tabes dorsalis,[12] tic douloureux,[13] and facial
spasm with synkinetic closure of the eyelids as a sequela of Bell's
palsy.[14] Other notable studies were those on occupational torticollis,[15] muscle wasting in disseminated sclerosis,[16] and so-called post-
hemorrhagic syringomyelia.[17] His *Les nerfs en schémas, anatomie et physiopathologie* with L. Testut (Paris, Doin, 1925) is a work,
which for clarity and brilliance of diagrammatic representation of
the cranial and spinal peripheral nervous system (many of the diagrams are in color) is hard to equal.

Pitres was highly erudite and his lectures were simple, clear and
captivating; he was, in fact, idolized by his students. Many honors
came to him; he was Commander of the *Légion d'honneur* and
member and one-time president of the *Académie des sciences de
belles lettres et arts* of Bordeaux—an academy in which Montesquieu
had figured so illustriously.

Pitres was tall and imposing and bore a close resemblance to
François I. Of liberal and tolerant mind, open to the appreciation of music, painting and the other arts, he had nothing of that
one-sidedness that some people claimed they could see in his
fidelity to cerebral localization of function. On the mantel of his
home, set off by many *objets d'art* were two small XVIIth century
statuettes—two saints—one engrossed in a book she was reading, and
the other ecstatic, with radiant face and half-bared breasts. "These
are the two friends of man," he told De Fleury, "Sainte Science and
Sainte Volupté." Although by inclination a pagan, he showed a
reverence for those who actively pursued Christianity. There was
no more fervent patriot than Pitres. After the defeat of France in
1870, his teacher, Henri Guitrac, made it possible for him to undertake an extended tour through the ravaged country, and it was this
experience that led him to dedicate his life to the restoration of

France's prestige. "Everyone," he said, "has the duty to work not only for his own advancement, but for the benefit of his country." He remained true to his precepts.

BORDEAUX, FRANCE   PAUL DELMAS-MARSALET

References

[1]C. rend. Acad. sc., 1880, 90: 1126–1128.   [2]C. rend Soc. biol., 1881, 2: 67–72.   [3]Arch. Physiol., 1883, 2: 1–40 et seq.   [4]Rev. mens. méd. chir., Par., 1877, 1: 1–18.   [5]Rev. méd., Par., 1888, 8: 609–631.   [6]Review by Lépine in Rev. mens. méd. chir., Par., 1877, 1: 721–722.   [7]Rev. méd., Par., 1884, 4: 855–873.   [8]L'aphasie amnésique. Paris, Alcan, 1898. [9]Rev. méd., Par. 1895, 15: 873–899.   [10]Progr. méd., Par., 1917, No. 36; p. 295–297 (with Marchand).   [11]Rev. méd. Par., 1886, 6: 193–229 (with Vaillard).   [12]Ibid., p. 574–610.   [13]Rev. neur., Par., 1902, 10: 850–858.   [14]Nouv. Iconog. Salpêtrière, 1913, 26: 365–396 (with Abadie). [15]J. méd., Bordeaux, 1905, 35: 589–591.   [16] Rev. mens. méd. chir., Par., 1877, 1: 893–908.   [17]C. rend. Congr. Internat. Méd. Moscow, 1897, 4 (pt. 1): 304–315 (with Sabrazès).

Reference to Biography: Progr. méd., Par., 1928, No. 16; p. 682–686 (De Fleury).

JAMES JACKSON PUTNAM (1846–1918)

*P*utnam was born in Boston, Massachusetts, and worked there most of his life. After graduating from Harvard (1866) he studied abroad with Rokitansky, Meynert and Hughlings Jackson. Returning to Boston he took a position at the Massachusetts General Hospital, started a clinic there and patiently persevered until his small beginnings grew into a department of neurology at the hospital and a laboratory of neuropathology at the Harvard Medical School. He was one of the seven founders of the American Neurological Association and served as president in 1888. In 1893 he was appointed professor of diseases of the nervous system at Harvard, a position he held until his retirement in 1912. In 1899 he delivered the Shattuck Lecture before the Massachusetts Medical Society on *Not the disease only, but also the man,*[1] treating the obligations of the physician "as a healer of the mind as well as of the body."

In 1907, he helped bring about Freud's visit to America, and for the next ten years his interest turned more and more to psychoanaly-

James Jackson Putnam

sis and the treatment of the psychoneuroses. In this field he wrote 25 papers and a book, *Human motives* (Boston, Little, Brown & Co., 1915), setting forth his personal ethical standard, which was of the highest order. Despite his advanced age and the outspoken skepticism of his colleagues, he was the first man in Boston and, at the time, one of the few in this country to study and expound the psychoanalytic teachings of Freud and to incorporate Freud's findings and methods into his own therapeutic work with patients.

In the neurological field he wrote many clinical and pathological papers. The most original was his description of subacute degen-

Portrait, courtesy of Dr. Marian C. Putnam, Roxbury, Massachusetts.

eration of the spinal cord in pernicious anemia.[2,3]   Of importance
also was his work on lead[4] and arsenic[5] poisoning.   Clinical endocrinology, too, attracted his attention,[6] and one observation for which
he is well-known is that Graves' disease may end in myxedema.[7]   He
also wrote on rabies, writer's palsy, tabes dorsalis, poliomyelitis, multiple neuritis, and on many other neurological conditions which he
saw in his active practice.

In reporting, in 1892, a case of bilateral athetosis in which lesions
were found in the lenticular nuclei and degeneration in the cerebral
peduncles, Putnam became one of the pioneers in the study of the
diseases of the basal ganglia.[8]   Gabriel Anton (1858–1933),[9,10] of
Graz, followed in 1896[11] with a detailed clinical and pathological description of the disorder, which he called "chorea"; he found scars in
the lenticular nuclei and even mentioned the presence of abnormally
myelinated fibers in the scars.   Then, in 1911, the classical papers
of Cécile Vogt[12–15] appeared, one of them in collaboration with Oppenheim.[14]   A feature of her cases of *athétose double*—as she called
the disorder—was the presence of patchy hypermyelination in
the striatum, which gave this structure a marbled or mottled appearance; hence she named the condition, status marmoratus, or état
marbré.   Cécile Vogt first expressed the opinion that status marmoratus is a congenital malformation, but later she and Oskar
Vogt[16–18] agreed with Scholz[19] and Bielschowsky[20] that most if not
all cases of status marmoratus and of plaques dysmyéliniques of the
cerebral cortex were exogenous in origin, i.e., the consequence of
asphyxia neonatorum, general paresis, etc.   This was discussed
in a recent biography of the Vogts.[21]

In his early years, Putnam reported at every meeting of the American Neurological Association.   His bibliography shows that he was
no narrow specialist, but was interested in medical as well as neurological disorders.   His broad interest is also shown by his preoccupation with psychiatry in later years.   It was in the year 1906 that this
transition of interests seems to have begun and from then on the
titles related to hysteria, psychasthenia, psychotherapy, and psychoanalysis.

He was a kindly, philosophical man.   His interests were broad in
scope but sensitive in detail, ranging from a deep concern for the
mentally afflicted individual to a philosophical interest in the nature
of man and his place in society as a whole.   He was one of the small

group who started and promoted social work until it became a profession. One of his charms was that he grew more interested in new things as he aged. He successfully combined liberalism with high ideals.

BOSTON, MASSACHUSETTS   STANLEY COBB

References

[1]Boston M. & S. J., 1899, *141*: 53–57 *et seq.*   [2]J. Nerv. Ment. Dis., 1891, *16*: 69–110.   [3]*Ibid.*, 1901, *28*: 74–101 (with Taylor).   [4]Boston M. & S. J., 1887, *117*: 596–601.   [5]*Ibid.*, 1888, *118*: 646–649 *et seq.*   [6]Tr. Congr. Am. Physicians, 1897, *4*: 122–143.   [7]Am. J. M. Sc., 1893, *106*: 125–148.   [8]J. Nerv. Ment. Dis., 1892, *17*: 124–126.   [9]J. Psychol. Neur., Lpz., 1928, *37*: 387–393 (C. and O. Vogt).   [10]Forsch. u. Fortschr., Berl., 1933, *9*: 55–56 (O. Vogt).   [11]Jahrb. Psychiat. Neur., Wien, 1896, *14*: 141–182.   [12]Neur. Cbl., 1911, *30*: 397–399.   [13]J. Psychol. Neur., Lpz., 1911, *18*: 479–488.   [14]*Ibid.*, 1911, *18*: 293–308.   [15]*Ibid.*, 1911, *18*: 489–500 (with Freund).   [16]*Ibid.*, 1920, *25*: 627–846.   [17]Psychiat. neur. Wschr., 1926, *28*: 85–87.   [18]J. Psychol. Neur., Lpz., 1928, *37*: 387–393.   [19]Zschr. ges. Neur. Psychiat., 1924, *88*: 355–382.   [20]*Ibid.*, 1924, *31*: 125–151.   [21]Neurology, 1951, *1*: 179–204 (Haymaker).

References to Biography: 1) Arch. Neur. Psychiat., Chic., 1920, *3*: 307–315 (Taylor).   2) Boston M. & S. J., 1918, *179*: 809–812 (not signed). 3) In *Addresses on psychoanalysis.* London, International Psychoanalytical Press, 1921; p. 457–466 (Jones).

HANS HEINRICH GEORG QUECKENSTEDT (1876–1918)

A native of Leipzig-Reudnitz, Queckenstedt was reared in an academic atmosphere accented by frugality, for he was the son of a poorly paid teacher. Early in his schooling he showed a bent for natural sciences, and to gain firsthand experience he would go tramping through the woods gathering botanical and zoological specimens. But he specialized in capturing vipers which he sold to the local dealer to add to his hard-won earnings. He attended the University of Leipzig and after having passed the state examination in 1900 he entered the service of Hofrat Professor S. J. M. Ganser (1853–1931) at the Städtisches Irren- und Siechenhaus in Dresden (then the Stadtkrankenhaus in Zwickau). Here, in 1904, he completed his doctoral thesis on *Carcinosarcom.* He then went to Ros-

Hans Heinrich Georg Queckenstedt

tock as assistant to Geheimrat Martius, devoting most of his energy to clinical work at the Medizinische Universitätsklinik. In 1913 his studies on iron metabolism in pernicious anemia[1] gained him the rank of Privatdozent, and later, in 1918, he became Extraordinarius. During the latter part of World War I, he was chief of the medical service at the Städtisches Krankenhaus of Harburg, near Hamburg.

The number of Queckenstedt's publications was small. According to his friend, Professor Hans Curschmann, of Rostock, Queckenstedt

Portrait, courtesy of Prof. Dr. A. Stender, Berlin-Charlottenburg, Germany.

was highly gifted but never had the urge to write. But what he wrote had the touch of finality. Most of his attention centered on the spinal fluid. Quincke had introduced in 1891[2] the procedure of lumbar puncture as we know it today, though more cumbersome methods had been used by Corning,[3] Wynter[4] and C. A. Morton;[5] Froin had described the syndrome of compression or obstruction of the fluid in 1903,[6] and Nonne in 1907;[7] Lange had announced his discovery of the colloidal gold reaction in 1912[8] and its application in 1913;[9] and Mestrezat's great monograph on the composition of spinal fluid in health and disease appeared in 1912.[10] From his youth, Queckenstedt had been keenly interested in physics and mathematics and thus by inclination turned to the problem of the dynamics of cerebrospinal fluid, which up to that time had been neglected. In his earlier experiences with lumbar puncture he was struck with the oscillation of the manometric fluid during respiration and he noted that the column of fluid fluctuated widely when the patient strained or coughed. What led him to study the effect of compression of the jugular veins on spinal fluid pressure is not known, but while carrying out this simple maneuver he observed that the pressure of the fluid sometimes failed to rise (a positive Queckenstedt test). Such a failure, he concluded, indicated the presence of an obstruction of the subarachnoid space between the foramen magnum and the lumbar region in which the needle had been inserted. His test, announced in 1916 in an article entitled *Zur Diagnose der Rückenmarkskompression,*[11] in which three cases were cited (echinococcus infection of a lumbar vertebra, sarcomatous angioma of the conus medullaris, and cord tumor of undetermined nature), was immediately recognized as a discovery of the first order. Interest in the liquor was in the air and it was not long afterward that Cushing, Weed and Dandy carried out their notable physiological studies in this field.

The other work for which Queckenstedt is particularly well known is that on albuminocytologic dissociation of the spinal fluid in polyneuritis, both diphtheritic and of unknown etiology.[12] What he demonstrated was not especially new, for the work of Roemheld,[13,14] Feer,[15] and Guillain, Barré and Strohl[16] had gone before, but what was lacking in priority was made up by the number of cases painstakingly scrutinized, 42 altogether.

The little that is known of the nature of the man is to be found in the biography by Stender. He never married. Those who knew him were agreed that he was a highly gifted person of unusual integrity. He met an untimely end two days before the Armistice of World War I was signed, when his service in the German Army would have been terminated: he was thrown from a shying horse and run over by a munitions truck. He was only 42.

WASHINGTON, D. C.   WEBB HAYMAKER

References

[1]Zschr. klin. Med., 1913, 79: 49–102.   [2]Verhandl. Congr. inn. Med., Wiesbaden, 1891, 10: 321–323.   [3]N. York M. J., 1885, 42: 483–485. [4]Lancet, Lond., 1891, 1: 931–932.   [5]Brit. M. J., 1891, 2: 840–841. [6]Gaz. hôp., 1903, 76: 1005–1006.   [7]Arch. Psychiat., Berl., 1907, 43: 433–460.   [8]Berl. klin. Wschr., 1912, 49: 897–901.   [9]Zschr. f. Chemotherap., 1913, 1: 44–78.   [10]Le liquide céphalo-rachidien normal et pathologique. Valeur clinique et l'examen chimique. Syndromes humoraux dans diverses affections. Paris, Maloine, 1912.   [11]Deut. Zschr. Nervenh., 1916, 55: 325–333.   [12]Ibid., 1917, 57: 316–329.   [13]Ibid., 1908, 36: 94–97.   [14]Deut. med. Wschr., 1909, 35: 669–671.   [15]Ibid., 1910, 1: 967.   [16]Bull. Soc. méd. hôp. Paris, 1916, 40: 1462–1470.

References to Biography and Works: 1) J. Neurosurg., 1949, 6: 337–340 (Stender).   2) Arch. Psychiat., Berl., 1925, 76: 6–20 (Nonne). 3) Cerebrospinal fluid in health and disease. St. Louis, Mosby, 1919; p. 17–29 (Levinson).

HEINRICH IRENAEUS QUINCKE (1842–1922)

Quincke would deserve a place in the history of medicine even if his only achievement had been the introduction of spinal puncture. No other single clinical method has done so much to clarify the understanding of diseases of the central nervous system. Quincke was born at Frankfurt-an-der-Oder, the son of a distinguished physician, who, with his family, later moved to Berlin. After studying medicine at Berlin, Würzburg and Heidelberg under such celebrated men as Virchow, von Kölliker and Helmholtz, Quincke in 1867 became assistant to the great Frerichs. He must have considerably impressed his fellow scientists, for in no other way can one account for his call to the chair of internal medicine at Bern only three years after obtaining his venia legendi in Berlin. In 1878

Heinrich Irenaeus Quincke

he went to Kiel where he remained for 30 years, retiring in 1908, only to continue his scientific work in the stimulating atmosphere of Frankfurt-am-Main. There he died at the age of 80, sitting quietly among his books.

The memory of this simple, kindly man, who was also an excellent physician, teacher and scientist, still lives among his students and colleagues. His numerous contributions to medical literature covered an amazing variety of subjects, among them his classic de-

Portrait, courtesy of Dr. Frederick Hiller, Chicago, Illinois.

scription of angioneurotic edema,[1] a clinical syndrome which bears his name.

Early in his career, Quincke became fascinated by the functions and dysfunctions of the nervous system. As far back as 1869 he began the studies of the mechanisms of body temperature that later led him to postulate the existence of a caloric center.[2] He recognized the syndrome of meningitis serosa,[3] described anosmia in traumatic brain lesions, and noted hyperthermia in the agonal states of lesions of the upper cervical cord.[4]

Quincke's idea of spinal puncture for the withdrawal of fluid occurred neither by intuition nor by accident, and it is interesting to reconstruct the steps that led him to it. Searching for a simple and harmless way to relieve the increasing tension in hydrocephalus in children and thus save their lives, he reasoned that removal of the spinal fluid would break the vicious circle of the over-production and under-resorption of liquor caused by compression of the pacchionian granulations. As Frerichs' assistant, he had studied in 1872 the anatomy and physiology of the cerebrospinal fluid in dogs by injecting red sulphide of mercury into the spinal subarachnoid space.[5] The knowledge gained thereby encouraged him to insert a fine needle with a stylet into the lumbar interspace of an infant, a procedure which he thought might cause slight injury to a root fiber of the cauda but would not cause paralysis. With his presentation of the method at the Wiesbaden Congress of 1891,[6] spinal puncture became indispensable. It is to Quincke's credit that from the very beginning he utilized his puncture for diagnostic as well as for therapeutic purposes.[7] He insisted on accurate manometric pressure readings both at the beginning and at the end of the puncture, he studied the cells and measured the total protein, found tubercle bacilli in the fibrinous pedicle, noticed diminution of liquor sugar in purulent meningitis, identified bacteria, and gave consideration to the basis for the presence of blood. Of special neurological interest is the fact that in one of his very first patients, an infant, Quincke described the occurrence of a transient bilateral abducens paralysis following repeated removal of a considerable amount of fluid.

We have only to realize the immense information which we derive from spinal puncture to understand how much Quincke's "new method" stimulated the medicine of his day and contributed to present day neurology.

CHICAGO, ILLINOIS   FREDERICK HILLER

References

[1]Mschr. prakt. Derm., Hamb. u. Lpz., 1882, *1*: 129–131. [2]Arch. Anat. Physiol., Lpz., 1869; p. 174–198 (with Naunyn). [3]Deut. Zschr. Nervenh., 1896, *9*: 149–168. [4]Arch. exp. Path., 1881, *15*: 1–21. [5]Arch. Anat. Physiol., Lpz., 1872; p. 153–177. [6]Verhandl. Cong. innere Med., Wiesb., 1891, *10*: 321–331. [7]Berl. klin. Wschr., 1895, *32*: 861–862 *et seq.*

References to Biography: 1) Arch. exp. Path., Lpz., 1922, *93*: 1–3 (Naunyn). 2) Zschr. klin. Med., 1923, *96*: 1–21 (G. von Bergmann). 3) *Classic descriptions of disease. With biographical sketches of the authors.* Springfield, Ill., Thomas, 1932 (Major). (Ed. 3, 3rd printing, 1948.)

FULGENCE RAYMOND (1844–1910)

Raymond was born in the small village of Saint-Christophe-sur-le-Nais (Indre et Loire), France. He entered the Army School of Alfort as veterinarian, where in 1866, although only 22 years old, he became chief of anatomy and physiology. Determined, however, to study medicine, he went to Paris in 1867, diligently pursued his medical studies and became externe in 1870 and interne under Charcot and Vulpian in 1871. A year later he received the *Médaille d'or des Hôpitaux*. He was made chef de clinique with G. See in 1877, and later médecin des hôpitaux and agrégé. In 1895 he was elected a member of the Académie de Médecine, and in 1908 the D.Sc. *honoris causa* was conferred on him by Oxford University.

After Charcot's death in 1894, the Faculté de Médecine unanimously elected Raymond his successor, as had been Charcot's wish. He was instrumental in enlarging and modernizing the old laboratories; his splendid lectures on neuropathology served as a stimulus to the many French and foreign workers who frequented them, and in other ways he enhanced the international reputation of the Salpêtrière as the great center of neurology.

Raymond was one of the most renowned of French clinicians. His contributions may be numbered by the score. Particularly outstanding were his monograph on *Étude anatomique, physiologique et clinique sur l'hémichorée, l'hémianesthésie, et les tremblements symptomatiques* (Paris, Delahaye, 1876), and his books on pathologic anatomy of the nervous system[1] and diseases of the nervous system.[2] He described several new neurological syndromes. Many

Fulgence Raymond

of his early papers were concerned with cerebral, particularly bulbar, localization,[3] while in later years syringomyelia,[4,5] myasthenia gravis,[6] progressive muscular dystrophy,[7] toxic-infectious diseases

Portrait, courtesy of Dr. Raymond Garcin, Paris, France.

of the nervous system such as polyneuritis and myelitis,[8] juvenile
general paralysis,[9] and brain tumors[10] evoked his special interest.
In his paper on "spastic tabes"[11] he contended that the disorder was
in the category of a syndrome in that its cause was diverse. Although this concept was in contradiction to that of his beloved chief,
Charcot, he defended it courageously, and had the satisfaction of
seeing his view accepted the world over.

One of his most notable activities was his teaching. His Tuesday
and Friday lectures, painstakingly prepared and eloquently delivered before a huge audience, were always concluded by spirited
discussions. His six volumes of clinical conferences belong to the
classics of French neurology. In spite of the separation of neurology
and psychiatry in France, he dedicated one day of the week to lectures on psychiatry. With Pierre Janet he wrote *Névrose et idées
fixes* (Paris, Alcan, 1898). Another treatise dealt with *Les obses-
sions et la psychasthénie* (Paris, Alcan, 1903).

Raymond had an unfailing optimism engendered by his never
ceasing efforts. Good fortune favored him to the last: on the eve of
his sixty-sixth birthday he was at his favorite place in the country,
Planche-D'Andille, sitting at his desk writing, when death came.
Guillain[12] said of him: "J'ai été l'interne de Raymond, je suis devenu
son chef de clinique, j'ai vécu dans son intimité, je puis affirmer qu'il
fut un grand neurologiste, un professeur d'une rare conscience, un
clinicien d'un rare mérite."

NEW YORK CITY   LOTHAR B. KALINOWSKY

References

[1]*Anatomie pathologique du système nerveux.* Paris, Delahaye & Lecrosnier, 1886.   [2]*Maladies du système nerveux, atrophies musculaires
et maladies amyotrophiques.* Paris, Doin, 1889–94.   [3]Mém. Soc. biol.,
Par., 1877, *3:* 126–127.   [4]Rev. neur., Par., 1906, *14:* 41–45 *et seq.*
[5]Nouv. Iconog. Salpêtrière, 1907, *20:* 261–275 (with Lejonne).   [6]Rev.
neur., Par., 1906, *14:* 709–717.   [7]Arch. gén. méd., Par., 1905, *13:* 742–746.
[8]Rev. gén. clin. thér., 1908, *22:* 659.   [9]Sem. méd., Par., 1900, *20:* 19–22.
[10]Encéphale, 1908, *3:* 264–272 (with Claude).   [11]Progr. méd., Par.,
1892, *15:* 449–453.   [12]*La Salpêtrière.* Paris, Masson, 1925 (Guillain
and Mathieu).

References to Biography: 1) Encéphale, 1910, *2:* i–iv (Claude).   2)
Bull. Soc. méd. hôp. Paris, 1910, 3.sér., *30:* 182–185 (de Beurmann,
Florand).

GEORGE RIDDOCH (1889–1947)

Riddoch was born at Keith in Banffshire, in the north of Scotland. He studied at the University of Aberdeen where he served as demonstrator in anatomy and graduated in medicine with high honors in 1913.

During World War I, it fell to him as Captain in the Royal Army Medical Corps in a military hospital to care for cases of traumatic paraplegia and head injury. Here he met Farquhar Buzzard, Campbell Thomson, Purves-Stewart and Henry Head. He became Head's favorite pupil and protégé. With Head he began a long and fruitful series of studies, including the classical investigation, published in 1917, of the reflex functions of the completely divided spinal cord in man.[1] His doctoral thesis dealt with dissociation of visual perceptions due to occipital injuries.[2] In 1918, in collaboration with Henry Head, he published his famous monograph on the automatic bladder.[3] Thus, by the end of the war, and at the age of 30, Riddoch had made very substantial contributions to neurology.

After the war Riddoch was appointed assistant physician to the London Hospital and the Hospital for Epilepsy and Paralysis, Maida Vale, and later to the National Hospital, Queen Square. In the following years he established many international contacts and became famed as a brilliant and stimulating teacher. At the same time he developed a large and successful consulting practice. During this period he collaborated with Buzzard on an important work concerned with reflex movements and postural reactions in quadriplegia and hemiplegia.[4]

His lectures on central pain[5] were a masterly exposition of this subject. Another of his better known lectures was that on the clinical aspects of hypothalamic derangement.[6] He wrote many excellent articles in textbooks.

Riddoch's original investigations were marked by a meticulous accuracy and attention to detail. If some of his conclusions in regard to reflex micturition and the mass reflex have been modified in the light of subsequent investigations, it is only because modern antibiotics have enabled greater recovery of function in isolated spinal segments. With the studies of Riddoch, Sherringtonian physiology made its first significant appearance in clinical neurology. In

George Riddoch

his application of the physiology of the nervous system to the clinic, Riddoch followed the footsteps of Hughlings Jackson and Henry Head. Although he inherited much of Head's dogmatism he lightened it by an Aberdonian wit, both dry and roguish, and a manner so warm and engaging that his companionship was sheer delight. There are those who may recall the incident of the billiard table at London Hospital. Just before Christmas each year the house staff gathered for the usual festivities and on one of these occasions Riddoch did such a vigorous Highland fling on the billiard table that the repair bill came to £40. Riddoch's fling became an

Portrait, courtesy of Dr. Macdonald Critchley, London, England.

annual pre-Christmas event, but each time the trustees of the hospital insisted that £40 be deposited beforehand.

In the recent World War, George Riddoch was appointed consultant to the British Army in 1941 and, in extraordinarily difficult circumstances, organized a most successful system of regional consultants and advisers in neurology. His tireless efforts in this undertaking, in addition to a heavy burden of teaching and private practice, rapidly undermined his health, which had never been robust, and his failure to recover from an operation for gastric ulcer was an unexpected and tragic loss to British neurology.

SAN FRANCISCO, CALIFORNIA   ROBERT AIRD

References

[1]Brain, Lond., 1917, *40:* 264–402.   [2]*Ibid.*, 1917, *40:* 15–57.   [3]*The automatic bladder. Excessive sweating and some other reflex conditions in gross injuries of the spinal cord.* London, Bale & Danielsson, 1918.   [4]Brain, Lond., 1921, *44:* 397–489.   [5]Lancet, Lond., 1938, *1:* 1093–1098 *et seq.*   [6]*The hypothalamus.* Edinburgh and London, Oliver & Boyd, 1938 (with LeGros Clark, Beattie and Dott); p. 101–130.

References to Biography: 1) Lancet, Lond., 1947, *2:* 672–673 (Brain, Walshe).   2) Brit. M. J., 1947, *2:* 711–712 (not signed).   3) Am. J. Psychiat., 1947, *104:* 506 (not signed).

DOUGLAS MORAY COOPER LAMB ARGYLL ROBERTSON
(1837–1909)

A mong those who added much to the medical ferment of Edinburgh was Douglas Argyll Robertson, the son of Doctor John Argyll Robertson, President of the College of Surgeons of Edinburgh in 1848. After preliminary medical training in Edinburgh, he received the M.D. from St. Andrews in 1857, and was appointed house surgeon to the Royal Infirmary. He then studied in Berlin under Albrecht von Graefe (1823–70), who was establishing ophthalmology as a definite medical specialty. Returning to Edinburgh, Argyll Robertson slowly developed a distinguished ophthalmologic practice. Meanwhile he taught the first laboratory class in physiology organized by the University of Edinburgh. In 1886 he became president of the College of Surgeons, and in 1894 was

Douglas Moray Cooper Lamb Argyll Robertson

president of the International Ophthalmological Congress in Edinburgh. From 1867 to 1896 he was ophthalmic surgeon to the Royal Infirmary.

It is not difficult to trace the factors influencing the major contributions of Argyll Robertson. His father had taught materia medica.

Portrait by permission of the President and Council of the Royal College of Surgeons of Edinburgh.

His friend, Thomas R. Fraser (1841–1919), made a systematic study of African arrow poisons while collecting them for the materia medica museum. Argyll Robertson was searching for an agent which would stimulate the sphincter pupillae in a manner opposite to the dilating effect produced by belladonna or atropine. Fraser suggested an extract of the ordeal bean of Calabar, which he had observed to cause pupillary constriction. Argyll Robertson's experiments were conducted on himself. He demonstrated that an active agent, later isolated as the alkaloid eserine or physostigmine, contracts the ciliary muscle of accommodation and the sphincter pupillae. Since both are supplied by the ciliary nerves, Argyll Robertson concluded that the action is due to their stimulation.[1] The early study of Argyll Robertson on the Calabar bean (physostigma venonosa) began a significant chain of chemical discoveries of great importance in neurology.

The pupillary condition to which Argyll Robertson's name is given was thoroughly described in two brilliant reports dealing with five patients.[2,3] Argyll Robertson's discussion of these cases was significant. He emphasized myosis, the peculiar reactions of the pupil to extracts of belladonna and of the Calabar bean, the associated color blindness, and the condition of the retinal vessels. He went on to describe the reduced dilatation of the pupil from belladonna, and the further contraction from Calabar bean; and he elucidated fully the action of belladonna in paralyzing the circular fibers of the sphincter pupillae, and of Calabar bean in stimulating them. He concluded from the five cases that "for contraction of the pupil under light it is necessary that the ciliospinal nerves remain intact and, as in these cases of myosis the ciliospinal nerves are paralyzed, light does not influence the pupil." In two of the five cases some locomotor ataxia was present, while in the others the form of spinal affection was doubtful.

These reports attracted much attention and the "Argyll Robertson pupil" soon became well established as an indication of syphilis of the central nervous system.

In his grey frock coat and top hat, Argyll Robertson was a classical figure in the days when such garments were typical of the dignity of the doctor. His tall, athletic figure, his handsome features, his air of distinction, and his old-world courtesy made him a conspicuous figure in any professional assembly, and endeared him to students and colleagues alike. A great golfer, he won many medals in tournaments. He and his wife travelled around the world in 1894 and became close friends of the Thakar of Gondal in India. They visited him again in 1900 before retiring to a farm in Jersey. In 1909 they again went to India to see their regal friend, and it was there that Argyll Robertson died.

GALVESTON, TEXAS   CHAUNCEY D. LEAKE

References

[1]Edinburgh M. J., 1863, 8: 815–820.   [2]Ibid., 1869, 14: 696–708. [3]Ibid., 1869, 15: 487–493.

References to Biography: 1) Edinburgh M. J., 1909, n.s., 2: 159–162 (Lundy).   2) J. Lancet, 1929, 49: 173–174 (Woltman).   3) Brit. M. J., 1909, 1: 191–193 (not signed).

MORITZ HEINRICH ROMBERG (1795–1873)

Romberg was a native of Meiningen. His medical studies were pursued at Berlin where, at the age of 22, he received the M.D. on the basis of a thesis in which he gave his classic description of achondroplasia.[1] He soon devoted himself to the study of nervous disease, the first physician in history to give particular attention to the structural diseases, thus founding neurology as we know it today.

A trip to Vienna in 1820 gained him the friendship of Johann Peter Frank, who was not only a pioneer in the study of diseases of the spinal cord (1792), but also the founder of modern public hygiene, and a humanitarian; his influence on Romberg was considerable and lasting.

Romberg derived much of his background from contemporary English neuroanatomy and neuropathology in translating Andrew Marshall's The morbid anatomy of the brain, in mania and hydrophobia (London, Longman & Co., 1815) into German in 1820, and, more significant still, Sir Charles Bell's The nervous system of the human body (London, Longman & Co., 1830) in 1832. He was conscious of the importance of having brought Bell's great landmark in neurology to the German-speaking world, for he stated: "The researches of Sir Charles Bell fill me with enthusiasm, and in 1831 I translated his great work and made known to my professional

Moritz Heinrich Romberg

brethren in Germany his investigations which will ever serve as models of scientific inquiry."

Portrait, courtesy of the Army Medical Library, Washington, D. C.

At the University of Berlin, he was appointed Privatdozent for special pathology and therapy (1830), then Extraordinarius (1838), and finally Director of the University Hospital (1840), where he began his study of patients, promptly recording his observations for inclusion in his textbook, which was published in parts from 1840 to 1846.[2] Three editions were called for before 1857. This, the first systematic book on neurology, well documented with full references to the literature, deals in admirable fashion with such disorders as neuritis, causalgia, ciliary neuralgia, facial neuralgia, sciatica, neuromas, chorea, tetany, epilepsy and facial paralysis. Romberg's discussion of tabes dorsalis, lucid in clinical details and brilliant in his surmise as to site of the initial pathological change, contains the classic remark that ataxics cannot stand with their eyes shut (Romberg's sign): "Lässt man ihn in aufrechter Stellung die Augen schliessen, so fängt er sofort an zu schwanken und zu taumeln . . ." (ed. 1, 1846; p. 795). His description of progressive facial hemiatrophy (Parry-Romberg's syndrome) appeared in 1846.[3] Romberg was also a neuropathologist of note, and was made Ordinarius in special pathology and therapy in 1845.

Romberg collected and incorporated into his precise clinical pictures of neurological diseases the scattered reports of experimental investigations from many sources. For his success at bringing some order into neurological thought, Romberg deserves enduring fame. He was acutely aware of the physiological work of Sir Charles Bell and of Magendie, and the acceptance of the difference between sensory and motor nerves led to a division of his textbook into two sections, one on sensation and the other on motion. The German text was translated into English in 1853[4] and the volumes had a wide influence not only in Great Britain but also in America.

Romberg excelled as a teacher, and he was always intent on closest personal relations with his students. He was particularly self-effacing during the Berlin cholera epidemic, when in 1831 and 1837 he was in charge of cholera hospitals.[5] He died of heart disease at the age of 78.

BOSTON, MASSACHUSETTS   HENRY R. VIETS

References

[1]*De rachitide congenita.* Berlin, Platen, 1817.   [2]*Lehrbuch der Nervenkrankheiten des Menschen.* Berlin, Duncker, 1840–46. (Ed. 2, 1851.)

[3]*Klinische Ergebnisse.* Berlin, Förstner, 1846. [4]*A manual of the nervous diseases of man.* 2 vol. London, Sydenham Society, 1853 (trans. and ed. by Sieveking). [5]Wschr. ges. Heilk., Berl., 1838, *6:* 33–39 *et seq.*

References to Biography: 1) Bull. N. York Acad. M., 1948, *24:* 772–782 (Viets). 2) Berl. klin. Wschr., 1873, *10:* 289–290 (Waldenburg). 3) Deut. Klinik, 1867, *19:* 109–110 *et seq.;* 1873, *25:* 245 (Göschen). 4) *Verdienste deutscher Ärzte um die Erkenntnis der Neuro-Pathologie.* Inaug.-Diss.-Düsseldorf, 1936 (Kleinjohann). 5) Dana, *Textbook of nervous diseases.* Ed. 10. New York, Wood, 1925; p. XV-LVI (Garrison, on the history of neurology).

OTTORINO ROSSI (1877–1936)

Rossi was born of hardy but poor parents in the village of Solbiate Comasco (Como), in Italy. As the result of a competitive examination he obtained a scholarship at the Collegio Ghislieri at Pavia; from this day on, he felt that he would always be successful. After his graduation from the University of Pavia (M.D., 1901) where Golgi had instilled in him his own enthusiasm for the histology and pathology of the nervous system, his financial needs forced him to accept a position as assistant at the Ospedale Civico at Varese. During the one year spent there, a Spartan way of life enabled him to put aside enough money so that he could return to his academic work at the University of Pavia. Here he spent four fruitful years (1902–06) as Assistant at the Hospital for Nervous and Mental Diseases. In 1910, after a few years as chief of the clinic at Florence and docente at the University there, he was appointed professor of neurology and psychiatry at Siena. A year later he was called to Sassari in the same capacity. In 1925 he returned to the University of Pavia where he remained the rest of his life.

Rossi's early training was with Golgi, from whom he learned the importance of morphological and functional anatomy of the central nervous system. Besides Golgi, Eugenio Tanzi, a leader of Italian psychiatry and professor in Florence, who claimed to have "discovered" Rossi, had a determining influence on Rossi in his approach to neurology. For his background in biology he was indebted to Kraepelin and Plaut.

Ottorino Rossi

Among Rossi's outstanding works in the field of biology were
his identification of glucose as the reducing agent in the cerebrospinal fluid;[1] his adaptation of the Wasserman test to the cerebrospinal fluid;[2] and his studies on neurotoxins and antigens,[3] forerunners of current contributions on allergy of the nervous system. In
neuropathology he distinguished himself for his work on the regeneration of the central and peripheral nervous systems[4] and the
histopathology of senile dementia and arteriosclerosis. In clinical
neurology one need only mention his comprehensive studies on
trauma of the central nervous system resulting from his large experience as a consultant during World War I.[5] His contributions to
neuroanatomy were many, and among them were his studies on the
afferent fibers associated with the plexus of Meissner and Auer-

Portrait, courtesy of Prof. Dott. Paolo Colombo, Verona, Italy.

bach[6] and the course of the visceral afferent fibers into the spinal cord.[7] Rossi's anatomic studies helped to pave the way to the under-standing of Hirschsprung's disease: Whitehouse and Kernohan, in 1948,[8] discovered that a defect existed in the plexus of Meissner and Auerbach in the part of the colon distal to the megacolon, and acting on this information, Swenson, Neuhauser and Pickett, in 1949,[9] achieved success in this hopeless condition by removing the defective part of the gut and suturing end-to-end the dilated portion to the sphincteric part of the rectum.

Although Rossi was not as well known abroad as his contemporary, Mingazzini, his influence in developing clinical neurology on the sound basis of anatomy, physiology and biology placed him with Mingazzini in the front rank of Italian neurologists. Several of his pupils subsequently received professorships at Italian universities— G. C. Riquier, in Milano; G. Berlucchi, in Pavia; P. Ottonello, in Parma; and V. Tronconi, in Sassari. Others became chiefs of neuro-logical services in Italian hospitals.

As a man, Rossi was straightforward, exacting, and an indefati-gable worker. Although on the surface he was stern, those of us who worked with him knew of his devotion to his pupils and recognized that the demands he made on them were modeled to his own dis-ciplined life. His fundamental kindness found expression in the fact that he gloried in one achievement only: that he had been able to do his duty in wartime without having to kill a fellow man. In doing this duty Rossi's valor was exemplary. When the Italian army, in June 1916, was for the first time confronted with a gas attack, he rushed to the front lines, thus restoring courage to the panic-stricken soldiers. His activities in peacetime extended to the field of uni-versity administration, and the city of Pavia owes him a great debt of gratitude for his work in reorganizing and consolidating its univer-sity. During later years he was active in national politics. Even though fourteen years have passed since his death, Italian neurology still is strongly permeated by the clinicopathologic trend which Rossi instilled as scholar and teacher.

NEW YORK CITY   ARMANDO FERRARO

References

[1]Hoppe-Seyler Zschr., 1903, 39: 183–189.   [2]Atti Accad. fisiocr. Siena, 1911, 5.sér., 3: 325–328.   [3]Ibid., p. 99–114.   [4]Riv. pat. nerv., 1935.

46: 1–369 (with Gastaldi). [5]*Osservazioni neurologiche su lesioni del sistema nervoso da traumi di guerra.* Sassari, Operaia, 1921. [6]Jahrb. Psychiat. Neur., Wien, 1934, *51:* 214–236. [7]J. Comp. Neur., 1922, *34:* 493–505. [8]Arch. Int. M., 1948, *82:* 75–111. [9]Pediatrics, 1949, *4:* 201–209.

References to Biography: 1) Riv. pat. nerv., 1936, *47:* 449–459 (Lugaro). 2) J. Nerv. Ment. Dis., 1936, *84:* 238–239 (Ferraro). 3) Arq. anat., 1938, *19:* 614–617 (contains bibliography; Santos).

GUSTAVE ROUSSY (1874–1948)

Gustave Roussy was born at Vevey, in Switzerland. He pursued his undergraduate studies at Lausanne, and spent his first three years in medicine at the University of Geneva; in 1897 he continued his studies at the Faculté de Médecine in Paris.

From then on he advanced steadily in the academic hierarchy. In 1902 he became interne des hôpitaux de Paris. He was Chef de travauz de physiologie pathologique in François-Franck's Laboratoire at the Collège de France from 1906 to 1908, Chef de travaux d'anatomie pathologique at the Faculté de Médecine in 1908, and Médecin en chef of the Hôpital Paul Brousse in 1913. His exceptional gifts were rewarded by appointments to positions of high place: successively he became Professeur d'anatomie pathologique at the Faculté de Médecine de Paris (1925); Directeur of the Institut du Cancer (1930), Doyen of the Faculté de Médecine (1933); and Rector of the Université de Paris (1937). On November 11, 1940, during the German occupation, he was dismissed from the university without any given reason. But in 1944, after the liberation of Paris, he was fully reinstated and again served the university with rare distinction.

Roussy was a Member of the Académie des Sciences and Sécrétaire Général of the Académie de Médecine, besides belonging to numerous other French and foreign learned societies. The Universities of Geneva, Lausanne, Athens, and Budapest bestowed upon him the Doctor's degree, *honoris causa.*

During the early part of his career, Roussy served as an intern under two eminent neurologists, Pierre Marie and Jules Dejerine, both of whom stimulated Roussy in his intense pursuit of neurology. With Dejerine he brought to light the thalamic syndrome (1906).[1]

and a year later, in his doctoral dissertation,[2] he explored the anatomy, physiology and pathology of the thalamus. A more detailed paper on the thalamic syndrome appeared in 1909.[3]

There was brilliance also in Roussy's papers on the degeneration of the cerebral cortex in amyotrophic lateral sclerosis; the experimental induction of syrinx in the spinal cord of the dog and cat; the pathology of the conus terminalis, a work in which he demonstrated the location in the spinal cord of the parasympathetic centers for micturition and defecation and the abdominal-pelvic sympathetic mechanism for the functional regulation and automatic activity of the bladder and rectum.

During World War I, Roussy wrote two important books in collaboration with J. Lhermitte, one on injuries of the spinal cord and

Portrait, courtesy of the Army Medical Library, Washington, D. C.

cauda equina[4] and the other on the psychoneuroses engendered by war;[5] and with J. Boisseau and M. d'Oelsnitz he published a volume on the treatment of the psychoneuroses of war.[6]

At the Réunion Neurologique Internationale Annuelle at Paris in 1930, Roussy read a highly stimulating and well documented paper on the neuroglia and their pathological reactions. With Mlle. G. Lévy he described, in 1932, a clinical entity, dystasie aréflexique héréditaire, which undoubtedly is related to Friedreich's disease.

The pituitary and tuber cinereum engaged Roussy's attention during the years 1912 to 1924. He and his distinguished collaborator J. Camus were the first to demonstrate that damage to the hypothalamus without removal of the pituitary could cause polyuria, gonadal atrophy, obesity and transient glycosuria; the conclusions reached were that gonadal atrophy was more likely due to a hypothalamic than a pituitary lesion and that the obesity was not necessarily dependent upon the existence of gonadal atrophy.[7,8] Subsequently, with M. Mosinger, he undertook the systematic study of the nuclei and fiber pathways of the hypothalamus and the diencephalic excito-secretory centers of the hypophysis, and insisted that the elaboration of endocrine secretions, such as pituitary colloid, occurred through the intermediation of a process which they termed *neurocrinie*. All these studies culminated in 1946 in a *Traité de neuroendocrinologie* (Paris; Masson), an important volume of 1100 pages.

Besides neurology, Roussy was particularly interested in the problem of cancer. Not only did many papers on experimental aspects of the subject come from his pen, but also a remarkable book,[9] written in collaboration with R. Leroux and M. Wolf.

Roussy was pre-eminent as a man of science, but he was also a great organizer and a leader in the battle against social injustices. He was highly cultured, the personification of simplicity, distinguished in his bearing, a gentleman down to his very finger tips. He was a stimulus to those with whom he came in contact; and at all times he was ready to help and welcome those who came from France or the outside world to acquaint themselves with his work. He was greatly admired not only by his colleagues and his students in France, but also by the international élite.

PARIS, FRANCE   GEORGES GUILLAIN

References

[1]Rev. neur., Par., 1906, *14*: 521–532.   [2]*La couche optique; étude ana- tomique, physiologique et clinique.* Thèse de Paris, 1907.   [3]Rev. neur., Par., 1909, *1*: 301–317.   [4]*Blessures de la moelle et de la queue de cheval.* Paris, Masson, 1918.   [5]*Les psychonévroses de guerre.* Paris, Masson, 1917.   [6]*Traitement des psychonévroses de guerre.* Paris, Masson, 1919.   [7]C. rend. Soc. biol., 1913, *75*: 483–486.   [8]Endocri- nology, 1920, *4*: 507–522.   [9]*Le Cancer.* Paris, Masson, 1929.

References to Biography: 1) Rev. neur., Par., 1948, *2*: 729–734 (Guil- lain).   2) Bull. Acad. Nat. Méd., 1949, 3.sér., *133*: 450–459 (Lher- mitte).

BERNARD SACHS (1858–1944)

*B*ernard Sachs, born in Baltimore, the son of a leading educator, received his early schooling and lived and worked almost all of his long, productive and distinguished life in the city of New York.   In his boyhood he was influenced particularly by his older brother, Julius, who took upon himself the task of molding the mind and character of the youngster.   For this he was well rewarded by a lifelong devotion and by the great strides his protégé, Barney (as he liked to be called), made under his tutelage.

At Harvard, four years (1874–78) of close contact with the prag- matic philosopher William James made psychology, and particularly psychopathology, Sachs' subjects of predilection.   They in turn led him to choose medicine as his life work, for there he hoped to find the opportunity to pursue further the study of the "intricacies of the human mind."

For his medical education he chose the new and vigorous faculty of Strassburg.   There he found Waldeyer (the anatomist), Goltz (the physiologist), Kussmaul (the internist), and von Recklinghau- sen (the pathologist)—all pioneers and forceful leaders in their respective disciplines.   Each one left a lasting impression on the future clinician.

On receiving his medical degree in 1881, he continued preparation for his life work under the guidance of Meynert, Hughlings Jack- son, Charcot and Westphal.   In spite of these divergent influences he adhered in thought and practice to the view that no sharp line can be drawn between neurology and psychiatry.   Their unity he

To my friend Joseph H. Globus

B. Sachs

symbolized by the term "neuropsychiatry"—a term which Forel[6] seems to have been the first to use; it was a term which had its heyday during World War I, having been adopted for purposes of convenience by the Medical Department of the U. S. Army, but which now is becoming extinct.[1]

Portrait, courtesy of Dr. Joseph H. Globus, New York City.

On entering private practice his interest in research did not abate; in fact, within a year or two (1887), he made a most significant contribution to neurology by recognizing a disease form which he first identified as *A family form of idiocy, generally fatal and associated with early blindness,* and later named "amaurotic family idiocy"— now often referred to as "Tay-Sachs disease."[2,3]

Another milestone in American neurology was his textbook on nervous diseases in children (1895),[4] containing many of his previously published (and unpublished) observations, including those on progressive muscular atrophies and dystrophies, cerebral hemorrhage, and thrombosis and embolism in the young. The book passed through three editions.

While neurology pertaining to early life constituted a major part of his interest, neurology, psychiatry and medico-legal problems in adults received no small share of his thought and work, as reflected in the 194 known publications under his name.

His dignified bearing, his tolerant but nonetheless unyielding viewpoint in argument, his clarity of expression, his frequently humorous approach, all contributed to his great success. His ability as an outstanding teacher was abundantly demonstrated as professor of neurology of the New York Polyclinic, chief of the Neurological Service of the Mount Sinai Hospital, and neurologist and alienist to Bellevue Hospital. His executive talents were displayed when he served as president of the American Neurological Association (twice), the New York Neurological Society, the New York Academy of Medicine, and the First International Neurological Congress at Berne in 1931.

At the age of 84 he was honored by a special issue of the *Journal of the Mount Sinai Hospital* in recognition of his valuable services to that institution during the 50 years he served as chief and consultant neurologist.[5] It contained tributes to his personality and accomplishments by many leading neurologists and psychiatrists. Outstanding among them was that of Adolf Meyer, who in his *Historical fragments on the neurological and psychiatric specialties,* published in that issue, painted in delicate colors the background of Barney Sachs—a great neurologist and a friend to mankind.

NEW YORK CITY   JOSEPH H. GLOBUS

References

[1]Neurology, 1951, *1:* 1–9 (P. Bailey).   [2]J. Nerv. Ment. Dis., 1887, *14:* 541–553.   [3]N. York M. J., 1896, *63:* 697–703.   [4]*A Treatise on the nervous diseases of children.* New York, Wood, 1895.   [5]J. Mount Sinai Hosp., N. York, 1942, 9: 213–271 (contains Sachs' bibliography).   [6]*Auguste Forel mémoires.* Neuchatel, Baconnière, 1941; p. 257.

Reference to Biography: Barney Sachs, 1858–1944. An autobiography. New York, privately printed, 1949 (with biographic notes by Nathan Straus and Foster Kennedy).

SANTE DE SANCTIS (1862–1935)

Sante De Sanctis, the founder of Italian experimental psychology, was born in the little village of Parrano in the mountains of Umbria. He received the M.D. in Rome in 1886, and acting on the advice of Cesare Lombroso, undertook clinical and anthropological studies of criminals. At the age of 31, while devoting himself to neuroanatomy and psychology, he attended the School of Anthropology in Rome where Giuseppe Sergi was his teacher in psychological psychiatry.

In 1892 he became assistant at the clinic of mental diseases at Rome, an activity interrupted in 1893 when he went to Zürich to study hypnotism under Forel and to the Salpêtrière in Paris to work in psychiatry. There he met, among others, Pierre Marie, and was deeply impressed by the ceremony commemorating the 30th anniversary of Charcot's death, which was held at the chapel of the Salpêtrière. On returning to Rome, he became associated with Mingazzini at the Ospedale Psichiatrico and spent four years with him, concentrating on neuroanatomic problems; he then turned again to clinical work under Marchiafava (1899), and to round out his experience, joined Luciani as physiologist (1902).

In 1906 he was appointed professor of physiologic psychology at the University of Rome, the first chair in this field in Italy. After the death of Augusto Tamburini in 1920, De Sanctis became director of the psychiatric clinic in Rome, and, when Mingazzini died in 1929, succeeded him to the chair of neurology and psychiatry of the university. De Santis' successor, in turn, was Cerletti, who, in collaboration with Lucio Bini, introduced electroshock in the treatment of psychoses.

Sante De Sanctis

De Sanctis was a prolific writer and his works were, for the most part, original. His 300 or more papers dealt with normal and pathological anatomy and physiology of the nervous system, clinical neurology, general, judiciary and criminal psychology, and psychiatry. Outstanding among his contributions to anatomy were those on the structure of the human mamillary bodies,[1] the nucleus funiculi teretis,[2] and myelination of the human cerebellum.[3] Hydromicrocephaly[4] was clarified by him. He initiated the study of mongolism[5] in Italy, and for many years worked on epilepsy in childhood.

His interest in psychiatry was also very broad. He was one of the first to trace a biological outline of psychopathology.[6] He devoted

Portrait, courtesy of Prof. Dott. Paolo Colombo, Verona, Italy.

himself particularly to problems concerned with the process of attention. These studies brought to light new symptoms which he called "paraprosexis," based on the postulate that when too much attention is concentrated on an impulse the impulse becomes inhibited.[7] This phenomenon found widespread confirmation and was later described as the basic disturbance in apraxia (Liepmann), perseveration (Pick, Liepmann and Kleist), and negativism (Kraepelin). He also made many noteworthy observations on the expression of thought, a subject which occupied him for some 25 years. His book on *La mimica del pensiero* (Palermo, Sandron, 1904) was translated into German in 1906. That on dreams, which appeared in 1899, preceded Freud's *Traumdeutung* by one year. His test for the measurement of intelligence was a forerunner of those of Binet and Th. Simon. We owe to him the first description of early dementia praecox. His fundamental contributions to child neuropsychiatry were condensed in his *Neuropsichiatria infantile* (Roma, Stock, 1930). But perhaps greatest of all were his studies in the field of experimental psychology, gathered in a comprehensive treatise,[8] in which many valuable data on neuroanatomy, neurophysiology and clinical neurology were included.

It is hard to find in the history of modern medicine a man who was so well grounded not only in the field of his endeavor, but also in philosophy, literature and law. De Sanctis used to say of himself that he suffered from "autophobia," for, like Balzac, he was made uncomfortable by rereading his work. This feeling may well have been due to a skepticism nourished by his immense and encyclopedic knowledge. With his quiet and even temper, his self control, and his endeavor to be guided by reason alone, he was the opposite of his distinguished contemporary Mingazzini.

The day before he died—at the age of 73—he delivered a lecture on psychoneurosis, and later called in his eldest son, also a physician and psychiatrist, and earnestly requested that his work not be allowed to die with him. He was referring to the institutions for poor, abnormal and retarded children which he had been establishing since 1898. As had been his wish, he was buried in the little village in which he was born.

MILANO, ITALY   CARLO L. CAZZULLO

References

[1]Ricer. lab. anat. norm. Univ. Roma, 1894, *4:* 125–136.   [2]Riv. sper. freniat., 1895, *21:* 547–579.   [3]Riv. quind. psicol., Roma, 1898, *2:* 117–122.   [4]Ann. nevr., Nap., 1900, *23:* 265–284 *et seq.*   [5]Riv. pat. nerv., 1907, *12:* 481–503.   [6]*I fondamenti scientifici della psicopatologia.* Como, 1900.   [7]Zschr. Psychol., Physiol. Sinnesorg., 1898, *17:* 205–214. [8]*Psicologia sperimentale.* Roma, Stock, 1929.

References to Biography: 1) Sez. Romana Soc. oto-neuro-oftalmol., April 30, 1935 (Fumarola).   2) Murchison (ed.), *History of psychology in autobiography.* Worcester, Mass., Clark Univ. Press, 1936; p. 82–120. 3) Rev. As. méd. argent., 1935, *49:* 1420–1436 (Ciampi).

JEAN ATHANASE SICARD (1872–1929)

Sicard was born and brought up in Marseilles and it was here that he began the study of medicine. Subsequently he completed his medical training in Paris, where he spent the remainder of his life.

In Paris he was associated with many of the leaders of French medicine. Widal was one of his first teachers and it was with him that Sicard pursued some of his immunological investigations. In 1894 he was externe to Raymond, and a year later became interne to Danlos, Widal, Troisier, Brissaud and Raymond. He owed most to his friend, Brissaud. He passed his thesis requirement in 1899, became chef de clinique in 1901, médecin des hôpitaux in 1903, agrégé in 1907, chef de service at the Hôpital Necker in 1910, and professeur de pathologie interne in 1923. During World War I he was director of the Neurological Center of the 15th Region.

Sicard was always preoccupied with what could be accomplished with the needle, both in diagnosis and in treatment. Numerous papers dealing with injections of many types came from his pen: alcohol for the relief of trigeminal neuralgia and other painful afflictions;[1,2] blood for the treatment of acute anterior poliomyelitis and other diseases; sera for direct intracranial therapy; bicarbonate of soda in the alleviation of tetany; milk in the treatment of migraine[3]; and sclerosing solutions for varicose veins, the last a procedure which he introduced.

He was one of the first to be interested in pneumoencephalography. His many papers on various manifestations and sequelae

Jean Athanase Sicard

of lethargic encephalitis,[4,5] and on the clinical manifestations and treatment of syphilis of the central nervous system were all significant contributions. He recognized that peripheral neuritis may develop as a consequence of injection of immunological sera and following the injection of quinine in the treatment of malaria. He took up where Ramsay Hunt had left off, by describing herpes zoster in the realms of the trigeminal and facial nerves.[6] In 1917 he put on record a case of traumatic injury of the neck in which the IXth, Xth, XIth and XIIth nerves were damaged,[7,8] and as a consequence his name became linked with that of Collet who, in 1915,[9] had described a similar case. Thus Sicard and Collet joined the

Portrait, courtesy of Dr. Paul Bucy, Chicago, Illinois. (Photographer: P. Simonet, Paris.)

long list of those—some obscure, some distinguished—whose names became eponyms in connection with syndromes of involvement of the bulbar cranial nerves: Avellis (X),[10] Schmidt and Hughlings Jackson (X, XI, XII),[11,12] Tapia (X, XII, and sometimes IX and the sympathetic),[13] Vernet (IX, X, XI),[14] and Villaret (X, XII and sympathetic).[15]

Sicard's fame rests, however, largely upon his introduction, with his pupil Jacques Forestier, of radio-opaque iodized oil (lipiodol).[16–18] This was unquestionably his greatest contribution to medicine and particularly to neurology. In the neurological field, lipiodol is usually thought of in connection with the diagnosis and localization of intraspinal neoplasms. But Sicard and his associates were well aware of the much wider application of this substance. They advocated its use in the diagnosis of intraspinal adhesions and inflammatory processes, urethral disorders, the outlining of sinus tracts, the demonstration of intra-arterial thromboses, the diagnosis of pulmonary disease, and even the diagnosis of intracranial tumors (through intraspinal injection of the lipiodol which ascended into the intracranial cavity). These and many other observations on the use of lipiodol were published with Forestier in book form[19] the year before Sicard died. Only recently has lipiodol been supplanted by pantopaque, introduced by Steinhausen and his associates.[20]

The day before his death, Sicard had invited friends to dinner, and with unaccustomed joie-de-vivre related the experiences he had had while on a trip to Cairo to attend the Congrès de médecine tropicale et d'hygiène. The next morning angina pectoris developed. He himself suggested the appropriate therapy, which consisted of injection of sympathetic ganglia with novocaine. The operation was to have been performed by his close friend, the surgeon Robineau. But before the needle, for which he had become famous, could be used, death supervened.

CHICAGO, ILLINOIS   PAUL C. BUCY

References

[1]Presse méd., Par., 1908, 16: 289–292.   [2]Lancet, Lond., 1918, 1: 213–214.   [3]Rev. neur., Par., 1925, 1: 944 (with Haguenau).   [4]Bull. Soc. méd. hôp. Paris, 1920, 3.sér., 44: 390–391 (with Kudelski).   [5]J. méd. fr., 1923, 12: 140–142.   [6]Rev. neur., Par., 1919, 26: 15–19 (with Roger

and Vernet). [7]Marseille méd., 1917, n.s., *1:* 385–397. [8]*Ibid.*, 1918, *55:* 886 (with Roger). [9]Lyon méd., 1915, *124:* 121–129. [10]Berl. Klin., 1891, *40:* 1–26. [11]*Die Krankheiten der oberen Luftwege.* Ed. 2. Berlin, Springer, 1897; p. 48. [12]Lancet, Lond., 1872, *2:* 770–773. [13]Arch. internat. laryng., 1906, *22:* 780–785. [14]Bull. Soc. méd. hôp. Paris, 1916, *40:* 210–223. [15]Rev. neur., Par., 1916, *1:* 188–190. [16]Rev. neur., Par., 1921, *28:* 1264–1266. [17]Bull. Soc. méd. hôp. Paris, 1922, 3.sér., *46:* 462–469. [18]Presse méd., Par., 1923, *31:* 885–887. [19]*Diagnostic et thérapeutique par le lipiodol.* Paris, Masson, 1928. [20]Radiology, 1944, *43:* 230–235.

References to Biography: Rev. neur., Par., 1929, *1:* 161–164 (Babonneix).

ACHILLE ALEXANDRE SOUQUES (1860–1944)

Souques was born in the central part of France in the village of Peyre, located on the southern fringes of the Cévenne mountains, not far from Les Gorges du Tarn. His medical studies were carried out in Paris, and among those in his class were Dupré, Sollier, and Mlle. Klumpke. In 1886 he became interne under Charcot at the Salpêtrière, and when Charcot died he continued on as chef de clinique to Charcot's successors, Brissaud and Raymond. A period was spent at the Bicêtre as successor to Pierre Marie, and in 1917 he returned to his beloved Salpêtrière. With his friends, Pierre Marie, Babinski and others, he was instrumental in founding the Société de neurologie of Paris.

All his medical activities were concerned with neurology. He was one of the best teachers of the art of performing the neurological examination, and counted among his pupils, de Martel, Clovis Vincent, Foix, Barré, Baruk, and myself. By keeping his private practice to a minimum he was able to pursue his studies uninterruptedly. His most outstanding contribution was that on *infantilisme hypophysaire*,[1] a peculiar variety of infantilism associated with nanism, due to a cystic tumor of the pituitary, a disorder quite different from the Babinski-Fröhlich syndrome. Also in the front ranks of clinical neurology were his numerous publications on parkinsonism. He was the first, in France at least, to recognize the importance of encephalitis lethargica in the causation of parkinsonism and more than any other neurologist was responsible for unifying the diverse manifestations of the disorder.[2] Under the designation, *kinésie paradoxale,* he

A mon ami le Dr Alajouanine,
a ffectueux souvenir.

J. Jugues

presented a curious disorder characterized by changes in hypertonia
and motility which suddenly make possible the performance of an
action which previously was impossible. He described an important

Portrait, courtesy of Prof. Th. Alajouanine, Paris, France. (Photographer: Manuel,
Paris.)

sign which accounts for the disharmonious movements in parkinsonism, namely the abolition of associated movements, as manifested, for instance, by the loss of automatic swinging of the arms while walking. He stated that the disorder may also be demonstrated by the lack of coordinated arm movements when the body is turned quickly to the side or the trunk is suddenly bent backward.

Always interested in the disorders of speech, he gave to aphasia new facets: one report dealt with an anatomic study of a case of Broca's aphasia with integrity of the third frontal convolution, and another with the anatomic basis of the anarthria of Pierre Marie. He provided the first description of that bizarre disorder of speech observed in pseudobulbar palsy and parkinsonism in which the same word or the same sentence is repeated many times; he referred to the condition, over which the patient has no control, as "palilalia."[3]

Among his other important works were the description of the *phénomenon des interosseux* in the hand of patients with organic hemiplegia, the study of vesico-rectal automatism in marked compression of the spinal cord, an anatomic and experimental study on subacute anterior poliomyelitis, the delineation of *camptocormie*, and a description—the first—of a special type of vertebral metastasis: the ivory vertebra.

In 1925, Souques retired from his duties as neurologist to the Salpêtrière. At first he was at loose ends. Many weeks were spent in exploring the beauties of the Louvre, and then he turned to the study of the neurology of antiquity. For some fifteen years he labored in this field, bringing to bear all the perspicacity and bent for detail which had taken him so far in the field of clinical neurology. He published many articles (e.g., one on Galen[4]—the first experimental neurologist) and a book, *Étapes de la neurologie dans l'antiquité grecque* (Paris, Masson, 1936) in which there may be found a full account of neurology as practised by the Greeks at the time of Hippocrates, and a masterly presentation of the anatomico-physiological works of Herophilus, Erasistratus and Galen. Jacksonian epilepsy and postdiphtheritic paralysis, he found, were well known to Hippocrates.

Souques was of small stature, blond and blue-eyed, as is characteristic of the men of the mountains in the center of France. He was an attractive person: his discretion and his kindliness endeared him to all who knew him; he had no enemies. A severe heart attack in

1939 took him back to his native locale, to Marvejols, where he summoned up enough energy to study the folklore and the dialect of that part of the country, a work carried out partly to assuage the moral agony which was then oppressing all of France. In 1942 he returned to Seine-et-Marne, but a carcinoma of the mouth deprived him of his speech: he wrote to Moreau and to me, "Comme c'est long de mourir."

A worthy pupil of Charcot—and his last one—Souques was emimently successful in perpetuating the anatomico-clinical approach which over the years has been the bulwark of French neurology.

PARIS, FRANCE   TH. ALAJOUANINE

References

[1]Nouv. Iconogr. Salpêtrière, 1913, *26*: 69–80 (with Chauvet).   [2]Rev. neur., Par., 1921, *28*: 534–573.   [3]*Ibid.*, 1908, *16*: 340–342.   [4]*Ibid.*, 1933, *1*: 297–340.

References to Biography: 1) Presse méd., 1945, *53*: 647–648 (Alajouanine).   2) Bull. Soc. méd. hôp. Paris, 1945, *61*: 55–57 (Vincent).

WILLIAM GIBSON SPILLER (1863–1940)

Spiller was the most distinguished American clinical neurologist of our time. He was born in Baltimore. After receiving an M.D. from the University of Pennsylvania in 1892, he spent four years abroad in specialized studies, at first in internal medicine and later in neurology with such savants as Obersteiner, Oppenheim, Edinger, Dejerine and Gowers. He often spoke of the clinical thoroughness of these men, especially Obersteiner and Oppenheim, and when in later years it was repeatedly suggested that he write a textbook on neurology his favorite retort was: "When I can write a better book than Oppenheim's, I'll do so."

On his return to Philadelphia he entered into neuropathological research in the William Pepper Laboratory of the University of Pennsylvania, a connection which was maintained until 1910. At the turn of the century, he became head of the neurological department of the Philadelphia Polyclinic Hospital. It was at about this time that he came to know Charles Karsner Mills (1845–1931), regarded as "the dean of American neurologists."[1] To both of them

William Gibson Spiller

the winning of prestige for the department of neurology was the great object of their lives, and when Spiller would drop into Mills' office every few days, his customary salutation, "What's new?" always meant "What's new in neurology?" Sometimes Mills would launch into an account of some of his experiences, such as those on the battlefield of Gettysburg; or Spiller, to save Mills's failing vision, would read to him. In 1915 Spiller succeeded Mills as professor of neurology to the University of Pennsylvania, and retained the chair until 1932, when he retired as professor emeritus.

Spiller's publications numbered almost 250 and all were important. The subject matter for his remarkably varied output was furnished by an enormous collection of specimens, many of them from the Philadelphia General Hospital. Like Mills, who was the first to de-

Portrait, courtesy of Dr. A. M. Ornsteen, Philadelphia, Pennsylvania.

scribe the syndrome of occlusion of the superior cerebellar artery[2,3] (Spiller did the pathologic study of this case[4]), Spiller became a pioneer in the field of vascular occlusions of the brain stem.[5-7] He was the first to postulate the medullary syndrome resulting from anterior spinal artery occlusion.[6] Equally impressive were his many papers on disorders of conjugate extraocular muscle movements,[8-12] in which he took up where Henri Parinaud (1844–1905)[13] had left off on the subject of paralysis of upward conjugate movements and provided a better understanding of the internuclear paralyses of Lhermitte.[14] His articles on cordotomy,[15] perhaps the most dramatic of all, showed the keen Spillerian instinct for research. The lion's share of his interest was centered for a time round trigeminal neuralgia, and his ten papers on this subject (the two most important being those on surgical intervention[16,17]) were regarded by him as his most important practical offering. Not least was his discovery that deep sensibility of the face is conveyed centrally by way of the facial nerve,[18] an observation confirmed subsequently by Souques and Hartmann[19] and many others. Mills, too, had made contributions to the clinical aspects of the facial nerve, and this may not have been a coincidence, for he himself suffered from Bell's palsy complicated by facial spasm. Patients would occasionally say to him: "Stop winking at me."

As editor of the *Journal of Nervous and Mental Diseases*, Spiller's daily pabulum was the current scientific literature, which was shared with students and associates. His command of the neurological literature —old and new—was phenomenal. Hours were spent every day in the outpatient neurological service of the Hospital of the University of Pennsylvania. His associates included McConnell, Cadwalader, Weisenburg, Camp, Wilson, Winkelman, and Hadden.

Spiller was of serious demeanor, a little stooped, rather quiet and contained, and wholly lacking in sartorial splendor. The story goes that he, delighting in an argument, would carry a spinal cord or some other specimen in his coat pocket, and whip it out on almost any occasion in the hope that his discourse on it would bring a disagreement of opinion. His office was as bare of decoration as that of an ascetic. He could never be considered extravagant. He and a friend were strolling down the boardwalk at Atlantic City one morning when the friend hailed a newsboy and gave him a quarter for a paper. "But you did not get your change back," said Spiller. "No," said the friend, "I wanted the boy to have it," to which Spiller replied, "That's wasting money; you could have borrowed the paper I bought last evening." Spiller was always invited to dinners and parties in Philadelphia given in honor of distinguished visitors but since he so rarely took over his share of the entertainment some of his associates grew a little piqued. A distinguished neurologist who came to Philadelphia was wined and dined, and only after he had gone was Spiller told of the banquet. "But I was not invited," he said. "That's odd," was the reply.

For years Spiller refused to enter the private practice of neurology, and when, in 1910, he finally yielded to the pleas of those of us who were his confreres, he seemed to feel that he had somehow been duped. In the sickroom he appeared doleful, and was regarded by some as coldly scientific—a case being a problem to be solved—but those who knew him well were aware of his capacity for great depth of feeling. When it was known that he was to lecture, the amphitheatre was always filled with his students, some to be entertained by the quotations from Shakespeare with which, in his rather soft voice, he frequently punctuated his discourses, and others to watch the dexterity with which he would solve one neurological mystery after another.

He was a master of neuroanatomy. Joseph D. Aronson relates that in the earlier days Spiller and Mills would match wits in the amphitheatre, and would argue down to the smallest detail—indeed, to exhaustion—and at the end one or the other would declare, "I wish only that the 'post' were done; then we'd see who is wrong." Spiller was a strong advocate for the use of potassium iodide in gumma of the brain; Mills was not. On one occasion over the autopsy table, a patient who had received much potassium iodide at the hands of Spiller was found to have massive gummas of the brain. Mills remarked to Spiller: "See, he's had barrels full of iodide; I told you it doesn't do any good."

In the ten years which have passed since his death, Spiller has, on the American scene, not been eclipsed.

PHILADELPHIA, PENNSYLVANIA   A. M. ORNSTEEN

References

[1]Arch. Neur. Psychiat., Chic., 1932, *28:* 1390–1410 (Frazier, Spiller, Burr, McConnell, Cadwalader).   [2]J. Nerv. Ment. Dis., 1908, *35:* 331–332. [3]*Ibid.,* 1912, *39:* 73–76.   [4]Arch. Neur. Psychiat., Chic., 1931, *25:* 1003– 1010 (Russel).   [5]J. Nerv. Ment. Dis., 1908, *35:* 365–387.   [6]*Ibid.,* 1908, *35:* 775–778.   [7]*Ibid.,* 1909, *36:* 601–613.   [8]Univ. Pennsylvania M. Bull., 1903, *16:* 362–366 (Potts).   [9]J. Nerv. Ment. Dis., 1905, *32:* 417–426 *et seq.*   [10]Am. J. M. Sc., 1919, *157:* 695–699.   [11]Brain, Lond., 1924, *47:* 345–357.   [12]Arch. Neur. Psychiat., Chic., 1932, *28:* 251–271. [13]Arch. Neur., Paris., 1883, *5:* 145–172.   [14]*L'encéphalite léthargique. Questions neurologiques d'actualité.* Paris, Masson, 1922.   [15]Arch. Neur. Psychiat., Chic., 1923, *9:* 1–21.   [16]Am. J. M. Sc., 1898, n.s., *116:* 503–532 (with Keen).   [17]Univ. Pennsylvania M. Bull., 1901, *14:* 341– 352 (with Frazier).   [18]*Ibid.,* 1907, *20:* 35–38 (R. H. Ivy and L. W. Johnson).   [19]Rev. neur., Par., 1924, *31:* 86–87.

Reference to Biography: Arch. Neur. Psychiat., Chic., 1940, *44:* 175–179 (McConnell).

MOSES ALLEN STARR (1854–1932)

*A*fter the early cradling of American neurology by Hammond and Mitchell and its adolescent growth under Mills, Sequin and others, a New York triumvirate composed of Dana, Sachs and Starr began to spotlight the then rapidly expanding neurological scene.

Starr was born in Brooklyn, New York. Descended from distinguished English ancestors who moved to New England in 1652, he was reared in a setting of security, scholarship and distinctive breeding. Precocious as a child, he was gifted in powers of precise observation and vivid recall, which were to serve him well in his later career as a neurologist.

Young Allen Starr entered Princeton University in 1872, where his academic interests became divided between classical history and science. Upon graduation from Princeton (1876) he first followed his more cultural leanings and went to Germany to study Roman and Greek history. However, a few visits to Helmholtz's laboratory in Berlin revived his latent interest in natural science, and in 1877 he decided to study medicine, shaping his ultimate aim to specialize in neurology.

Moses Allen Starr

Portrait, courtesy of Mrs. Katherine Starr Oliver, Mount Kisco, New York.

After graduating in 1880 from the College of Physicians and Surgeons, Columbia University, he served a two-year residency at Bellevue Hospital and then embarked again for Europe. Thus, in 1882 we find him at Heidelberg in the laboratories of Erb and Schultze, and subsequently training in Vienna under Nothnagel and Meynert, in the company of such illustrious fellow students as Sigmund Freud, G. Anton of Halle, and Bernard Sachs. He then went to Paris to be with Charcot, who was at the height of his fame.

Upon his return to New York in 1883 he began his career as a neurological investigator. Lacking laboratory facilities, he constructed a laboratory in his own residence and, as a result of this "home" research, published, in 1884, his famous essay on *The sensory tract in the central nervous system*,[1] which further elucidated the many problems opened by Flechsig and his students. In 1888, at the Congress of American Physicians and Surgeons, he participated with Ferrier and Horsley in a symposium on cerebral localization of function, and from then on was regarded as an American pioneer in this field, along with Mills and Dana. His special contributions were to sensorimotor neurology,[1,2] aphasia,[3] and localization of brain tumors.[4,5] In all, he published well over 100 articles and several textbooks and monographs.[2,5-8]

Though renowned as an investigator, Starr was even better known as a teacher. He climbed the academic ladder rapidly, succeeding Sequin in 1889 as the second professor of nervous diseases at the College of Physicians and Surgeons. At the height of his career his appearance and peppery personality created a striking picture. He was of less than medium height and stocky build, with sprightly eyes deeply set in a ruddy, determined face bedecked by a winged white mustache. Always moving quickly and thinking fast, he exuded an enthusiasm and drive which were contagious. Foster Kennedy has likened him to a retired Anglo-Indian Colonel but with more drive; and Kinnier Wilson, after observing him in Horsley's laboratory, described him as "a great little fellow, keen as mustard, hopping all over the place . . ." To those who knew him well there was beneath this exuberant exterior a warm human touch and an unfailing patience and sympathy for the other person's point of view.

Starr's teaching approach was direct, schematic and forceful. Though lacking the subtle profundity and literary skill of Weir Mitchell and Dana, he probably excelled them in the vivid clarity of the clinicoanatomic pictures he painted. His lectures and clinics were invariably crowded. From 1889 to 1915 he was the central teaching figure in New York neurology. Among his students were Pearce Bailey, Sr., Charles A. Elsberg, Smith Ely Jelliffe, Walter Timme, Louis Casamajor, and Henry Alsop Riley.

Many academic honors were conferred upon him, including the degrees of Ph.D. and LL.D. from Princeton and Sc.D. from Columbia. He held office in several leading medical societies, having been president of the American Neurological Association (1897) and of the New York Neurological Society, and vice-president of the New York Academy of Medicine.

Starr died quietly in his sleep in Marienbad, Czechoslovakia, when he was 78. The M. Allen Starr Research Laboratories in Neurology at Columbia University were dedicated to his memory with a stirring eulogy by Frederick Tilney.

WASHINGTON, D. C.   PEARCE BAILEY

References

[1]J. Nerv. Ment. Dis., 1884, *11*: 327–407.   [2]*Familiar forms of nervous disease*. Baltimore, Wood, 1890.   [3]Brain, Lond., 1888, *12*: 82–101. [4]Med. News, 1889, *54*: 29–37.   [5]*Brain surgery*. Baltimore, Wood, 1893. [6]*Atlas of nerve cells*. New York, Macmillan, 1896.   [7]*Organic nervous diseases*. Philadelphia, Lea, 1903.   [8]*Organic and functional nervous diseases*. Ed. 3. Philadelphia, Lea & Febiger, 1919.

References to Bibliography: 1) *Semi-centennial volume of the American Neurological Association*. Albany, New York, Boyd, 1924 (contains bibliography).   2) Arch. Neur. Psychiat., Chic., 1932, *28*: 1411–1413 (Casamajor).

ERNST ADOLF GUSTAV GOTTFRIED VON STRÜMPELL
(1853–1925)

Von Strümpell was born in Neu-Autz, Kurland (a part of the Baltic Provinces of Russia), but spent his youth in nearby Dorpat (now Estonia), where his father was professor of philosophy. The high intellectual level of his family and the way of thought and life among the German minority of the Baltic Provinces were important elements in von Strümpell's development, character and career. Already at the age of six he showed much promise as a violinist. While

Prof. Dr. Adolf Strümpell

still a "Gymnasiast," he played chamber music and on one occasion took part in a performance of Mozart's *Entführung*.   In his auto-

Portrait from frontispieces in *Aus dem Leben eines deutschen Klinikers.*   Leipzig, Vogel, 1925; by von Strümpell.

biography he tells of his embarrassment when during the overture he heard the orchestra play along in prestissimo while he still held the half notes of the first measures.

After a semester in Prag, where he studied philosophy and psychology, he turned to medicine, first in the German university of Dorpat under L. Stieda and E. von Bergmann. Later he went to Leipzig, following his father who had been called to the University there. His teachers included Wunderlich, Thiersch, Credé and Carl Ludwig. After graduation in 1875 he was appointed assistant in Wunderlich's clinic of internal diseases. The winter of 1877–78 was spent in Vienna where he was impressed by Meynert and Benedikt, and where he met Johannes Brahms. In 1878 he was appointed Privatdozent, and came into close scientific and personal contact with Wagner, Cohnheim, Weigert and Erb. His first course of lectures at the University on acute infectious diseases attracted just one student, who fled, however, at the teacher's approach, evidently frightened by the lonely atmosphere of the classroom.

When Erb was called to Heidelberg in 1883, von Strümpell became Director of the Medizinische Poliklinik and Professor extraordinarius. The brilliant P. J. Möbius was his assistant. He was the chief of internal medicine in Erlangen from 1886 to 1903 and in Breslau from 1903 until 1909. After a short intermezzo in Vienna he was, after 30 years, back in Leipzig (in 1910), as successor to Heinrich Curschmann.

Von Strümpell won much of his fame and international reputation through his textbook of internal medicine, which first appeared in 1883; he worked on subsequent editions until the day he died. There were more than 30 editions, many translated into foreign languages. Being written almost entirely on the basis of personal observation, it was, indeed, a one-man performance. His lasting achievements were due to most careful observation and a critical and constructive analysis of the functional disorders resulting from lesions of the nervous system. He described several disease entities, among them hereditary spinal spastic paralysis[1] and polioencephalomyelitis.[2] His name is linked with Westphal's as pioneer in the study of pseudosclerosis. Alexander Karl Otto Westphal (1833–90), of Berlin, who was well-known for his observation that patellar reflexes are lost in tabes dorsalis (1873),[13] proposed in 1883 the term "pseudosclerosis" for a condition characterized by tremors, difficulty in speech, and poverty of movement; he could find no changes in the brain and did not mention hepatic cirrhosis.[3] Similar cases were reported by von Strümpell in 1889[4] and 1890,[5] but he contributed nothing really enlightening. Another paper, in which he coined the term "amyostatic symptom-complex" to include pseudosclerosis, paralysis agitans, etc., appeared in 1899.[6] The term pseudosclerosis, born under an inauspicious star, took hold, however, as more cases were assembled, and finally the condition was established as an entity by Hösslin and Alzheimer.[7] In time the gap which separated this disorder from Wilson's disease (1912) was bridged, mainly through the writings of W. Spielmeyer,[8] H. C. Hall,[9] and F. Lüthy.[10]

Von Strümpell wrote also on tabes, multiple sclerosis, and aphasia. Several reflexes bear his name.[11,12] Not only his clinical sense, but also his broad education and his general culture, his alert interest in human affairs, science and art, enabled him to detect and describe the psychogenic element in nervous symptoms at a time when the organic approach was all-powerful among neurologists. Such was the background of his numerous contributions to the study of mental hygiene, alcoholism, education and, above all, traumatic neurosis, a term coined by him.

His personality as reflected in his autobiography and the testimony of his pupils, was that of a modest, kind, serene and optimistic individual, a devoted physician, a faithful friend and colleague, a man of the highest moral standards. In his search for knowledge, he had an undeniable trend toward the general; his analysis of neurotic behavior, for instance, seems cursory. In all matters of science and life he was a liberal with a healthy respect for tradition. His devotion to music brought him into personal contact with outstanding artists of his time. He believed teaching to be the most precious contribution man can make to his time.

RICHMOND, VIRGINIA   WALTHER RIESE

References

[1]Arch. Psychiat., Berl., 1868, 17: 217–238.   [2]Jahrb. Kinderh., 1885, 22: 173–178.   [3]Arch. Psychiat., Berl., 1883, 14: 87–134 et seq.   [4]Deut. Zschr. Nervenh., 1898, 12: 115–149.   [5]Ibid., 1899, 14: 348–355. [6]Ibid., 1915, 54: 207–254.   [7]Zschr. ges. Neur. Psychiat., 1912, 8: 183–209.   [8]Ibid., 1920, 57: 312–351.   [9]La dégénerescence hépatolenticu-

laire. Paris, Masson, 1921.   [10]Deut. Zschr. Nervenh., 1931, *123:* 101–181.   [11]Neur. Cbl., 1899, *18:* 617–619.   [12]Deut. Zschr. Nervenh., 1899, *15:* 254–273.   [13]Arch. Psychiat., Berl., 1875, *5:* 803–834.

References to Biography and Works: 1) *Aus dem Leben eines deutschen Klinikers. Erinnerungen und Beobachtungen.* Leipzig, Vogel, 1925 (von Strümpell).   2) Klin. Wschr., 1925, *4:* 382–383 (His).   3) *Diseases of the basal ganglia and subthalamic nuclei.* New York, Oxford Univ. Press, 1946 (Denny-Brown).

HENRI VERGER (1873–1930)

*H*enri Verger, a genuine Girondin, was born at Saint-Fort-sur-Gironde, the son of a physician. On completing his undergraduate work at the Lyceum of Bordeaux, with emphasis on the classics, he pursued his medical studies at the University of Bordeaux, where, in time, he became agrégé (1904) and professor of medical jurisprudence (1914) and clinical medicine (1923).

His first work, in 1897,[1] was concerned with muscle sense and with disordered sensibility following cerebral hemiplegia. He demonstrated that it is necessary to take into consideration two categories of sensibility: the simpler, consisting of pain, thermal and tactile, and the more complex, the stereognostic sense (or, as he called it, the "sens du toucher actif") which subserves motor performance. He contended that through the stereognostic sense, images are perceived and impressed indelibly in the memory and find representation at the level of the rolandic cortex.

He is best known in some quarters in connection with the thalamic syndrome, which he produced in the dog (in 1898) by means of electrolytic lesions.[2]   Although marked sensory disturbance occurred, pain sensibility of the contralateral side was never abolished. A decade later the observations of Verger and those made by Dejerine and E. Long[3] were substantiated in the monkey by Roussy. The disorder is generally known in France as the syndrome of Verger-Dejerine, but the real pioneer was Edinger, who first described the disorder in man in 1891.

The neuralgias also engaged much of his attention. In collaboration with Pitres, he devised in 1904 a practical classification of the neuralgias through the use of cocaine injected intraneurally.[4] His concept of neuralgic torticollis was particularly illuminating. Also

Henri Verger

he discovered a new method of treating neuralgia, namely the intra-
neural injection of 60 to 70 per cent alcohol. The procedure, especially in trigeminal neuralgia, is still referred to as the *méthode
bordelaise*.

Portrait, courtesy of Prof. Paul Delmas-Marsalet, Bordeaux, France.

Verger's work on hysteria was also notable. Dominant in France at the turn of the century was Babinski's view that hysteria could be cured by persuasion, and that deep hypnosis was not necessary; and to emphasize the point he coined a new term, *pithiatisme*, from the Greek words meaning "persuasion" and "curable." Verger vigorously opposed Babinski's concept that "hystero-traumatism" is little more than simulation, publishing his first observations on the subject under the title, *Conception nouvelle des névroses traumatiques et leur retentissement médico-légal.*[5]

From 1930 onward, he concentrated on epidemic encephalitis, and it was his contributions in this field which brought him near the pinnacle of his profession. In France this disorder is generally referred to as "Cruchet's disease," because Cruchet's description of it[6,7] appeared one month before that of von Economo. Verger was concerned with many clinical aspects of the disease, including neuralgic and poliomyelitic and bulbar forms.[8-14] His brilliant monograph with Cruchet on parkinsonism and the bradykinetic syndrome appeared in 1925.[15] Of importance also were his studies of painful spasticity in acutely progressive syringomyelia[16] and Gerlier's disease.

Verger's activity extended far beyond the realm of his immediate neurological interests. He was one of the most ardent defenders of *l'Ordre des Médecins* and wrote a history of medical ethics (*Précis de déontologie médicale*) which was published in the Collection Testut. He worked in the field of social medicine and wielded much influence in the "syndicalistes" (labor unions). He became "the symbol of the modern progressive physician whose isolation from his colleagues was, if not desertion, at least anachronistic." During World War I he was chief of the ambulance corps of the French Army, and for distinguished service at the front he was awarded the Croix de la Légion d'honneur. As expert in medical jurisprudence he presented numerous reports before military tribunals on cases in which the life and honor of soldiers were at stake.

Verger was endowed with wisdom, a spirit of tolerance, and a sense of humor. Where he differed on scientific matters with his beloved master Pitres—their points of divergence were numerous— he would bring his arguments to bear only with the greatest reserve, but in disagreeing with others there was nothing halting about his verbal sallies. Lhermitte relates that when he heard Verger discuss sciatic neuralgia, he was "seduced" by the charm of his words, the precision of his observations, and the skill with which he presented his arguments, but he could not share Verger's concepts.

Verger died suddenly and unexpectedly from "pulmonary edema" at the age of 57.

BORDEAUX, FRANCE   PAUL DELMAS-MARSALET

References

[1]Arch. Clin., Bordeaux, 1897, 6: 443–457.   [2]Arch. physiol., norm. et path., 1898, 5.sér., 10: 706–713 (with Sellier).   [3]Rev. neur., Par., 1910, 19: 197–204.   [4]Rev. méd., Par., 1904, 24: 34–63.   [5]Arch. anthrop. criminol., 1913, 28: 15–38.   [6]Lancet, Lond., 1925, 2: 263–268. [7]Practitioner, Lond., 1930, 124: 174–187.   [8]Bull. Soc. méd. chir. Bordeaux, 1920; p. 19–24 (with Anglade).   [9]Ibid., p. 61–63.   [10]Ibid., p. 260–270 (with Hesnard).   [11]Ibid., p. 435–442.   [12]Ibid., p. 541–547. [13]Encéphale, 1922, 17: 409–423 (with Hesnard).   [14]Presse méd., 1926, 34: 737–739 (with Cruchet).   [15]Les états parkinsoniens et le syndrome bradykinétique. Paris, Baillière, 1925.   [16]Encéphale, 1907, 2: 21–28.

References to Biography: 1) Paris méd., 1930, 78: 479–480 (Delmas-Marsalet).   2) Rev. neur., Par., 1930, 2: 528–529 (Lhermitte).

JULIUS WAGNER VON JAUREGG (1857–1940)

Wagner von Jauregg was born in Wels, Austria. His father, a native of Austrian Silesia and state official, was born "Wagner," but on being ennobled in 1883 he added the name Ritter von Jauregg, an adaptation of his mother's maiden name, Jauernigg. Since the ennobling took place rather late in his father's life some of the early publications of young Julius were under the name "Julius Wagner." On the termination of World War I, ennobled Austrians were deprived by law of their titles, but Julius was granted permission to use the name Wagner-Jauregg.

Wagner von Jauregg, as we shall call him, studied medicine at the University of Vienna, where he received his doctorate in 1880. As a student, and after graduation, he worked in Stricker's Institute of Pathology in Vienna (1876–82). Being unsuccessful in his effort

Julius Wagner von Jauregg

to obtain a position at one of the clinics of internal medicine, he accepted a post at the psychiatric clinic in Vienna with Leidesdorf even though, as he later confessed, he knew nothing about the subject. In 1885 he became Privatdozent. He moved to Graz in 1889 to head the department of psychiatry of the University, but upon Meynert's death in 1892 he returned to Vienna, taking charge of the Psychiatric Clinic of the Allgemeine Krankenhaus. In 1902 he succeeded Krafft-Ebing as professor of neurology and psychiatry.

One of his first publications dealt with cerebral symptoms following the resuscitation of strangulated individuals.[1] In this paper he expressed ideas which could easily have become the basis of "shock therapy": the use of large amounts of chemical and physical agents

Portrait, courtesy of Prof. F. Jahnel, Munich, Germany.

for the induction of violent metabolic changes in the brain in the treatment of psychoses.

Wagner von Jauregg's best known contribution to medical science was the introduction of malarial fever for the treatment of general paresis. He conceived the idea that fever might be of therapeutic value in 1887, when he observed that "not rarely psychoses were healed through intercurrent infectious diseases," and he proposed that "one should intentionally imitate this experiment of nature."[2,3] He first attempted to induce fever with erysipelas, tuberculin, and typhoid vaccines. In 1917 he resorted to the inoculation of tertian malarial organisms into paretics, blood containing the organisms being taken by syringe from the cubital vein of a wounded and shell-shocked malarious soldier who had been admitted to Wagner von Jauregg's clinic. Of the nine patients thus treated, six were definitely benefited and three of them were still at their occupations four years later. For his discovery of the therapeutic value of malaria inoculation in the treatment of dementia paralytica, Wagner von Jauregg was awarded the Nobel Prize for Physiology and Medicine in 1927. He was the first psychiatrist to be thus honored, and to date the only one.

Wagner von Jauregg was also a pioneer in the prevention of cretinism, being the first to suggest obligatory addition of iodide to table salt for protection of the population in endemic goiter areas.[4] Many of his papers convey the concept that mental diseases are caused by somatic rather than by psychic disorders.[5] The effects of heredity in the field of neurology and psychiatry also commanded his most careful attention.[6] His last monograph, published posthumously by his son, Dr. Theodor Wagner-Jauregg, dealt with the duration of life as determined by heredity.[7] He was also a wellknown figure as psychiatric expert in numerous famous forensic cases, and for many years played an important part in shaping legislation concerned with psychiatry. Many of his ideas have been worked out with the assistance of his pupils von Economo, Pilcz, Stransky, Bonvicini, Gerstmann, Kauders, and Poetzl, the last named of whom became his successor.

After recovering from typhoid fever in his childhood he became exceptionally strong of body, an athlete every inch of his five-foot-seven frame. During his student days he was stricken with tuberculosis, and not having the means to go to a sanatorium and being a person of great determination, he continued his studies, relaxing between classes in a nearby park until the hemoptysis ceased. Soon his health and strength were restored. His son, Dr. Theodor Wagner-Jauregg, tells of his out-performing the champion weight lifter Jagendorfer by raising with his foot a 30 kilogram iron dumbbell from the floor to the seat of a chair. Like Cajal, he conquered tuberculosis, developed superb biceps, was addicted to chess. When the nights in Vienna were wintry he would often play chess with a friend by telephone, and when he had insomnia—he seldom slept more than five or six hours at night but always had a 20-minute nap after lunch—he would usually get up and play a game with an imaginary opponent.

Wagner von Jauregg was a conservative. The style of his clothes never changed. It was because of his appearance and personal characteristics, his athletic body, his bushy eyebrows, his deep voice, his imperturbable calm, and his dry humor that Vienna society recognized him as one of its most conspicuous figures. On retirement from the University in 1928, he remained at his home in Vienna, continually putting his pen to its accustomed use. His almost completed autobiography was at his bedside when death came to him at the ripe age of 83. Much of it has been used by Schönbauer and Jantsch in their recent book on Wagner von Jauregg and other celebrities of Vienna.

NEW YORK CITY   BERNHARD DATTNER

References

[1]Jahrb. Psychiat. Neur., Wien, 1889, 8: 313–332.   [2]*Fieber und Infektionstherapie. Ausgewählte Beiträge 1887–1935.* Wien, Weidmann, 1936.   [3]J. Nerv. Ment. Dis., 1922, 55: 369–375.   [4]Jahrb. Psychiat. Neur., Wien, 1894, 12: 102–137 et seq.   [5]*Ibid.*, 1892, 10: 180–198. [6]Wien. klin. Wschr., 1929, 42: 925–927 et seq.   [7]*Über die menschliche Lebensdauer.* Innsbruck, Deut. Alpenverl., 1941.

References to Biography: 1) *Die medizinische Welt.* Wien, Urban & Schwarzenberg, 1944 (Schönbauer).   2) Wien. med. Wschr., 1928, 78: 892–894 (contains bibliography; Pilcz).   3) Arch. Neur. Psychiat., Chic., 1940, 44: 1319–1322 (Bruetsch).   4) *Julius Wagner-Jauregg. Lebenserinnerungen.* Wien, Springer, 1950 (Schönbauer and Jantsch).

CARL WERNICKE (1848–1904)

Wernicke was born in Tarnowitz, a small town in Upper Silesia which at that time was German. After graduating in medicine at Breslau, he worked as assistant of Neumann in Breslau and of Westphal at the Charité in Berlin. Neumann gave him the chance to go to Vienna for six months, where he studied under Meynert. Years later, Meynert's portrait was the only one which hung on the walls of the auditorium in Wernicke's clinic, and his name was one of the few ever mentioned by Wernicke in his lectures. From 1878–85 Wernicke carried on a private practice in nervous diseases in Berlin, and then gladly accepted a call to his alma mater at Breslau as Extraordinarius. In 1890 he received the Ordinariat in psychiatry. Years later (1904) he moved on to Halle in the same capacity, but had barely become well settled when he met with a fatal accident while riding a bicycle in the Thuringian forest.

Wernicke began his scientific career in anatomy, in which he was influenced particularly by Meynert. The first product of his studies was his distinction of three primordial convolutions ("Urwindungen") in the cerebral cortex. This was followed by his 3-volume *Lehrbuch der Gehirnkrankheiten* (Kassel u. Berlin, Fischer, 1881–83), an astounding accomplishment for so young a man. Particularly interesting was his postulation of the symptomatology resulting from thrombosis of the posterior inferior cerebellar artery, based in his anatomic investigations of the arterial supply of the medulla oblongata—an assumption confirmed in 1895 by Wallenberg.[1] Also he was the first to predict the occurrence of pseudo-ophthalmoplegia,[2] that rare disorder, sometimes accompanying pseudobulbar palsy, in which the patient is unable to move his eyes voluntarily on command or to fix his gaze on an object in the peripheral visual field, but is able to follow to some degree slowly moving objects; the patient reads a line only by letting his eyes wander aimlessly until finally all the words of the line are perceived. In his *Lehrbuch* (vol. 2, p. 229) he brought to light the clinical syndrome of polio-encephalitis superior haemorrhagica, which now bears his name. Years were to pass before it was realized that the basis of the disorder was an alteration in the blood-brain barrier, which allowed blood plasma to escape into the parenchyma and cause it to disintegrate.

Portrait from *Mschr. Psychiat.*, 18: i, 1905.

The work for which Wernicke became internationally famous was a small book on aphasia,[3] published when he was 26. In it the influence of Meynert was apparent. The originality of his work lies in his attempt to interpret the various aphasic symptom-complexes as consequences of impairment of various elementary psychic processes which are localized in different parts of the cerebral cortex. In the course of these studies he described, for the first time, sensory aphasia and its localization in the posterior part of the first temporal convolution. The simple graphic presentation of his ideas on the structure of language in relation to the cerebral cortex became the mainspring of the many so-called brain maps so characteristic of this era of research in the field of aphasia. His work helped to place on a secure foundation the concept of unilateral cerebral dominance, first proposed by Dax in 1836 at a Congress in Montpellier (Dax's son published this paper in 1877 and 1878).[4,5]

For Wernicke, mental disorders were diseases of the brain, making the separation of psychiatry and neurology artificial: "Geisteskrankheiten sind Gehirnkrankheiten." As soon as he had the chance to observe psychiatric patients in greater number, he tried to apply to them the principles which had proved so successful in his study of aphasia. Not liking to discuss results of individual cases in papers, Wernicke published a system of psychiatry in three parts (1894–1900). Today one may have a critical attitude toward his physiologic concepts as the basis for an understanding of the various psychiatric syndromes, but he nevertheless will find them a source of stimulation; his *Krankenvorstellungen*[6] is a good example. One may miss descriptions of clinical entities in Wernicke's psychiatry. That is not accidental. Wernicke considered the time not yet ripe for distinction of separate psychiatric diseases. Thus he was and remained always an ardent adversary of Kraepelin, whose method he considered not sufficiently scientific.

Wernicke was a taciturn and reserved man, not easy to deal with. He was close to his older co-workers, particularly Ernst Storch, whom he held in high esteem. He had not much contact with his younger pupils, but his way of examining patients and his demonstrations were so elucidating and stimulating that we who had the good fortune to attend his clinics were deeply influenced in our further consideration of neurological and psychiatric problems. We could never forget him. His influence can be seen in the work of each of his many pupils, not a small number of whom became men of stature in their own right in the profession.

NEW YORK CITY   KURT GOLDSTEIN

References

[1]Arch. Psychiat., Berl., 1895, 27: 504–540.   [2]Ibid., 1889, 20: 243–275.
[3]Der aphasische Symptomenkomplex. Breslau, Cohn & Weigert, 1874.
[4]Montpel. Méd., 1877, 38: 233–237.   [5]L'aphasie. Paris, Delahaye, 1878.
[6]Krankenvorstellungen aus der psychiatrischen Klinik in Breslau. Breslau, Schletter, 1889–1900. (Also in Psychiat. Abh., Heft 10; p. 13–15.)

References to Biography: 1) Arch. Psychiat., Berl., 1905, 40: 1016–1019 (Siemerling). 2) Med. Klin., 1905, 1: 735–736 (Rothmann). 3) Mschr. Psychiat., 1905, 18: i–iv (Ziehen). 4) Zschr. ges. Neur. Psychiat., 1939, 165: 38–47 (Schröder).

SAMUEL ALEXANDER KINNIER WILSON (1878–1937)

Kinnier Wilson was born in New Jersey, United States of America, and was brought up and educated in Scotland. He took his medical degree at the University of Edinburgh in 1902, and was awarded the B.Sc. in physiology with honors in 1903. Immediately after this he was house physician at the Royal Edinburgh Infirmary under Sir Byrom Bramwell, whose inspiration directed him toward neurology. He then studied in Germany and France, notably under Pierre Marie and Babinski. Returning to London in 1904, he began work at the National Hospital, Queen Square, as house physician, then registrar and pathologist, and on up to honorary physician until his death, by cancer, which occurred at the height of his powers. Most of his active life was spent in London as one of the group of brilliant neurologists at the National Hospital, which included Gowers, Hughlings Jackson, Bastian and Horsley.

Kinnier Wilson's written contributions were many, and all of them had a distinction rare in scientific literature. He became established as a master in the field in 1912—he was then 33—when he published his doctoral thesis on *Progressive lenticular degeneration: a familial nervous disease associated with cirrhosis of the*

Samuel Alexander Kinnier Wilson

liver,[1,2] a disorder since known as "Wilson's disease." This work was the beginning of the modern study of the anatomy, functions and disorders of the structures which he christened the "extra-pyramidal system." In this publication, Wilson made only passing reference to Westphal-Strümpell's pseudosclerosis, and when in later years, during lectures at "Queen Square," the matter would be

Portrait, courtesy of Dr. Foster Kennedy, New York City.

brought up by a pupil, he would slowly roll up the collar of his white coat, with infinite grace bringing the lapels together beneath his chin, cross his arms on his expansive chest—this series of movements was a mannerism of his—and with his resonant voice and penetrating eye would transfix his audience like Demosthenes on the steps of the Parthenon by telling them the story of the disorder, putting each character of the drama into proper perspective. Westphal and von Strümpell never fared too well! Denny-Brown relates that he once asked Kinnier Wilson his opinion on certain aspects of "hepatolenticular degeneration," whereupon Wilson eyed him with some circumspection and replied, "Do you mean Kinnier Wilson's disease?"

Kinnier Wilson's description of hepatolenticular degeneration was only the beginning. The paper on *The old motor system and the new*,[3] given at the meeting of the American Neurological Association in 1923, was a fine example of his keen analytical powers; his Croonian Lectures in 1925 on *The disorders of motility* and his Harveian Lecture in 1926 on *The epilepsies* had the same quality, and his volume on *Modern problems in neurology* (London, Arnold, 1928) showed remarkable insight. However, his unfinished 2-volume *Neurology* (London, Arnold, 1940) with its rare clarity and a style reminiscent of that of Samuel Johnson, was his magnum opus: it was the greatest since Oppenheim's. Many other subjects were elucidated by his facile pen, among them apraxia,[4] aphasia,[5] epidemic encephalitis,[6,7] and tics and allied conditions.[8] He reopened the field of pathological laughing and crying and their counterpart, paralysis of emotional facial movements, suggesting that the supranuclear pathways for emotional facial movements ran in the part of the brain supplied by the posterior communicating artery.[9] Sir Charles Bell (1774–1842) was well aware that emotional expression is dependent on the integrity of the facial nerve, as shown in his report of the type of facial paralysis since called Bell's palsy,[10] and Gowers recognized the dissociation between emotional and voluntary innervation in cerebral facial paresis,[11] an observation which Monrad-Krohn expanded,[12] but it was Wilson who set down the problem of expression in its then anatomical entirety.

Kinnier Wilson will remain an important figure in science because of his original work on hepatolenticular degeneration and because

of the great handbook of neurology he wrote. By his hundreds of
students he will be remembered as the great teacher at "Queen
Square" in the period between the wars, one who carried into
England the fine traditions of the Bicêtre and the Salpêtrière. His
commanding physique, his rich voice, his keen, quick analysis of
a situation, his ironical humor, and his masterful showmanship, made
of him a figure of Olympian stature.

WASHINGTON, D. C.   WEBB HAYMAKER

References

[1]Brain, Lond., 1912, 34: 295–509.   [2]Lewandowsky, M. H., Handbuch
der Neurologie. Berlin, 1910–19, 5: 951–990.   [3]Arch. Neur. Psychiat.,
Chic., 1924, 11: 385–404.   [4]Brain, Lond., 1908, 31: 164–216.   [5]Apha-
sia. London, Paul, Trench, Trubner, 1926.   [6]Lancet, Lond., 1931,
2: 1143–1147.   [7]Ibid., 1918, 2: 7–12 et seq.   [8]J. Neur. Psychiat.,
Lond., 1927, 8: 93–109.   [9]Ibid., 1924, 4: 299–333.   [10]Philos. Tr. R.
Soc. London, 1829, 119: 317–330.   [11]A manual of diseases of the nervous system. Vol. 2. London, Churchill, 1888; p. 72.   [12]Brain, Lond.,
1924, 47: 22–35.

Reference to Biography: Arch. Neur. Psychiat., Chic., 1937, 38: 388–389
(Kennedy).

V

NEUROSURGEONS

HARVEY CUSHING (1864–1939)

*H*arvey Cushing, the fourth in his line to practice medicine, was born in Cleveland, Ohio. He received his education at Yale College and Harvard Medical School and, following an internship at Massachusetts General Hospital in Boston, he spent four years (1896–1900) in general surgery under William S. Halsted at The Johns Hopkins Hospital.

During 1900–01 he worked in laboratories and clinics in England and on the Continent, his major investigation being an experimental study on the interrelation between intracranial pressure and systolic blood pressure, which he carried out under the supervision of Theodor Kocher of Bern whose interests were then turning to neurological surgery. In the summer of 1901 he returned to England for a month with Sherrington who was at that time commencing his celebrated studies with A. S. F. Grünbaum (later Leyton) on the anthropoid motor cortex. Cushing's surgical skills were utilized in performing the craniotomies.

On returning to the Johns Hopkins, Cushing directed his attention to neurological surgery. He had earlier devised an approach to the Gasserian ganglion for relief of tic douloureux, and he now began to develop technical procedures for minimizing hemorrhage in operations involving the brain and spinal cord. He started to remove brain tumors in 1902 and persevered for some years despite heavy mortality. Although the removal of a meningioma from Major General Leonard Wood in 1910 was regarded for a time as Cushing's first success at complete extirpation of an intracranial tumor, the meningioma recurred and General Wood died some years later during the second operation.

Following the visit of Edward Schäfer to Baltimore in 1908, Cushing undertook an experimental study of the functions of the pituitary gland, developing both in dogs and human beings a successful surgical approach to this well-concealed body. He established that the canine pituitary was not essential for life and could be removed in its entirety.[1] By 1912 he had fifty well-studied cases of pituitary disease in man, and in the monograph which he published in that year[2] he enunciated the concept of hyper- versus hypo-pituitarism,

recognizing that acromegaly was due to hyperactivity of the anterior lobe and dwarfism the result of diminished activity.

For the next twenty years, first at the Peter Bent Brigham Hospital in Boston and then at Yale University, Cushing consolidated his position as the founder of a great specialty, each year lowering his mortality rate through improvements in his surgical technique. His chief scientific contributions lay in his study of the natural history of the various histological types of brain tumor with an analysis of the life expectancy of each.[3,4] The clinical histories and meticulously documented case reports in all Cushing's papers and monographs are a model of medical writing, especially his *Tumors of the nervus acusticus and the syndrome of the cerebello-pontile angle* (Philadelphia, Saunders, 1917), which is regarded as a classic in this respect.

Portrait from *A bibliography of the writings of Harvey Cushing prepared . . . by the Harvey Cushing Society.* Springfield, Illinois, Thomas, 1939.

Cushing's preëminence as a surgeon and his compelling personal charm brought students to him from all over the world, and at the meeting of the First International Neurological Congress at Bern in 1931, the school he had founded was compared to that of John Hunter. Cushing was a vigorous advocate of reform in medical education and worked throughout his life for broader postgraduate opportunities. But his foremost contribution outside neurosurgery lay in the field of medical humanism, his best known literary work being his *Life of Sir William Osler* (2 vol.; Oxford, Clarendon Press, 1925), for which he received a Pulitzer Prize in 1926.

When Harvey Cushing died he left his distinguished private collection of rare volumes on the history of medicine and science to Yale University; and the Historical Library in the School of Medicine, where the books have come to rest, will stand as his most enduring monument.

NEW HAVEN, CONNECTICUT   JOHN F. FULTON

References

[1]Bull. Johns Hopkins Hosp., 1909, *20:* 105–107 (with Reford).   [2]*The pituitary body and its disorders.* Philadelphia, Lippincott, 1912.   [3]*Intracranial tumors.* Springfield, Ill., Thomas, 1932.   [4]*Meningiomas. Their classification.* Springfield, Ill., Thomas, 1938 (with Eisenhardt).

References to Biography: 1) *Harvey Cushing: A biography.* Springfield, Ill., Thomas, 1946 (Fulton).   2) *Harvey Cushing: surgeon, author, artist.* New York, Schuman, 1950 (Thomson).

Reference to Bibliography: A *bibliography of the writings of Harvey Cushing.* 2nd printing. Springfield, Ill., Thomas, 1940 (Harvey Cushing Society).

WALTER EDWARD DANDY (1886–1946)

Walter Dandy, who by his exemplary teaching did more to advance the technique of neurosurgery than any other pioneer in this specialty, was born in Sedalia, Missouri. After receiving the B.A. at the University of Missouri, he studied medicine at The Johns Hopkins School of Medicine, graduating in 1910. For the next few years he served as house officer in surgery at The Johns Hopkins Hospital. During this period he was a prolific writer, his most

Walter Edward Dandy

important articles being on the production and absorption of spinal fluid and the pathogenesis of hydrocephalus, written in collaboration with Blackfan.[1]

Dandy's greatest contribution to neurosurgery came in 1918, when he introduced ventriculography and pneumoencephalography,[2] which now are routine diagnostic procedures.

Following these experimental studies, Dandy's interest turned more and more toward the development and perfection of neurosurgical techniques. In 1925 he described a posterior approach for the section of the trigeminal root to relieve tic douloureux. In his skillful hands this operation was easier, simpler, safer, and less likely to be complicated by keratitis and facial paralysis, than the retro-

Portrait, courtesy of Dr. A. Earl Walker, Baltimore, Maryland.

gasserian neurectomy introduced a quarter of a century earlier by Frazier and Spiller. In 1928 Dandy devised an operation for the relief of Ménière's syndrome,[3-5] a procedure suggested by Mills 20 years previously.[6]

With his amazing skill he was able to perform difficult feats of surgery with a relatively low mortality. Thus, he demonstrated that intraventricular tumors could be safely removed without producing serious neurological deficits. He advocated the complete extirpation of acoustic tumors—a radical procedure previously considered entirely too hazardous. Then he showed that cerebral aneurysms were amenable to surgical attack. In the preface to his scholarly monograph on the subject,[7] he stated: "Intracranial arterial aneurysms, always considered rare and almost impossible both of diagnosis and of treatment, are now added to the lengthening line of lesions that are curable by surgery. This is another example of the results that can be attained from intensive cultivation of a seemingly barren field . . . they are now known to be quite common, and many at least are amenable to cure with a surprisingly low mortality."

Dandy's contributions to medical literature were diverse and many. Besides the numerous papers on hydrocephalus, trigeminal neuralgia, glossopharyngeal neuralgia, Ménière's disease, and his monographs on intraventricular tumors, orbital tumors and vascular abnormalities of the brain, he wrote the section on the brain for Lewis's *System of surgery*.[8] This treatise on neurological surgery, beautifully illustrated as were all his papers, is still the best text available on the technique in brain surgery.

Visiting surgeons and students from all parts of the world came to watch Dandy operate. In his intense preoccupation with his work he seemed to stand aloof from the rank and file of the growing specialty of neurosurgery. But the privileged friends who knew Dandy intimately were aware of his congenial home life, his personal interest in his pupils and associates, and his generous nature. His greatness, which did not make him lose the common touch, is well described in an editorial on his death in the *Baltimore Sun:* "The imaginative genius to conceive of new and startling techniques, courage to try them and skill—superb skill—to make them successful."

BALTIMORE, MARYLAND   A. EARL WALKER

References

[1]Am. J. Dis. Child., 1914, 8: 406–482.   [2]Ann. Surg., 1918, 68: 5–11. [3]Arch. Surg., 1928, 16: 1127–1152.   [4]Arch. Otolar., Chic., 1934, 20: 1–30.   [5]J. Am. M. Ass., 1937, 108: 931–937.   [6]Arch. Neur. Psychiat., Chic., 1932, 28: 1390–1394 (Frazier).   [7]Intracranial arterial aneurysms. Ithaca, N. Y., Comstock, 1944.   [8]Lewis (ed.), System of surgery, Hagerstown, Md., Prior, 1945, 12: 1–671.

References to Biography and Works: 1) Surgery, 1946, 19: 577–579 et seq. (Blalock).   2) Ann. Surg., 1947, 126: 113–115 (Firor).   3) Klin. Wschr., 1928, 7: 169–173 et seq. (Wartenberg).   4) J. Neurosurg., 1951, 8: 249–262 (Campbell).

CHARLES ALBERT ELSBERG (1871–1948)

Charles Elsberg was one of the American pioneers in neurosurgery. He belonged to the heroic age, which included Cushing, Frazier, and others, when the foundation of neurosurgery was laid in America. All those pioneers were general surgeons first, who grew into neurosurgery as they literally created the discipline. While Elsberg did considerable work in the whole field of neurosurgery, his most important and lasting contributions were to surgery of the spinal cord.

Elsberg was born in New York City. Upon finishing his undergraduate studies at the College of the City of New York in 1890, he entered the College of Physicians and Surgeons of Columbia University and received his medical degree in 1893. After his return from Europe, where he did postgraduate work under von Mikulicz, he was appointed to the surgical staff of the Mount Sinai Hospital, which he served as attending surgeon until 1929. In 1909 he became neurosurgeon of the Neurological Institute of New York and was associated with it until his retirement in 1937. It was during those years, both at the Mount Sinai Hospital and at the Neurological Institute, that he made his important contributions to the surgery of the spinal cord.

As early as 1912 he reported on 43 laminectomies.[1] In 1916 his important work on *The diagnosis and treatment of surgical diseases of the spinal cord and its membranes* (Philadelphia; Saunders) appeared, and in 1925 another on tumors of the spinal cord.[2] The latter was brought up-to-date and amplified in a volume on surgical diseases of the spinal cord[3] which appeared in

Charles Albert Elsberg

1941. He also did original investigation on vision, and entered into a long series of studies on smell with Levy and Brewer in which new clinical tests of olfaction were provided; most of these papers appeared in the *Bulletin of the Neurological Institute of New York*. Localizing aspects of the tests he devised were summarized in an article in 1937.[4] In all, Elsberg published about 150 papers dealing with refinements in diagnosis and treatment. In 1944, long after his retirement, he wrote a history of the Neurological Institute.[5]

In addition to holding the position of chief of neurosurgery at the Mount Sinai Hospital and the Neurological Institute, he was professor of neurosurgery at the College of Physicians and Surgeons

Portrait, courtesy of Dr. I. S. Wechsler, New York City.

of Columbia University. Many honors came to him. He was vice-president of the New York Academy of Medicine from 1924 to 1928, and in 1947 was awarded an honorary degree by the College of the City of New York. In 1937 he was elected President of the American Neurological Association.

Elsberg was of a retiring disposition. He had an extraordinary capacity for work and spent all his time either in the operating room or in the laboratory. He had few friends. Somewhat late in life (1937) he married Jane Stewart, with whom he spent happily the years of retirement to his country home.

NEW YORK CITY   I. S. WECHSLER

References

[1]Ann. Surg., 1912, 55: 217–226.   [2]*Tumors of the spinal cord and the symptoms of irritation and compression of the spinal cord and nerve roots.* New York, Hoeber, 1925.   [3]*Surgical diseases of the spinal cord, membranes and nerve roots.* New York, Hoeber, 1941.   [4]Arch. Neur. Psychiat., Chic., 1937, 37: 223–236.   [5]*The story of a hospital; the Neurological Institute of New York.* New York, Hoeber, 1944.

Reference to Biography: J. Mount Sinai Hosp., N. York, 1948, 15: 266–269 (Cohen).

OTFRID FOERSTER (1873–1941)

*F*oerster, son of a professor of archeology, studied medicine at the Universities of Freiburg, Kiel and Breslau and received the M.D. in 1897 at Breslau. After two years' study under Dejerine in Paris and Frenkel in Switzerland, he returned to Breslau in 1899, where he remained the rest of his life, refusing calls to other universities. In 1922 he was made Ordinarius of neurology. He was head of the neurological department of a municipal hospital (Wenzel Hancke Krankenhaus), which was built into a neurological institute in 1934 with the help of the Rockefeller Foundation. It is now called the "Otfrid Foerster Neurologisches Institut." For nearly two years, with some interruptions, he was physician to Lenin at Moscow. A number of neurologists had been called to Moscow in consultation and ultimately Lenin became annoyed at seeing so many doctors around and ordered them all home. The Russian

Government requested Foerster to stay on, and he remained for a year in an adjoining room, often having to watch Lenin through a keyhole. He was on hand at the autopsy in 1923.

Foerster, the clinical neurologist, began to practice neurosurgery at the age of 40. At heart he was a neurophysiologic experimenter. He helped his patients, but they had to pay the price by being subjected to physiological experimentation. He wrote 300 scientific works, all in longhand. Originality was their outstanding character-

Portrait, courtesy of Yale Medical Library, New Haven, Connecticut. (Photographed in Breslau by R. U. Light, 1935.)

istic, with therapy their final goal. In the 44 years of his scientific career, motility was his favorite subject, but he boldly attacked neurological problems of any level of the cerebrospinal axis. He was an enthusiastic therapist. His skeptical chief, Wernicke, once said of him: "I now have an assistant who makes lame walk and blind see."

Foerster wrote on tabes,[1] coordination,[2] associated movements,[3] and spastic contractures.[4] Two operations bear his name: rhizotomy in the treatment of spastic paralysis,[5] and rhizotomy in the relief of gastric crises.[6,7] In 1913, independently of Spiller and Martin, he introduced cordotomy.[8] In 1924, independently of Rosett, he reported on a hyperventilation test in epilepsy.[9] His work on extrapyramidal diseases[10] was a revealing masterpiece. In the *Handbuch der Neurologie* of Lewandowsky (1929), and that of Bumke and Foerster (1936),[11] he revised the entire concept of motility and sensibility on the basis of his extensive experience in war neurosurgery. Decades will be needed to plumb the depths of this immense work. Epilepsy, localization, muscle physiology, brain tumors, pain were his favorite subjects during his last years. All his life Foerster fought for the independence of neurology, and his resolution declaring that "... neurology represents an entirely independent specialty in medicine" was unanimously accepted by the First International Neurological Congress at Bern in 1931. To him fell the honor, during the meeting of the Second International Neurological Congress in London in 1935, of delivering the Lecture in commemoration of the 100th anniversary of the birth of Hughlings Jackson, and on this occasion he received the Hughlings Jackson Memorial Medal. His famous cytoarchitectonic map of the human cerebral cortex appeared in an article on *The motor cortex in man in the light of Hughlings Jackson's doctrines*, published in 1936.[12]

This was a man! At neurological meetings which he brilliantly addressed as chairman, everyone could feel his the strongest personality among them, the undisputed master, the most revered and most admired. In the 20's I had the opportunity of seeing the leading neurologists and neurosurgeons of Europe at work. In depth and breadth of knowledge, in the wide range of investigative work, in the happy blending of physiology with neurology and neurosurgery, of theory with practice, in his enthusiatic, stimulating drive, Foerster stood out as the foremost. On a visit to Boston he was invited by Harvey Cushing to act as surgeon-in-chief *pro tem*. The phrenetic tempo of his work was too much even for the staff of the Peter Bent Brigham Hospital.

He had one goal, one purpose: the search for helpful knowledge. This sacred fire burned within him and devoured him! He knew no holidays, no recreation, no regular vacations. He was a frail, a sick man. He suffered from chronic gastro-intestinal disturbances, from thromboangiitis obliterans, arteriosclerosis, tuberculosis, chronic nicotinism. But he was merciless to himself. His implacable spirit extracted the maximum from his delicate, fragile body. He completely disregarded physical pain. Once he said of himself that through year-long exercises he had learned ". . . to influence the intensity of bodily pain to complete disappearance." Few mortals have put as much enthusiasm, devotion and self-sacrifice into their research work as did Otfrid Foerster.

SAN FRANCISCO, CALIFORNIA   ROBERT WARTENBERG

References

[1]Deut. Aerzte Ztg., 1901, 7: 101–102.   [2]*Die Physiologie und Pathologie der Coordination.* Jena, Fischer, 1902.   [3]*Die Mitbewegungen bei Gesunden,* etc. Jena, Fischer, 1904.   [4]*Die Kontrakturen bei den Erkrankungen der Pyramidenbahn.* Berlin, Karger, 1906.   [5]Zschr. orthop. Chir., 1908, 22: 203–223.   [6]Beitr. klin. Chir., 1909, 63: 245–256.   [7]Tr. Internat. Cong. Med. 1913. Sub-sect. VII (a) Orthopaedics, pt.2. London, 1914; p. 7–16.   [8]Berl. klin. Wschr., 1913, 50: 1499–1502.   [9]Deut. Zschr. Nervenh., 1924, 83: 347–356.   [10]Zschr. ges. Neur. Psychiat., 1921, 73: 1–169.   [11]*Die Leitungsbahnen des Schmerzgefühls und die chirurgische Behandlung der Schmerzzustände.* Berlin, Urban & Schwarzenberg, 1927.   [12]Brain, Lond., 1936, 59: 135–159 (the Ninth Hughlings Jackson Lecture).

References to Biography: 1) J. Neurophysiol., 1942, 5: 1–17 (contains bibliography).   2) Deut. Zschr. Nervenh., 1941, 153: 1–23 (von Weizsäcker).   3) Arch. Psychiat., Berl., 1941, 114: 1–16 (contains bibliography; Gagel).

CHARLES HARRISON FRAZIER (1870–1936)

*F*razier was one of the small group of pioneers who created neurosurgery as a new branch of surgery. He was, as a surgeon, an autodidact in the best tradition of his time. He was born in Philadelphia. After internships at the University of Pennsylvania Hospital and the Episcopal Hospital, he went to Europe for study in surgery, neurology and pathology (1895). He always said that the men to whom he owed the most were Ernst von Bergmann (1836–1907) and Rudolf Virchow (1821–1902). Young Frazier did well to seek out von Bergmann, who at that time dominated the surgical field in Berlin. As veteran of three wars including the Russo-Turkish War (in which he served on the Russian side), von Bergmann had mastered the scalpel and had instituted an aseptic operative ritual as modern as that of today. Through his association with von Bergmann, Frazier was well equipped when he returned to the University of Pennsylvania Hospital in Philadelphia.

Frazier's academic career began in 1896 as instructor in surgical pathology. In 1901 he was elected clinical professor of surgery, a position he held with great distinction for some 15 years. His decision in 1919 to devote himself almost exclusively to neurosurgery was influenced by his work as neurosurgeon during World War I in the Base Hospitals in Foxhills and #11, Cape May, to which many of the wounded were sent from France. A report on 500 cases of peripheral nerve injury and reconstruction and 200 cases of gunshot wound of the head treated there, gives testimony of the direction his interests in surgery had taken. In 1922 he was appointed John Rhea Barton professor of surgery and head of the surgical department of the Hospital of the University of Pennsylvania. Here his interest in the surgical approach to intracranial and intraspinal tumors was stimulated by Charles K. Mills (1845–1931) and William G. Spiller (1863–1940), successive professors of neurology in the University of Pennsylvania.

His close cooperation with Spiller had much to do with his success. It was Frazier's merit to make workable Spiller's suggestions. Others had cured trigeminal neuralgia by operation before him. Not until after Frazier introduced the subtotal retrogasserian neurotomy in 1901[1] did the operation change from a serious procedure, en-

Charles Harrison Frazier

dangering life and eye, to a safer intervention. In the 700 or more cases of tic douloureux operated on by Frazier, the mortality rate was less than 0.5 per cent, keratitis was minimal, and motor function undisturbed. Always ready to give credit where it was due, Frazier often referred to retrogasserian neurotomy as "Spiller's operation."

The second great success of the Spiller and Frazier collaboration was the development of Spiller's idea to cure pain by section of the anterolateral column of the spinal cord. At Spiller's suggestion,

Portrait, courtesy of Dr. F. H. Lewey, Philadelphia, Pennsylvania.

E. Martin had performed this operation in 1911.[2] Three years later, Frazier devised a more practicable operative technique, and thus placed cordotomy among the routine surgical procedures. Although Frazier's name is most closely linked with trigeminal neuralgia and cordotomy, his and his associates' fundamental contributions to the problems of pituitary and parasellar tumors and of neoplasms of the sphenoidal ridge should not be overlooked.

Frazier was sturdily built, had a ruddy complexion and piercing, keen, blue-grey eyes topped by a head of hair which was always as orderly as he was precise. He had an intuitive, commanding temperament, made all the more impressive by his rich resounding voice. He began many an operation with a group of assisting residents and interns, only to finish with an operating nurse as his sole aid. The great demands which he made on his co-workers, as on himself, gave him a strictness which sometimes seemed to approach harshness, but this appearance was wholly superficial. Fundamentally, he was a gentleman, gracious, righteous, and helpful. He seldom talked to the gallery during an operation, but after operations, while he swept the floor of the operating room with a kitchen broom—to relax his shoulder muscles (this was in the early 1930's)—his discourses always captivated his audience. Six of his assistants occupy important positions in neurosurgery—Grant became his successor at the University of Pennsylvania, Monroe is at Harvard, Gardner at Western Reserve, Watts at George Washington University, Kwan at Union Medical College in Peking, and Groff at the Graduate School of Medicine in Philadelphia. Others were the late Dr. Max Peet of the University of Michigan and the late Dr. Alfred W. Adson of the Mayo Clinic. It was natural that these and many other associates of Frazier should join in 1935—the 65th anniversary of his birth—to present him with a *Festchrift*.[3]

PHILADELPHIA, PENNSYLVANIA   F. H. LEWEY

References

[1]Univ. Pennsylvania M. Bull., 1901, *14:* 341–352 (with Spiller).   [2]J. Am. M. Ass., 1912, *58:* 1489–1490 (Spiller and Martin).   [3]Ann. Surg., 1935, *1:* 1–390.

References to Biography: 1) Ann. Surg., 1937, *105:* 638–640 (Grant). 2) *Ibid.*, 1935, *1:* vii–viii (Stengel).   3) Lancet, Lond., 1936, *2:* 291– 292 (Harris).

SIR VICTOR ALEXANDER HADEN HORSLEY (1857–1916)

*V*ictor Horsley, an early pioneer in neurosurgery, was born in Kensington into a prominent family noted for its accomplishments in music, art and surgery. In childhood, Victor, as the result of his father's persistence, decided to be a surgeon. In preparation for this profession, he started very early to investigate the interiors of birds and animals. His school life was not particularly noteworthy, but at the University of London, where he matriculated in medicine in 1873, his abilities were such that he received a gold medal in anatomy. In 1880 he passed his qualifying examination at the Royal College of Surgeons and a year later received the B.M. and B.S. Meanwhile he had become closely associated with Bastian, and with him published in 1880 his first work, which dealt with arrested development of the left upper limb in the presence of a parietal lobe defect.

During his early postgraduate years, Horsley's interests were varied and included such subjects as myxedema and cretinism[1] and the preventive treatment of rabies. His interests became firmly fixed on the nervous system only after he joined Schäfer at University College and Beevor at the Brown Institution in researches on the functions of the cerebral cortex. With a view to extending the work of Fritsch and Hitzig and Ferrier, Horsley analyzed in minute detail by means of faradic stimulation the motor responses of the cerebral cortex, internal capsule and spinal cord of the higher primates.[2] His work in this field, carried out in association with Schäfer, Beevor, Semon, Spencer and Gotch over a period of seven years, is to be counted among the remarkable achievements of British neurophysiology. Moreover he had the distinction of being the first to achieve success in hypophysectomy, two dogs surviving five and six months after this operation,[3] but his data were exceedingly scant. Marinesco's work in this field in 1892[4] was more carefully documented, but his animals survived only as long as 18 days. It was not until 1912 that Aschner,[5] by perfecting the operation so as to avoid damaging the hypothalamus, was able to keep hypophysectomized dogs alive indefinitely.

In 1886—he was then 29—Horsley was appointed surgeon to the National Hospital, Queen Square, London, a position for which

Sir Victor Alexander Haden Horsley

his physiologic studies had admirably prepared him. Until that time brain surgery had been confined to traumatic injuries, in which the site of the brain damage was known by the location of the scalp laceration or bruise. With the new knowledge of cerebral localization it was possible to make a topical diagnosis on the basis of clinical examination. Two years before Horsley's appointment, the first successful removal of a brain tumor had been accomplished by Godlee, although equal credit should be given Bennett, who localized the tumor and persuaded Godlee to operate.[6] Much the same might be said of the first successful removal of an intraspinal tumor. As Critchley relates, Gowers had referred to Horsley an army offi-

Portrait, courtesy of Dr. Foster Kennedy, New York City.

cer of 45 whose legs had become spastic. The diagnosis was spinal tumor. Horsley was invited by Gowers to operate, and on June 9, 1887, in the theatre at "Queen Square," the task was undertaken by Horsley with the assistance of Stedman and Ballance. The tumor proved to be a benign "fibromyxoma" of the fourth thoracic root.[7] A year later "the patient was working sixteen hours a day, which entailed much standing and walking."

In 1888 Horsley described decompressive procedures for the relief of inoperable brain tumors. In 1890, at the International Medical Congress in Berlin, he discussed the 44 operations he had performed upon the brain. In this series there had been 10 deaths, most of which were in cases of malignant glioma. At a time when brain operations were usually fatal, and speed was a prime factor in surgery, this astonishing record is a tribute to Horsley's manual dexterity. In 1908 he aided R. H. Clarke, physiologist at St. George's Hospital in London, in building a stereotaxic instrument for the study of cerebral function.[8] A brief account of the historical aspects of the Horsley-Clarke instrument is to be found in a volume by Rasmussen.[9]

In the early 1900's Horsley's interests turned to medical politics, a field in which his enthusiastic and energetic spirit fared not too well. He became an ardent, almost fanatic crusader for medical, social, and educational reforms. His rigid views on the use of alcoholic beverages, propounded at both temperance and medical meetings, alienated some of his friends. For his leadership in medical administration and for his professional accomplishments, Horsley was knighted in 1902. Although he was 57 years of age at the outbreak of World War I, he requested active duty, and was given an assignment in charge of a surgical service of a General Hospital. Later he was made consultant to the Mediterranean Expeditionary Force. It was in the discharge of these duties that he met his death at Amara, in Mesopotamia, of heatstroke.

BALTIMORE, MARYLAND   A. EARL WALKER

References

[1]Brit. M. J., 1885, 1: 111–115.   [2]Philos. Tr. R. Soc. London, 1888, ser.B., 179: 1–45 (with Schäfer).   [3]Lancet, Lond., 1886, 1: 3–5.   [4]C. rend.

Soc. biol., 1892, *4:* 509–510.   [5]Virchows Arch., 1912, *146:* 1–146.
[6]Brit. M. J., 1885, *1:* 988–989.   [7]Med-Chir. Tr., 1888, n.s., *71:* 377–430
(with Gowers).   [8]Brain, Lond., 1908, *31:* 45–124.   [9]*Some trends in
neuroanatomy.* Dubuque, Iowa, Brown, 1947 (Rasmussen).

References to Biography and Works: 1) *Sir Victor Horsley; a study of
his life and work.* London, Constable, 1919 (Paget).   2) *The life of
Sir William Osler.* Vol. 2. Oxford, Clarendon Press, 1925 (Cushing);
p. 677.   3) Rev. Neur. Psychiat., Edinb., 1916, *14:* 583–588 (Russell).
4) Penfield (ed.), *Neurological biographies and addresses.* London, Oxford Univ. Press, 1936 (Evans); p. 65–70.   5) *Sir William Gowers
1845–1915. A biographical appreciation.* London, Heinemann, 1949; p.
46 (Critchley).

CLOVIS VINCENT (1879–1947)

Clovis Vincent, who established modern neurological surgery in
France, was born in Ingre, Loiret, the son and grandson of
physicians. He studied medicine in Paris and came under the influence of Babinski. In 1913 he became Babinski's assistant at the
Pitié. During World War I, Vincent served in the French Army,
making a brilliant record. He was particularly well-known for his
work in the treatment of the psychoneuroses. He referred to his
method of electrotherapy as "rééducation intensive," though the
soldiers called it "torpillage" (torpedoing). The treatment was not
without pain, and one of his patients, Private Deschamps, proceeded to sue the French state, naming Vincent as codefendant. In
this "cause célèbre," known as the "procès de Tours," famous medical
authorities of France testified on Vincent's behalf, among them Huet,
Babinski and Teissier. Vincent was vindicated and many soldiers
were then reactivated by being "torpedoed."

After the war, Vincent returned to his revered master Babinski
and under his guidance investigated hysteria, chronic syphilitic meningitis, epidemic encephalitis, paraplegias-in-flexion of cerebral origin,[1] and spinal compression. His work in these years firmly established him as a highly original investigator and careful clinician.

In 1927 Vincent visited the United States, where he studied the
methods of Harvey Cushing and Percival Bailey. He became pain-
fully aware of the shortcomings of French neurological surgery,
which had been handled by busy general surgeons. In May 1928, at

Clovis Vincent

the age of almost 50 years, he performed his first operation, at the Pitié, extirpating a hydatid cyst from the fissure of Sylvius.

During the next few years Vincent patterned his life after Cushing's as he had formerly after Babinski's. Lacking even elementary surgical training, he performed abdominal operations in order to master the fundamental principles and techniques of surgery. He transformed the neurological wards at the Pitié into neurosurgical ones. In a rather short time he made himself one of the most accomplished neurosurgeons in Europe. When Cushing watched Vincent operate in 1933, he was profoundly impressed by his skill, and this despite Cushing's well-known insistence on a long general surgical training for prospective neurosurgeons.

Portrait, courtesy of Prof. Ludo van Bogaert, Antwerp, Belgium.

Of particular importance in this field were his observations with Marcel David and François Thiébaut on the temporal lobe pressure cone in the presence of cerebral tumors.[2] He also developed a method of total extirpation of cerebral abscess and cerebellar tubercle.[3] One of his earliest contributions to neurosurgery, made in collaboration with Lardennois, was the use of periarterial sympathectomy for reflex disturbances and disordered sensation following amputation.[4] With Schiff, Puech and David, he described the injection of air as a treatment for the sequelae of head injuries.[5] Vincent also wrote on the diagnosis of tumors of the frontal lobes,[6] and on the functions of the frontal lobes.[7]

In collaboration with van Bogaert, Vincent published in 1936[8] a valuable study of Hallervorden-Sptaz's disease. This disorder was first brought to light in 1922 by Hallervorden and Spatz,[9] who at that time were associated with Spielmeyer at the Deutsche Forschungsanstalt für Psychiatrie at Munich. Hallervorden had performed an autopsy on a young girl of eight in neighboring Landsberg a.d. Warthe, and on sectioning the brain, he and Spatz found, to their surprise, that the globus pallidus and the red zone of the substantia nigra bilaterally had taken on an intense rust-brown color. Microscopically, as Vincent and van Bogaert were later to confirm,[8] the nerve cells and myelin in these locations were found to have degenerated, and an enormous amount of iron deposited. Four other children of this family also came down with the disorder —extrapyramidal motor disturbances, athetotic hyperkinesias and dementia were the chief signs—and section, by Hallervorden,[10] disclosed the same degeneration and iron deposit. Vincent and van Bogaert's case, which also concerned a girl aged 8, was especially clear cut, for mental disturbances were lacking until the end. Vincent and van Bogaert[8] and van Bogaert[11] regarded Spatz-Hallervorden's disease as a form of "status dysmyelinisatus" of C. and O. Vogt,[12] and felt that it should be distinguished from Hunt's juvenile paralysis agitans. The peculiarity of the disease consisted then, in the selective involvement of the globus pallidus and the red zone of the substantia nigra, both of which have been shown in other ways by Spatz[13-15] to be closely interrelated. One of the more recent reports on the disorder was by Hallervorden's associate, Eicke.[16]

Vincent's accomplishments in the early 1930's were quickly recognized. In 1933 a neurosurgical service was created for him at the

Pitié, where he had been Babinski's chosen successor. With the aid of the Rockfeller Foundation, a chair of neurosurgery was established for him at the Faculté de Médecine of Paris.

Throughout the German occupation of Paris during World War II, Vincent worked harder than ever. He lived in the hospital and fought for his patients and his work, struggling almost single-handed to keep the doors of his neurosurgical clinic open. Although he was worn out when the war ended, his clinic was preserved.

Babinski, on his deathbed, was asked what would remain of him after his death, and he replied: "I have shown the way to de Martel and Vincent."

SAN FRANCISCO, CALIFORNIA   WALTER F. SCHALLER
                                         LEON J. WHITSELL

References

[1]Rev. neur., Par., 1925, *1*: 337–348 (with Krebs and Chavany).   [2]*Ibid.*, 1936, *65*: 536–545.   [3]Schweiz. med. Wschr., 1938, *68*: 101–105. [4]Rev. neur., Par., 1921, *1*: 748–752.   [5]*Ibid.*, 1931, *1*: 651–653.   [6]*Ibid.*, 1928, *1*: 801–884.   [7]Deut. med. Wschr., 1936, *62*: 41–45.   [8]Rev. neur., Par., 1936, *65*: 921–959.   [9]Zschr. ges. Neur. Psychiat., 1922, *79*: 254–302. [10]Deut. Zschr. Nervenh., 1924, *81*: 204–210.   [11]Rev. neur., Par., 1940, *72*: 448–456.   [12]J. Psychol. Neur., Lpz., 1920, *25*: 747–762.   [13]Zschr. ges. Neur. Psychiat., 1922, 77: 261–390.   [14]Anat. Anz., Erg. Heft, 1922, *55*: 159–180.   [15]Deut. Zschr. Nervenh., 1923, *77*: 275–296.   [16]Arch. Psychiat., Berl., 1940, *111*: 514–546.

References to Biography: 1) J. Neurosurg., 1945, *2*: 530–534 (Rabinovitch).   2) Arch. Neur. Psychiat., Chic., 1949, *61*: 74–78 (Bailey). 3) Arq. neuropsiquiat., San Paulo, 1948, *6*: 73–81 (contains bibliography; Gama).

NAME INDEX

A

Abadie, on Bell's palsy, 350
Achard, as associate of Foix, 286
Achúcarro, 5–7
  his influence on Río Hortega, 86–87
Addison, as pioneer in galvanotherapy, 82
  on diapedesis of leukocytes, 95
Adie, 231–34
Adler, as friend of Pick, 203
Adrian, as pupil of Langley, 145
  as symposium co-president, 106
Adson, as pupil of Frazier, 428
Aird, on Lasègue, 323–26
  on Riddoch, 362–64
Alajouanine, on Souques, 385–88
  on subacute necrotic myelitis, 287
Alcock, on hemiballismus, 55
Alexander, as editor, 60
Algieri, on osmic acid stain, 62
Alpers, as pupil of Jakob, 185
  on Landouzy, 317–20
Altschul, on Mingazzini, 194
Alzheimer, 165–68
  as associate of Nissl, 195
  as predecessor of Spielmeyer, 216
  as teacher of Achúcarro, 5
    of Brodmann, 13
    of Jakob, 184, 185
  on basal ganglia diseases, 307
  on general paresis, 197
  on pseudosclerosis, 398
  on Weigert, 224
Amundsen, and Charcot, 268
Anderson, E., on Goltz, 131–35
Anderson, H. K., on sympathetic system, 144
André-Thomas, as associate of Dejerine, 274
  on Dejerine, 275
  on Friedreich's disease, 273
  on hypertrophic neuritis, 273
  on olivopontocerebellar atrophy, 273
Anglade, on parkinsonism, 402
Anton, as associate of Starr, 394
  as teacher of Schilder, 211
  on athetosis, 352
  on Meynert, 67

Apáthy, as teacher of Benedek, 211
  on neuron theory, 209
Aran, on spinal muscular atrophy, 278
Arey, on Ranson, 79
Ariëns Kappers, 7–10
  as student of Winkler, 100
  on Edinger, 30, 31
  on olfactory system, 29
  on striatum, 29
Aronson, on Mills and Spiller, 391
d'Arsonval, as pupil of Brown-Séquard, 265
  his debt to Claude Bernard, 110
Aschner, on hypophysectomy, 429
  on hypothalamus, 255
Astruc, on Lasègue, 325, 326
Athanassio-Benisty, on nerve injuries, 216
Atlas, on basis of Argyll Robertson pupil, 79
Auerbach, plexus of, 144, 371–72
Avellis, syndrome of, 30, 384
Ayala, as pupil of Mingazzini, 194
Azoulay, on Achúcarro, 7

B

Babès, as preceptor of Marinesco, 189
  on histopathology of nervous system, 190
Babinski, 234–36
  as a founder of the Société de neurologie, 385
  as associate (or pupil) of Charcot, 268
    of Marie, 331
    of Marinesco, 189
    of Vincent, 432, 433, 435
    of Wilson, 409
  on cerebrospinal fluid, 68
  on hysteria, 257, 349, 401
  on syndrome of medulla oblongata, 68
  sign of, 270
Babkin, on Pavlov, 155
Babonneix, on Sicard, 385
Babukin, as neurohistologist, 24
Bach, identification of skeleton of, 51
Baer, K. A., on Goethe, 74
von Baer, on germ layers, 82
Baglioni, on Luciani, 148

SUBJECT INDEX

A

Abiogenesis, 243
Abscess, brain, treatment of, 239, 434
Acalculia, 181
Achondroplasia, 367
Acoustic sense, center of, 55
  pathways of, 33, 40, 100, 181, 339, 342
Acromegaly, 189, 329, 416
Adie syndrome, 233
Adiposogenital dystrophy, 235, 375
Adrenal medulla, functions of, 115
Adrenalectomy in 1856, 265
Adrenalin, action of, 144, 145
Agnosia, 206, 270, 328
  introduction of term, 30
Agrammatism, 202
Agraphia, 181, 273, 347
Alcohol, as fixative, 45, 195
Alcoholism, brain changes in, 187
  campaigns against, 182, 431
  corpus callosum in, 187
  neuritis in, 311–12, 344
  psychosis (etc.) in, 16, 311–13, 328,
    342, 398
Alexia, 206
Alimentary canal, movements of, 114
  secretions of, 152
Allergy and CNS, 371
Allochiria, 199
Allocortex, 65
Alzheimer's disease, 6, 166
  fibrillary change of, in encephalitis,
    287
Amaurotic family idiocy, 60, 170, 191,
    210, 215, 378
Amblystoma, behavior of, 23, 24
Ammon's horn, anatomy of, 65
  in anoxia, 216
Amputation of limbs, effect of, on cord,
    160, 191
  sympathectomy for pain after, 434
Amusia, 181
Amyostatic symptom-complex, 398
Amyotonia congenita, 270, 346
Amyotrophic lateral sclerosis, 184, 266–
    68
  pathology of, 315, 374

Anarthria, 387
Anemia
  pernicious, 269, 352
    iron metabolism in, 354
Anesthetics, action of, 160
Aneurysms
  intracranial, 270
  removal of, 419
Angioarchitectonics of brain, 33
Angioneurotic edema, 358
Anomalies, brain, 220
Anosmia, 358, 421
Anoxia, brain, 40, 216, 352
Anthropology, 9, 51, 83, 91, 113, 260
  criminal, 99, 113, 248, 380
Antivivisection, 125
Ants, studies of, 35, 36, 37
Aphasia, 40, 270, 301, 330–31, 339, 347,
    394, 398, 411
  amnesic, 347
  basis of, 181, 192, 202, 243, 387
  in multilingual persons, 348
  motor, 260, 273, 330–31, 387
  psychological aspects of, 212
  sensory, 243, 261, 273, 328, 408
Aphémie, 260
Apoplexy, turning of eyes in, 318
Apraxia, 202, 270, 328, 281, 411
  and corpus callosum, 329
  introduction of term, 30
Archicortex, 8, 30
Argyll Robertson pupil, 79, 232, 234, 366
  effect of drugs on, 366
Arsenic poisoning, 352
Art in histology, 89
  deformities depicted in, 268
Artists, 30, 292
Arteries, structure of, 200
  syndromes of occlusion of, 60, 234–35,
    286, 390, 406, 411
  spinal, 205
Arteritis, syphilitic, 187
Arteriosclerosis, cerebral, pathology of,
    166, 371
  of spinal cord, 205
Arthropathies, 266

463

This Book

The FOUNDERS *of* NEUROLOGY

Edited *by* WEBB HAYMAKER, M.D.

was set and printed by the Mack Printing Company of Easton, Pennsylvania and bound by the J. F. Tapley Company, Long Island City, N. Y. The engravings were made by G. R. Grubb and Company of Champaign, Illinois. The page trim size is 6 × 9 inches. The type page is 27 × 44 picas. The type face is Linotype Caledonia, set 11 point on 13 point. The text paper is 60-pound Newfield Enamel. The cover is Du Pont Fabrikoid, Quality 700, Color 1022, Grain Shoe-4, Pliability medium, Finish Cordoba P-2032.

With THOMAS BOOKS careful attention is given to all details of manufacturing and design. It is the Publisher's desire to present books that are satisfactory as to their physical qualities and artistic possibilities and appropriate for their particular use. THOMAS BOOKS will be true to those laws of quality that assure a good name and good will.